Human navigation and
magnetoreception

To Thomas, Howard *and* David
for tolerating a father who puts magnets on people's heads

Human navigation and magnetoreception

R. Robin Baker

Reader in Zoology, Department of Environmental Biology,
University of Manchester

Manchester University Press

Manchester and New York

Distributed exclusively in the USA and Canada by St. Martin's Press

Copyright © R. Robin Baker 1989

Published by Manchester University Press
Oxford Road, Manchester M13 9PL, UK
and Room 400, 175 Fifth Avenue,
New York, NY 10010, USA

Distributed exclusively in the USA and Canada
by St. Martin's Press, Inc.,
175 Fifth Avenue, New York, NY 10010, USA

British Library cataloguing in publication data
Baker, R. (Robin), *1944*–
  Human navigation and magnetoreception.
  1. Man. Orientation. Effects of earth's
  magnetic field
  I. Title
  612′.813

Library of Congress cataloging in publication data
Baker, Robin, 1944–
    Human navigation and magnetoreception/R. Robin Baker.
    p. cm.
    Includes indexes.
    ISBN 0–7190–1810–2.   ISBN 0–7190–2627–X (pbk.)
    1. Magnetoreception.   2. Orientation.   I. Title.
  QP435.B35   1989
  152.1′882—dc19

ISBN 0 7190 1810 2 *hardback*
      0 7190 2627 X *paperback*

Typeset in Hong Kong
by Best-set Typesetter Ltd

Printed in Great Britain
by Billings and Sons Ltd., Worcester

Contents

Preface and acknowledgements

On 29 June 1979 at Barnard Castle, England, a group of 31 sixth-form pupils climbed on board a coach in their school car park and blindfolded themselves. They placed magnets on their heads, settled back in their seats, and started to concentrate. Through steady drizzle, the coach travelled tortuously through the town centre before emerging onto a fairly straight trunk road and setting off for the southwest. After 5 km or so, the vehicle stopped briefly, then turned through 135° and set off eastwards to a second position, this time 5 km southeast of the school. At each stop the passengers were asked, while still blindfold, to write on a card an estimate of their current compass direction from school. After the second stop, the cards and magnets were collected and later examined. The pattern that emerged was as dramatic as it was unexpected.

In retrospect, the final sentence of this paragraph, which began my previous book on human magnetoreception (Baker 1981b), was ill-chosen. Compared with results obtained since, those first data were suggestive rather than dramatic. Nor should the pattern that emerged have been unexpected. Every animal seriously tested has been found to have a magnetic sense, and it now seems that the final search will be for an animal that is magnetically blind. It would be more surprising to discover that Man just happened to be that animal than to discover he was not.

Moreover, even early in the nineteenth century, many biologists had already postulated that Man had a separate sense devoted to the judgement of direction. The following passage, for example, was written by Bellamy (1839) under the heading 'Notice of a peculiar faculty in Man and certain animals' in a book on the natural history of South Devon:

There is an extraordinary power possessed by man, (at least by those individuals whose faculties are in due development) of directing his course in any required direction of the compass... My own experience informs me that this power is retained after a long succession of turnings and windings in all possible directions, and what is more I have further noticed that the mind, or one especial portion of it, continues engaged in ascertaining or observing the direction being pursued through all these deviating courses, without our consciousness of the activity of this sense, and in short it operates while the aggregate of the reflecting powers are abstracted on some given question.

Later, von Middendorf (1855) suggested that the sense of direction of animals may be based on sensitivity to the Earth's magnetic field. In 1873, *Nature* invited correspondence on the sense of direction of Man and other animals, to which one of the contributors was Charles Darwin (Darwin 1873).

From the beginning, for some inexplicable reason, the idea that any animal might be sensitive to the Earth's magnetic field has generated intense and heated opposition from the more conservative sections of the scientific community. Alfred Newton, for example, the first professor of zoology at Cambridge, when accused of believing in a magnetic sense, replied 'I had no need to declare my disbelief in Dr. von Middendorf's magnetic hypothesis, for I never met with any man that held it' (Cherfas 1980). Perhaps partly under the influence of such vehement opposition, nineteenth century hypotheses concerning the sense of direction of humans and other animals retreated from prominence. It was 1965 before Merkel & Wiltschko (1965) produced the first effective demonstration that an animal (the European Robin (*Erithacus rubecula*)) had a magnetic compass sense. Their results, after a brief series of skirmishes with opponents, eventually triggered similar demonstrations for more and more animals by more and more authors. The hypothesis of a magnetic sense of direction in humans, however, was not resurrected until the Barnard Castle and associated experiments carried out by myself and my colleagues at Manchester University between June and November 1979 (Baker 1980c, d).

One might have thought that, given the age of the magnetoreception hypothesis, and the demonstrated reality of the sense in other animals, the results of the Barnard Castle experiment should not have been unexpected and should simply have taken their place alongside those other results for other animals. Instead, these first publications (Baker 1980b, c, d, e; 1981a, b, c) triggered a series of what can only be described as hostile reactions, reminiscent of Alfred Newton's reaction to von Middendorf.

These reactions passed through a number of stages. Particularly invigorating was the article by Jacobs (1982) which appeared in the *Los Angeles Times* for 19 July. In it, various of my American colleagues were credited with such comments as: 'He's just careless' (J.L. Gould); and 'To get Baker's results, you'd really have to be a sloppy scientist' (J.L. Kirschvink). Of course, I am sure neither scientist would ever have made any much comment! The scientific reaction to my work eventually culminated in the collected papers published by Kirschvink *et al.* (1985a).

The most perplexing aspect of the reaction of my fellow-scientists over the past seven years is the way that their resistance has borne such little relation to the data that they themselves collected as they set about repeating the Manchester experiments. I have explored this paradox elsewhere (Baker 1985b, 1987c). It may be illustrated by the titles different authors have given to their publications.

Three present only data for subjects that are clearly disoriented. However, all three series of experiments were based on small sample sizes (e.g. 7, 9, 25) and the authors chose titles that were suitably neutral:

(1) 'Magnetic sense in humans?' (Zusne & Allen 1981);
(2) 'A study of the homeward orientation of visually handicapped humans' (Judge 1985); and
(3) 'An attempt to replicate the spinning chair experiment' (Kirschvink *et al.* 1985b).

Contrast these titles with those chosen by authors who obtained data that were either unequivocally supportive of my claims or were at worst equivocal, perhaps containing a mixture of significant and non-significant results:

(1) 'Human homing: an elusive phenomenon' (Gould & Able 1981);
(2) 'Human orientation with restricted sensory information: no evidence for magnetic sensitivity' (Fildes *et al.* 1984);
(3) 'Human homing orientation: critique and alternative hypotheses' (Adler & Pelkie 1985);
(4) 'Absence of human homing ability as measured by displacement experiments' (Gould 1985);
(5) 'Human navigation: attempts to replicate Baker's displacement experiment' (Able & Gergits 1985);
(6) 'Human homing: still no evidence despite geomagnetic controls' (Westby & Partidge 1986).

In general, the phenomenon of negative titles and comments in the face of positive or equivocal results remains enigmatic. It is, of course, unthinkable that any of these scientists could have interpreted and presented their data with anything other than an open mind. We are forced, therefore, to look for other explanations. Perhaps, sometimes, the paradox may reflect faulty analysis or lack of familiarity with the literature. These, and other, possibilities are explored later in this book.

It has to be said that, since 1981, the atmosphere surrounding the study of human magnetoreception has, both publicly and less publicly, been just a little unpleasant. This may have had the unfortunate effect of discouraging other, uncommitted scientists from entering the field. The result has been the stagnation of literature in what potentially is an important area of biological and medical research.

I am pleased to say, however, that, with the publication of the papers collected together by Kirschvink *et al.* (1985a) and the demonstration that other authors have, in fact, clearly replicated the Manchester data (Baker 1987c), the air now seems to have cleared and the field is once more on the move. Even throughout the period of literature stagnation, research at Manchester has continued with vigour. There now exists a vast set of data which not only reveals many aspects of the magnetic sense itself but also identifies some of the more and less effective ways of pursuing its study. In contrast to the lack of public progress in the past seven years, the next seven should be years of published discovery by an increasingly wide range of scientists. Hopefully, other researchers in other laboratories will be reassured by the published demonstration that the Manchester data have been replicated by others and thus have confidence that there is a real and important phenomenon to be studied. They may also be reassured that they will no longer bring down upon themselves the same hostility that has plagued the field of magneto-reception since 1855. Perhaps, with these reassurances, such scientists will be encouraged to embark on programs of investigation to evaluate more precisely the nature of the human magnetic sense, its place in our sensory armoury, and its role in our everyday lives. The data already collected at Manchester could act as a springboard for such investigations.

It is the aim of this book to establish such a springboard; to summarise the multifaceted aspects of human magnetoreception that have emerged from the recent studies and to offer guidance in the design of experiments so that the pitfalls of the past can be avoided. The amount of progress over the next few years in our understanding of this novel feature of human physiology will be a measure of the extent to which this aim has been realised.

The study of human navigation and magnetoreception has become widely identified with the University of Manchester. It seemed appropriate, therefore, that, as the study expands to laboratories around the world, a summary of the pioneer studies (at Manchester and elsewhere) should be published by the University of Manchester's own Press. To allow this to be possible, I am extremely grateful to Hodder & Stoughton, my usual publishers, for releasing me from my contract for this one book. I also thank Thomas Baker, for writing some of the computer programs used in these studies, Wolfgang Wiltschko for pointing out shortcomings, errors and omissions in an early draft of the manuscript and Liz Oram for correcting the proofs and compiling the index.

Since my studies of human navigation began in 1976, many students, friends, family and acquaintances have assisted in the carrying out of experiments. These people are now far too numerous to thank by name, though, where particular people actually carried out particular projects, appropriate credit is given in the text. Here, I simply thank them all. Without their energy and expertise, the data-set on which the Manchester analyses are based would be far less substantial. I thank, also, the thousands of people who have now taken part in the various types of experiment. Almost without exception they have reacted with tolerance and good humour to treatments that are often bizarre and uncomfortable.

R. Robin Baker
29 May 1988

1

Introduction

'I don't go far in the beginning; I go some distance and come back again, then, in another direction, and come back, and then again in another direction. Gradually, I know how everything is, and then I can go out far without losing my way.' With these words, an anonymous Australian aborigine described (in Gatty 1958) the way he built up his knowledge of his surroundings during 'walkabout', that period of adolescence during which young males go solitarily out into the bush for several years and finally graduate in the art of survival and navigation.

Until the last few decades, training in navigation and the tracking of animals began for the young Australian aborigine as soon as he left his mother's cradle (Magarey 1899). Even before leaving on 'walkabout', a young child would have gained some knowledge of his surroundings through accompanying the family group on its wanderings. Not until adolescence, however, did an aborigine explore solitarily over any distance. According to Howitt (1873), the aborigine's ability to find his way over such large, inhospitable areas depended on intense familiarity: specific knowledge of the district belonging to his own tribe or family; general knowledge of the country occupied by neighbouring tribes. He knew the land thoroughly because he was born in it and had roamed over it ever since.

Any student or ex-student that reads this book will probably remember vividly their own 'walkabout': that time, probably in their late teens, when they arrived in a strange new city and needed to build up a whole new area of familiarity that was their own, not their parents'. Mostly the need was to find the best places to do or buy this or that and to pioneer the best, most economical routes between them. The aborigine's description of how he builds up his familiar area could just as easily be a description of the new student's movements in an unfamiliar city. The first few days and weeks in a new place are a period of intensive exploration.

Fig. 1.1. Australian aborigine. Photo by courtesy of Axel Poignant.

Of course, the city-dweller has a major advantage over a nineteenth-century Australian aborigine. This advantage derives from access to printed maps and a plethora of signposts and place-names. Even more valuable is the ubiquity of other, usually non-hostile, people from whom navigational information can easily be obtained by inquiry. There is another, vital difference. For an aborigine to become lost in the Australian outback could be fatal. Rarely is the penalty so extreme for the average student and city-dweller of the late twentieth century. Even so, there can be few people who, at some stage in their lives, have not experienced those moments of panic that come with the realisation that they are lost; that their navigational mechanisms have failed.

There is a widespread misconception that only long-distance migrants, such as some birds, need to be able to navigate and then only as they travel along the longest and most difficult parts of their lifetime track. In fact, navigational ability is essential to any animal with a home base to which the animal returns after exploratory forays into surrounding unfamiliar terrain (Fig. 1.2). As all mammals, including Man, and perhaps even all vertebrates, seem to organise their movements in this way (Baker 1978a, b), an ability for navigation is expected to be widespread, if not universal, among such animals.

All animals studied in any detail have been found to use a variety of senses and a wide range of environmental sources to solve the problems of navigation and orientation that confront them every day of their lives. One of these senses is **magnetoreception**, the ability to perceive the Earth's magnetic (= geomagnetic) field. So many animals are now known to possess a magnetic sense that I confidently believe the final search will be to find an animal that is magnetically 'blind'. Against such a background, it would be suprising if Man just happened to be that animal.

This book is concerned with the role of a magnetic sense in 'natural' human navigation (i.e. navigation without the use of printed maps or instruments). The techniques by which this role has been evaluated owe much to the techniques by which biologists have studied the navigation

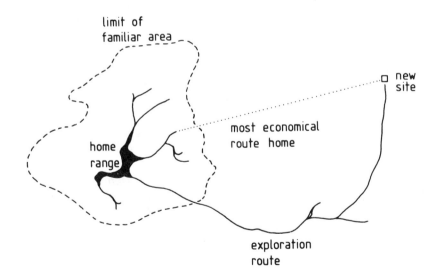

Fig. 1.2. Unless the outward journey is a straight line, the most economical route back to the starting point after exploration can be determined only by navigation. Re-drawn from Baker (1981b).

of other animals, particularly other mammals and birds. Throughout the chapters that follow there will be frequent reference to work on these other species. One aim is to view human abilities against the general perspective of vertebrate navigation.

For any animal to show magnetoreception, some means of perceiving the geomagnetic field must exist. One possibility is that animals possess a discrete sense organ, a **magnetoreceptor**, for which magnetoreception is the sole or primary function. A number of biologists are seeking such a sense organ in a wide range of animals, yet the magnetoreceptor remains elusive. Hypotheses abound but even the nature of the receptor is still obscure. Chapter 3 describes the search for the magnetoreceptor in Man and other animals.

The study of animal navigation has always been a subject rife with controversy and argument. Nowhere is this more true than in the study of human navigation and magnetoreception. One major area of contention has been the rigour necessary in the design and analysis of experiments before any conclusions may be drawn. Details of the experimental and analytical techniques that have been developed and the main arguments that surround them are discussed in detail in Chapter 4.

Numerous experiments on human navigation and magnetoreception have now been performed in Britain, the United States and Australia. Levels of performance in the different types of experiment have now been measured (Chapter 5) and the influence on these levels of different magnetic treatments investigated (Chapter 6). Using the most effective of these treatments, the role of magnetoreception in human orientation and navigation under a variety of other conditions (e.g. day, night, sun, cloud) has been established (Chapter 7).

The example of natural navigation by Australian aborigines given earlier is notable for its chauvinism. Throughout human, and perhaps even primate (Baker 1978a, 1982), evolution, females seem to have avoided long-distance, solitary exploration. Throughout Chapters 5 to 7 the question is considered of whether males and females might differ in their use of magnetoreception.

Chapter 8 discusses whether the behavioural evidence presented in Chapters 5 to 7 offers any new clues for the location, physiology and structure of the human magnetoreceptor. It also considers whether there are any clinical implications from the discoveries so far. Finally, Chapter 9 looks ahead to the next eight years in the study of human magnetoreception and identifies the areas most urgently in need of investigation. We begin, however, in Chapter 2, with the most basic of considerations: the role of navigation in the lives of humans and the value of magnetoreception.

2

Human navigation: the value of magnetoreception

Individual people share with all individual organisms the fact that they are each born at a site determined for them by their mother. Some time later they die at a site determined by their own migration. Between these two events and places they trace through time and space an invisible path, their **lifetime track** (Baker 1978a).

2.1. *Familiar areas and home ranges*

As humans, it is our subjective experience that we organise our lifetime tracks around an area of familiarity within which, most of the time, we know where we are and where we are going. In particular, we know when and where to obtain this or that 'resource'. Most often, also, we know the most economical route between any pair of resource sites.

The sum total of sites and routes with which we are each familiar make up our personal **familiar area**. In theory, this area could consist of all the places we have ever visited in our lifetime. Memory being what it is, however, we can probably claim to be familiar with only a fraction of these. Moreover, we are more familiar with some places than others. During any given 24 hours, we use only a small proportion of all the sites and routes familiar to us: our daily 'range' is much smaller than our familiar area.

When a range is part of a familiar area, it is termed a **home range**. Not only is a day's home range smaller than the familiar area but so too is a month's and a year's home range. Indeed, we each have parts to our familiar area that we shall probably never visit again. Perhaps these parts are now too difficult or costly to visit or perhaps the 'resources' they offer are no longer required or can be obtained more readily elsewhere. A major feature of our familir area, therefore, is that the sites are in some way ranked according to their suitability. The result is that whenever a resource is needed we know the best source. Such memorised information is being used continually as we decide where to go and how to get there.

Even for humans, it is by no means easy to find objective evidence for what, subjectively, we know to be true about our life within a familiar area. Suitable data may be obtained from: (1) observation of the frequency with which individuals return again and again to the same site while ignoring adjacent sites of apparently equal suitability; and (2) displacement-release or 'homing' experiments (Baker 1982). From such data, we conclude that use of a familiar area by humans manifests itself by site faithfulness and homing after experimental displacement. Yet, if we apply these same tests to virtually any other vertebrate, we are likely to obtain the same picture as for humans: site faithfulness and homing. Perhaps this should not be so surprising. Life within a familiar area has many advantages, leading, as it does, to economy of travel and efficient exploitation of available resources. With such advantages, it would be even more surprising if man were the only vertebrate to organise its movements in this way.

It is a safe assumption that all who read this book have little seasonal pattern to their shifts of home range. There are people, however, with a distinct annual cycle to their lifetime track (Fig. 2.1). Examples are some Lapps, moving to and fro between winter and summer home ranges in Scandinavia, and some Bedouin, travelling huge annual migration circuits within the deserts of Arabia (Baker 1978a). Few readers, however, would suggest that such Lapps or Bedouin are any less familiar than themselves with the area in which they each live and move.

This insight into the universal use of a familiar area by our own species has ramifications for our understanding of other vertebrates. The possibility emerges (Baker 1978a, 1981c, 1982) that perhaps all vertebrates share with us the sense of location that comes from life within a familiar area, even if some of them show long-distance seasonal shifts of home range.

Such evidence that exists (Baker 1980a, 1982, 1984b) tends to support the widespread relevance of the Familiar Area hypothesis, and probably few people would resist its application to the movements of terrestrial mammals, such as, for example, monkeys, elephants, horses, dogs, cats and mice, or perhaps even to birds. However, there has been some reluctance to accept the hypothesis for vertebrates such as reptiles (e.g. Swingland 1983, for the Aldabran Giant Tortoise, *Geochelone gigantea*).

2.2. *Exploration*

When a human or any vertebrate is born, it has no familiar area. By the time it is old enough to reproduce, it should ideally be exploiting with

(a) (b) (c)

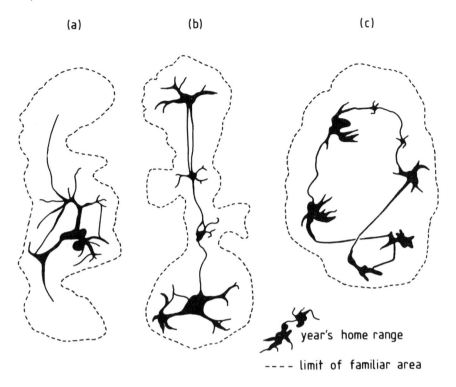

year's home range

---- limit of familiar area

Fig. 2.1. Variation in form of year's home range. Three examples are given: (a) static home range, e.g. most city-dwellers; (b) seasonal to-and-fro migration, e.g. Lapps; (c) annual migration circuit as for many nomadic pastoralists, e.g. Bedouin. Solid black shows the area used during the course of a year. The dashed line marks the limits of the familiar area. In effect, whatever the form of the year's home range, it crystallises out from a much larger familiar area. From Baker (1981b).

economy and efficiency the resources available within a suitably large familiar area. In some way, between birth and maturity, unfamiliar areas have to become familiar.

Often, a person first contacts a previously unfamiliar site through social communication, usually some form of written or verbal information. Such communication, of course, is in no sense a modern phenomenon, nor is it peculiar to humans. Even some invertebrates, such as Honey Bees, first collect information about unfamiliar sites through communication with other individuals (von Frisch 1967).

The role of communication in forays by North American Indians was vividly described by Colonel Dodge in his book *Our Wild Indians* (Dodge 1890). Ask a nineteenth-century Amerindian how to go to a distant place and he would simply point out the direction, even if it were 100 km away. Press him closely and if he had been there he would describe in minute detail the landmarks by which to navigate. Similar and monotonous as they may have appeared to a stranger, each hill and valley, each rock and clump of bushes, had its own distinguishing feature which he could describe. With this facility, it was customary for older men to assemble youngsters for instruction a few days before the latter were to go into unknown country.

The method of instruction was described to Dodge by an old guide, Espinosa, who had been a boy prisoner among the Comanches. When all were seated in a circle, a bundle of sticks was produced, each one marked with notches to represent the days. Starting with the stick with one notch, an old man would draw on the ground with his finger the first day's journey. Rivers, streams, hills, valleys, ravines, hidden waterholes were all shown in relation to prominent and carefully described landmarks. When all understood the first day's journey, the first stick was put away, the stick with two notches was taken out, and the second day's journey was drawn; and so on until the end. Espinosa described one party of young men and boys, the eldest not more than 19 years old. None had ever been to Mexico. Yet they set out from the main camp on Brady's Creek in Texas to make a raid into Mexico as far as the city of Monterey (an air-line distance of over 600 km) solely from the information fixed in their minds by these sticks.

Useful though social communication may be to ease the course of familiarisation, it cannot by itself be enough. Eventually, either solitarily or with others, individuals can only extend their useful familiar area by **exploration**; travelling beyond the current limits of their familiar area, visiting and evaluating new sites, and incorporating those that are useful within the expanded familiar area (Fig. 1.2).

Exploration is a means of collecting information for future use. Indeed, an exploring animal, as it travels through unfamiliar terrain with unappraised dangers and resources, is, in effect, trading the short-term disadvantages of exploration for the long-term advantages of life within a larger familiar area.

Characteristically, vertebrates seem to be more motivated to explore as adolescents than as adults (Baker 1978a, b, 1982). There is some evidence for rodents from breeding experiments and gonadectomy that this motivation to explore during adolescence is genetically based and hormonally mediated (Baker 1981c). The change in incidence of migration with age shown by humans (Baker 1978a) closely mirrors that by rodents, and it has been hypothesised (Baker 1981c, 1982) that in humans, also, the motivation to explore is genetically based and hormonally mediated.

The combined Familiar Area and Exploration models successfully account for a large part of the behaviour associated with the lifetime tracks of vertebrates and have the added advantage of providing a common interpretation for humans and other vertebrates. 'Evidence' that such behaviour is actually shown by non-human vertebrates, however, was initially (Baker 1978a) more anecdotal than experimental, and some authors (e.g. Swingland 1984) suggest that the models are, in fact, untestable (and therefore unscientific). Yet, since 1978, a variety of predictions based on these models have been made (Baker 1980a, 1982, 1984b) concerned primarily with rodents and birds. For example, it was predicted that when a bird is observed to change its migration pattern over the course of a few years, the change will be in the behaviour of the adults, not the young first-time migrants. Other predictions also involve specific differences between adults and young in terms of their activity-, search-, and migration-patterns and in their use of resources. All are testable by combinations of observation, radio-tracking, banding and experiment, and the first results have been published (Baker 1980a; Mather 1981). So far, the Familiar Area and Exploration models are supported.

In addition to such formal testing of predictions, recent radio-tracking studies of captively bred animals released into the wild (e.g. Oryx (*Oryx leucoryx*) (Fitter 1984); Otters (*Lutra lutra*) (Jefferies *et al.* 1986); Servals (*Felis serval*) (van Aarde & Skinner 1986)) reveal movement patterns and behaviour that can scarcely be interpreted in any other way than exploration and familiarisation. Nor can the few detailed observations of the establishment of an independent home range separate from that of their mother, by, for example, young rodents (e.g. sciurids (Holekamp 1984)). In their study of released and radio-tracked Otters in East Anglia, England, Jefferies *et al.* (1986) noted what they could only describe as 'bursts of exploration' followed by periods of consolidation and familiarisation.

2.3. *Navigation*

2.3.1. *Navigation as part of exploration*
Exploration has three major facets (Baker 1982): (1) the exploratory migration by which the animal travels beyond its pre-exploration familiar area; (2) habitat assessment, to determine which habitats are to be ranked high in suitability and incorporated within the expanded, post-exploration familiar area; and (3) **navigation**.

Schmidt-Koenig (in Baker 1985c) has questioned whether, by definition, navigation may be considered part of exploration. His point is that the familiar area expands as the animal explores. At no time, therefore, is the animal beyond its familiar area. Thus, if navigation is the means by which an animal returns from unfamiliar to familiar locations, it cannot by definition be considered part of exploration.

Sometimes, of course, an animal will return from exploration by retracing its steps or at least steering between landmarks passed on the outward journey. This is **pilotage** rather than navigation (Baker 1981b, 1982, 1984b). Except when the outward route of exploration is a straight line, however, the most economical route home will take the explorer across terrain that it has never before travelled (Fig. 1.2). Thus, if navigation is the means by which an animal finds its way to a familiar destination over terrain that is unfamiliar *in that* the animal has never before travelled that same route, then semantically we can accept navigation as part of exploration.

In the laboratory, rats are able to pioneer short cuts through mazes (John F. Shepard, unpublished work illustrated in Ellen 1987). When horses throw their rider and bolt, they, too, have been known to return home by a more direct route than the outward journey. Otters pioneer short cuts overland to avoid bends in rivers (Green *et al.* 1984). However, clear evidence that animals involved in *natural* exploration ever return home by navigating a direct route rather than by retracing their steps is frustratingly elusive. One of the problems is that, unless the animal has been tracked from birth (or release, in the case of the reintroduction of captively bred animals), it is not possible to know whether the animal is actually exploring (i.e. visiting areas it has never before visited) or simply revisiting familiar but rarely used locations. For example, Wolton (1985) shows some fascinating tracks of radio-tracked Woodmice (*Apodemus sylvaticus*). Individuals spent most of their time in woodland, travelling distances of up to 40–50 m or so from their nest site. Occasionally, however, such as every five to ten nights, individuals would make a rapid, long-distance excursion (150 m in 30 min) to an adjacent potato field, returning home about 2 h later. Wolton considered such excursions to be 'exploratory', but the mice may well have been familiar with the site from earlier (pre-telemetry) exploration. In any case, radio fixes were too infrequent (every 30 min) to be certain that the return routes did not retrace the outward routes (Wolton 1985, Fig. 7).

Definite explorations have been monitored in the several recent attempts to reintroduce, or reinforce, populations of particular mammals by releasing captively bred individuals back into the wild (e.g. Otters, Serval, Oryx, as above). In each study, at least some of the released individuals have been fitted radio-transmitters and their movements radio-tracked. Exploratory movements of surprising dimensions have been documented, such as the night that a herd of ten Oryx travelled through unfamilar terrain to a position 60 km away from their previous home range, only to return the following night all the way back to the starting site. Unfortunately, of the published studies of such releases that I have found, none maps in detail both the outward and return tracks. Although relevant data must exist, therefore, there are none so far published to show how often natural explorations by free-living or feral animals involve the retracing of steps and how often navigation.

Although not exactly relating to 'natural' exploration, perhaps the most controlled data on this question are available for geese. Led by human foster mothers, young birds walked along unfamiliar paths away from their home. When deserted, the birds rarely retraced their circuitous outward track but most often returned home by pioneering a more direct route (Fig. 2.2).

I know of no formal data for humans on how often we retrace our steps during exploration and how often we pioneer more direct routes; our own subjective experience, however, tells us that sometimes we do one, sometimes the other.

It is usual, as in Chapter 1, to view navigation in the short term as the means by which humans and other animals avoid becoming lost when

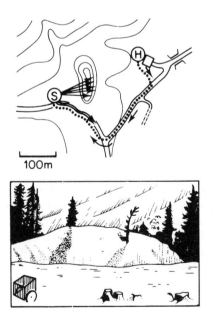

Fig. 2.2. Departure directions of seven domestic geese after passive displacement one by one in an uncovered cage. H = Home; dotted line = outward journey; arrows = departure directions. Drawing shows the view towards home from the release site, S, in a forest clearing. Redrawn from Saint Paul (1982).

in unfamiliar areas. Viewed in the context of exploration, however, navigation is much more than this; it is the means by which an animal pioneers the most efficient route from one resource site to another. In the long term, therefore, the efficiency with which an animal travels around within its final familiar area depends ultimately on its navigational ability. Of course, the route pioneered through navigation the first time an animal returns home from a new site may not be its final solution; on future occasions, when more information may be available, the initial solution may well be modified and improved by further navigational assessment.

In terms of an urbanite driving around a modern city in a car, inefficient routing within a familiar area may mean no more than a few lost hours per year and wasted petrol and money. Moreover, efficiency is likely to depend as much on ability to interpret the best routes from maps as on any ability to sense and pioneer the most economical routes while exploring. In terms of an aborigine trying to eke out a living over hundreds of kilometres of Australian outback, however, efficiency of routing may influence such major factors as age at death and success at providing for, protecting, and raising a family. For only a few generations at most, even in industrial societies, have humans in their everyday lives enjoyed relative freedom from the need to navigate efficiently without maps and instruments.

2.3.2. *Route-based and location-based navigation*

There are two broad categories of navigation (Baker 1981b): (1) route-based; and (2) location-based (Fig. 2.3). In route-based navigation the animal collects information during exploration, thus maintaining a more or less continuous awareness of home direction throughout the journey. Location-based navigation uses information available at a specific site.

Usually, we should expect these techniques to be complementary, but perhaps if one mechanism becomes, or is rendered, impossible, navigation could be achieved solely by the other.

When humans explore without instruments in the bushlands of, for example, Africa and Australia, they maintain a constant anxiety about the location of their home and often look back to fix their position in relation to their last point of departure (Gatty 1958). Lewis (1972) describes exploratory forays along winding trails in the flat, featureless scrub of the African bush in the company of indigenous tribesmen. At each change of direction his companions would require him to point out the direction of their camp until, in a day or two, he was reorienting quite automatically at each major twist of the trail.

Surprisingly, the demonstration that other animals show route-based navigation is relatively recent. In the 1950s and 1960s, studies of birds concentrated on mechanisms for location-based navigation (e.g. Matthews

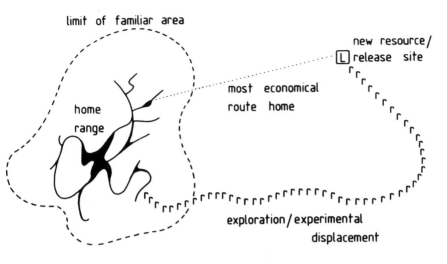

Fig. 2.3. Route-based and location-based navigation during exploration. From Baker (1981b).

1968). Since the first indication (Papi 1976) from detour experiments that pigeons also use route-based navigation, more attention has been given to the latter, particularly the possible use of smells (e.g. Papi 1982a) and magnetism (Kiepenheuer 1978; R. Wiltschko and Wiltschko 1978) by birds denied visual cues while being displaced. There is also some evidence for route-based navigation by mammals (Mather & Baker 1980, 1981a,b; Etienne *et al.* 1986; Etienne 1987).

2.4. *Magnetoreception*

2.4.1. *A role in navigation*
There are obvious advantages in maintaining an awareness of home direction by route-based navigation during exploration (Fig. 2.4). There are also disadvantages. Not least is the mutual interference caused by the conflicting demands of exploration and navigation on particular senses. If exploration is to be adaptive, there has to be continuous vigilance, both for dangers and resources. Vision, smell and/or hearing will be in continuous demand. Any background navigational sense that functions without interfering with these other senses should be advantageous. Magnetoreception, either to monitor the compass direction of travel or to follow the twists and turns of the journey, would seem

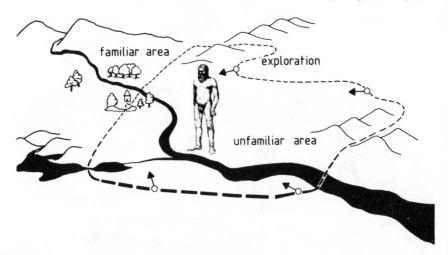

Fig. 2.4. When experienced navigators explore, they maintain an awareness of the direction of home. From Baker (1981b).

to meet most of these demands and to be a valuable supplement to the navigational armoury of an exploring animal.

Analogy may be drawn with the sense of time (Baker 1981a). The need is for a continuous 'background' sense, yet one that does not interfere with the concentration necessary for other activities. If time were only monitored consciously, its perception could interfere with the efficiency of other senses. Subconscious perception, with a facility to produce a conscious answer when needed, is of undoubted value. The same selection pressure seems likely to have acted on magnetoreception during exploration.

Three main potential roles for magnetoreception in navigation may be recognised (Fig. 2.5). These are the detection and use of: (a) the geomagnetic axis, to monitor angles of turn; (b) the geomagnetic compass, to fix directions relative to other environmental compass cues such as sun, moon, stars and wind; and (c) geomagnetic intensity, to judge position on a magnetic map. Of these three, there is clear evidence (Chapters 6 and 7) that humans use the geomagnetic field in their assessment of routes and judgement of compass direction. Whether any animal makes use of a magnetic map remains a matter for conjecture and controversy (Yeagley 1947; Moore 1980; Walcott 1982; Gould 1982a, b; Papi 1982b; Wallraff 1982, 1983; Baker 1984b; Able 1987; Klinowska 1987).

2.4.2. *Integration with other cues*
Although magnetoreception should be of major value for background

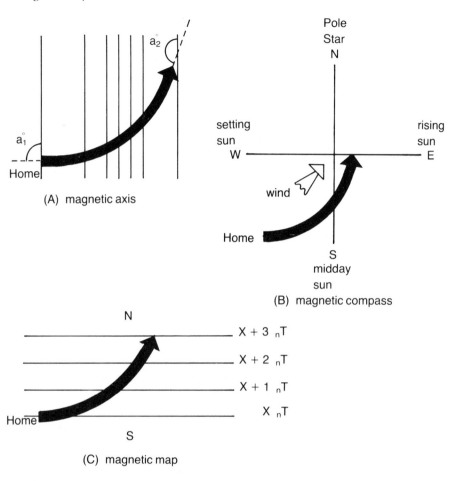

(A) magnetic axis

(B) magnetic compass

(C) magnetic map

Fig. 2.5 Three roles for magnetoreception in navigation during exploration. Solid black arrow shows an exploration route in which a person heads initially to the East and then veers gradually to the North. (A) Initially, the route is at right angles ($a_1°$) to the North-South axis and then bends until it is nearly parallel ($a_2°$). The difference between $a_1°$ and $a_2°$ is a measure of the angle through which the explorer has turned. Integrated with relative walking speeds on different parts of the turn, this allows estimation of the direction of home relative to the direction facing. In practice, this 'integration' is most likely to take the form of continual assessment of home direction relative to the body (i.e. initially 'behind'; eventually 'over left shoulder'). (B) The direction of home determined as in (A) may be fixed relative to absolute compass direction as judged from the geomagnetic field. At any time, absolute geomagnetic compass direction may be transferred to compass direction relative to celestial cues or even the wind. (C) In the Northern Hemisphere, the intensity of the geomagnetic field (XnT) increases with travel to the North. By comparing local field intensity with remembered intensity at home, it is theoretically possible to assess whether exploration has ended North or South of the East–West axis through the home site.

navigation by all vertebrates, including humans, there is no suggestion that any animal should navigate solely by reference to the Earth's magnetic field. Magnetoreception is just one element in an integrated navigational armoury that involves all the available senses and uses a wide range of environmental information (Keeton 1972).

If magnetoreception is used to monitor the twists and turns of complex exploration routes, home direction is in effect monitored continuously in relation to the axis of the body. Thus, in Fig. 2.5, home is initially directly behind the departing explorer but after a slow turn to the left it is over his left shoulder. The direction of home from the new site may then be fixed as a compass bearing or relative to major landmarks. The accuracy of this positional fix depends in part on the original accuracy with which the angle of turn is judged.

Clearly, the geomagnetic field is not the only reference system to allow twists and turns to be monitored. Fixed and distant points are particularly useful. Hence, celestial cues such as the sun, moon and stars, distant visual landmarks such as mountains and hills, or even acoustic landmarks such as the sound of surf may be used. So, too, may the direction of movement of clouds or the feel of wind direction on the body.

Geomagnetism, celestial cues, wind and landmarks are all external reference systems. Twists and turns may also be measured without any external reference. Information could in theory be derived from an inertial system based on an internal gyroscope (Barlow 1964), such as the semi-circular canals.

Magnetoreception and a sense of inertia share the advantage that they do not interfere with vigilance for resources and dangers. Nevertheless, the most accurate judgement of twists and turns should be achieved by some integrated use of the range of cues available. Suppose that: (1) accuracy of navigation is greatest if all senses are used continuously for navigation; and (2) vigilance for dangers and resources is greatest when senses such as sight, smell and hearing make a minimum contribution to navigation. The best trade-off between these conflicting demands during exploration is achieved when the frequency of integration of information from the different senses maximises the combined benefit to accuracy and vigilance.

Similar integration of information is valuable in the judgement of compass direction so that orientation to one set of cues may, if necessary, be transferred to another without loss of direction. Sun, moon and stars, as well as less reliable cues such as wind direction or moss growing on the poleward side of trees (Gatty 1958), may all be integrated with geomagnetism. The result is a coordinated reference system that allows constant orientation as, for example, day gives way to night, thick forest gives way to open country, or overcast skies give way to clear.

Finally, in theory at least, perception of the intensity of the geomagnetic field may be integrated with such information as height of the sun, moon or stars above the horizon.

2.5. *Summary*

Humans share with other vertebrates the habit of organising their lifetime track in a way that allows them to spend the major part of their lives within a familiar area. Such a habit permits efficient exploitation of resources. The actual level of efficiency depends in part on the accuracy of navigation: the mechanism by which economical routes are identified and pioneered during the explorations by which the familiar area is initially established.

Accurate navigation thus imparts two major benefits: (1) individuals are less likely to become lost during exploration; and (2) the eventual familiar area allows efficient exploitation of resources. Throughout their evolution, humans will have been as sensitive to the benefits of accurate navigation as any other animal. Only the most recent of generations have had the luxury of relative immunity to any shortcomings in their navigational ability.

Magnetoreception, the ability to perceive the geomagnetic field, can contribute to the accuracy of navigation in at least two ways. Judgement of the twists and turns of the exploration route permits continuous awareness of the direction of home relative to the body. Judgement of compass direction allows home direction to be fixed relative to external sources of reference. Moreover, magnetoreception may function as a continuous, subconscious, 'background' sense, perhaps similar to the sense of time. The result could be a navigation mechanism that for long periods during exploration frees other senses, such as vision and hearing, to contribute to exploration in other ways (e.g. in vigilance for dangers and resources).

Even so, the most powerful navigational armoury would involve integrated use of magnetoreception, other senses and a variety of navigational reference systems. Exploration is most efficient when the various senses are deployed in a way that is optimum for the conflicting demands of navigation and vigilance.

In theory, therefore, navigation and magnetoreception should have made an important contribution to the fitness of humans and other vertebrates throughout their evolution. An ability to perceive the geomagnetic field may or may not involve a discrete sense organ, a magnetoreceptor. The next chapter describes the progress that has so far been made in the search for this elusive organ in Man and other vertebrates.

3

The search for the magnetoreceptor

Humans see through their eyes and hear through their ears. Each sense is based on a discrete and separate sense organ (or, to be precise, pair of sense organs). Smell and taste are based on an array of sensory units scattered over specialised epithelia and collected together in more or less discrete areas of the body. However, not all senses are based on such clear-cut structures. Touch, for example, is based on sensory units scattered over the surface of the entire body. The sense of time seems to be based on a variety of scattered 'pacemakers', each perhaps involved with specific behaviour patterns or physiological cycles. The sense organ concerned with balance is located within a coalition of sensory structures that constitutes the ear.

Thus, some senses derive from discrete and separate organs. Others use parts of organs which have a variety of quite different functions. Yet others are based on information collected throughout the entire body. It would, of course, be very convenient if magnetoreception, like sight, were based on a discrete and separate sense organ that may be found, identified and delimited. Moreover, some hypotheses for the physical basis of magnetoreception do indeed predict such a discrete magneto-receptor and have sent biologists scurrying on a search through the animal kingdom in the hope of finding just such a sense organ. Other hypotheses, however, do not predict a discrete structure and warn that there may be nothing tangible to find.

In Chapter 8, I attempt a critical synthesis of relevant data to try to decide where the sense organ(s) is likely to be and how it might function. Here, however, I simply outline major hypotheses for the physical basis of magnetoreception. Where these hypotheses have given rise to anatomical investigations, the latter are also described. Each hypothesis is presented in a basic, even optimistic, light, without contradictory data. My uncritical aim is simply to provide a background to the experimental investigations that make up the chapters to follow.

3.1. *Hypotheses of magnetoreception*

Magnetoreception may be said to occur when a specific change in the ambient magnetic field, or in the orientation of an organism relative to that field, is converted within the organism into a characteristic pattern of nerve impulses (Baker 1985a). The magnetoreceptor is the site at which the ambient magnetic field is converted into nerve impulses. Hypotheses of the physical basis of magnetoreception are concerned with where and how this conversion takes place.

3.1.1. *Whole-body hypotheses*

When I lecture on human magnetoreception and describe the current search for a discrete and identifiable sense organ, it is commonly suggested to me from the audience that such an organ is unnecessary; that the whole body could be a magnetoreceptor. For example, when an impulse travels along a nerve, there must be some interaction with the geomagnetic field. The precise pattern of a given set of impulses may well depend, therefore, on geomagnetic orientation. Nerves within the brain, or even a network of nerves throughout the entire body, could, in effect, be the magnetoreceptor.

Over the years, a number of more specific hypotheses have been advanced that also involve the entire body. Most have been postulated with respect to birds. Thus, Yeagley (1947) suggested that the magnetic field could be detected by a flying bird acting as a linear conductor moving through the lines of force. Theoretically, this would set up a small potential difference between the two ends of the conductor. To be useful, the induced voltage would have to be measured to within a millionth of a volt. Stewart (1957) suggested that air friction on a bird's feathers sets up electrostatic forces which react to the geomagnetic field. Wallraff (1978) envisaged a bird as a form of magnetic probe which measures magnetic intensities. The principle of measurement is based on electromagnetic induction. Important parts of the probe are suggested to be located in the wings, and normal function would depend on flapping flight.

All such hypotheses require the animal to move before the geomagnetic field may be detected. The minute voltages involved would then have to be measured against a background of the far more powerful electrostatic field of the Earth (about one volt) and of the fluctuating effect of charged clouds (Slepian 1948). An additional problem for most humans would be the detection of small, induced voltages within a powerful electrostatic cocoon (generated by clothes made from synthetic fabrics) against the background of the electrostatic jungle that is the modern urban environment.

3.1.2. *Hypotheses based on modification of other sense organs*

Three sense organs, known primarily for their role in the perception of other features of the environment, have been suggested to have a second role as magnetoreceptors. These are electroreceptors, ears and eyes.

Electroreceptors   Sharks and rays have electroreceptors, the ampullae of Lorenzini, capable of detecting electric fields as low as 0.01 µV/cm. These organs allow the fish to detect the electric fields that surround their prey and are used in the final stages of a predatory attack. Kalmijn (1978) has suggested that they may also be used for compass orientation and to judge the direction of flow of water currents.

As an ocean current flows, its movement relative to the vertical component of the geomagnetic field generates an electric field. This induced field passes from left to right through a fish carried along head first by the current. If the fish turns to its right, the field through the fish is now from tail to head.

Active movement of the shark relative to the horizontal component of the geomagnetic field induces an electric field through the fish which passes from its dorsal to ventral surface. The intensity of the field is greatest when the shark swims at right angles (i.e. East or West) to the field. In theory, therefore, electroreceptors may be used to judge compass direction from the geomagnetic field.

Brown *et al.* (1979) have shown that the ampullae of Lorenzini in the Barents Sea Skate (*Raja radiata*) can detect the electric field induced by natural variations in the geomagnetic field. The receptor is sensitive not to the absolute value of the electric field but to its rate of change. The level of sensitivity is sufficient to detect a change in the electric field as small as 0.006 µV/cm/s. However, by itself this is not evidence that the electroreceptors are used for magnetoreception during orientation. Although we know that sharks and rays have a magnetic compass sense (Kalmijn 1978), and that the ampullae of Lorenzini have the necessary sensitivity, we do not yet have direct experimental evidence that these ampullae *are* the magnetoreceptors concerned. Appropriate experiments are in progress (Kalmijn 1988). Magnetoreception via electroreception is a possibility for marine fish because they live in a medium (salt water) that has a low-resistance return path. Fresh-water, and particularly terrestrial, animals do not have this advantage; nor, as far as we know, do they have such sensitive electroreceptors.

Ears   Wilkinson (1949) suggested that terrestrial animals might be able to detect the geomagnetic field if a conducting loop were to be oscillated in the field. This would generate an alternating current by the dynamo principle. Such a current might be easier to measure than the potential

differences postulated by some of the whole-body hypotheses. Rosenblum & Jungerman (1981) and Rosenblum *et al.* (1985) have predicted
the size and shape of such a magnetoreceptor. They conclude that a
structure only millimetres in size would be required to sense the Earth's
field by such induction and point out that the labyrinth of the inner ear
has many of the required characteristics. Measurement of the generated
current would have to be made against powerful background currents,
such as those generated by other physiological processes.

Eyes Talkington (1967) argued for birds that the lymph tubes in the
pleats of the pecten (a heavily pigmented projection into the eye from
the optic disc) could act as conductors in which an electromotive force
is generated. Danilov *et al.* (1970) also suggest a role for the pecten in
magnetoreception, but in a detailed search of the structure using an
electron microscope and other, histological, techniques, Southern *et al.*
(1982) could find nothing that looked like a magnetoreceptor.

Leask (1977), also, suggested that detection of the magnetic field might
take place in the eye, in the molecules of the retina, as a by-product of
the normal visual process. Specifically, Leask proposed an optical or
radio frequency double-resonance process involving the lowest excited
triplet state of a particular molecule (e.g. rhodopsin). The triplet states of
such a molecule have a magnetic moment and their energy variations
with the magnetic field are anisotropic, depending on field magnitude
as well as on field direction.

As originally formulated, Leask's model predicts that some light is
necessary for magnetoreception to occur.

3.1.3. *A discrete and separate magnetoreceptor: the magnetite hypothesis*
Despite much initial interest, Leask's model was superseded in the late
1970s by a hypothesis which, in fact, had its origins in a discovery made
as long ago as 1962. It was then that Lowenstam found that the radular
teeth of chitons (Polyplacophora) were capped with the magnetic material, magnetic (FeO.Fe$_2$O$_3$, sometimes known as lodestone). Until 1962,
it had been thought incorrectly that magnetite could be made only at
temperatures and pressures never found in living tissue. Eventually,
biochemical pathways by which magnetite could be manufactured bio-
logically were identified (Towe and Lowenstam 1967; Frankel *et al.*
1979).

The next, and main, impetus to the new hypothesis came with the demonstration that magnetotactic bacteria contained conspicuous inorganic
particles (Kalmijn and Blakemore 1978) that were also magnetic (Frankel
et al. 1979) (Fig. 3.1). It was these particles that allowed the bacteria concerned to orient to the geomagnetic field, a phenomenon first discovered
by Blakemore (1975). Perhaps magnetic particles embedded in specia-

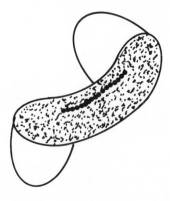

Fig. 3.1. The bacterium, *Aquaspirillum magnetotacticum*, contains a string of magnetite particles. Drawn from a micrograph by R. & N. Blakemore (in Maugh 1982).

lised, innervated tissue could constitute a magnetoreceptor even in insects (Gould *et al.* 1978) and vertebrates (Walcott *et al.* 1979).

Theoretical models have been developed to explore ways in which the unique magnetic and conductive properties of magnetite (Banerjee & Moskowitz 1985) might impart to animals the observed characteristics of magnetoreception (Kirschvink & Gould 1981; Kirschvink & Walker 1985; Yorke 1985). Of the suggestions made, two examples follow.

Perhaps, as the body of an animal moves within the geomagnetic field, the magnetite particles rotate, or try to rotate, to realign with the Earth's field. As they do so, they could trigger sensitive cells which would relay information to the brain by nerves.

Alternatively, magnetic deposits may exist in the form of a large, fixed and ordered array, particles with a particular size and spacing exerting a magnetic influence on each other. As the array turns within the geomagnetic field, electric, magnetic or even pressure changes could occur which trigger nerves ramifying through the tissue that holds the array. These nerves, again, would relay information to the brain.

Walcott (1982), on the basis of data collected for pigeons, has postulated that the acuity of magnetoreception might depend on the degree of alignment within an array of magnetic particles: strongly aligned arrays impart accurate perception of the geomagnetic field; 'scrambled' arrays impart reduced or no perception.

If magnetoreception depends for its accuracy on the degree of alignment of magnetite particles, an immediate question is when and how these particles become aligned. Gould *et al.* (1978) show that live Honey Bees possess in the front third of their abdomen a magnetic remanence that is naturally aligned. This natural alignment first appears in the late pupal stage and disappears rapidly on death. Remanence, with new alignment, reappears in dead bees if they are exposed to a strong magnetic field.

When a magnetite particle is first laid down in tissue, its alignment may be influenced by the geomagnetic field (Kirschvink & Gould 1981). In arrays, the alignment of later particles may also be influenced by the alignment of adjacent particles, depending on their size, strength and proximity. For any given individual animal, particles may be deposited only once, their alignment fixed throughout life. Alternatively, particles may be aligned and realigned, perhaps absorbed and redeposited, at frequent intervals or even continuously throughout life. The latter system would be of particular benefit if magnetite particles in arrays sometimes clump through magnetic attraction and if clumps are inefficient for magnetoreception (Baker 1985a).

Gould *et al*. (1978) found individual differences in the natural alignment of magnetic remanence in Honey Bees. These differences may well have depended on the pharate bees' alignement within the geomagnetic field while stationary as pupae (Gould *et al*. 1978). An equivalent process for vertebrates would be for particles to be deposited, aligned or realigned while the animal is at rest or asleep. If alignment is continuous or frequent, individual differences may reflect differences in orientation within the geomagnetic field while at rest or asleep (Baker 1984a, b, 1985a). For humans, such differences should relate to differences in bed orientation.

3.2. *Anatomical investigations*

Ideally, those of us involved in the study of animal magnetoreception would one day wish to be able to point at a particular piece of tissue and say 'This is the magnetoreceptor'. At the same time, it is clear that not all of the above hypotheses for magnetoreception would allow this wish to be realised.

If the entire body is involved in detection of the geomagnetic field, there is no discrete magnetoreceptor. Even the nerves that convey information to the central nervous system are likely to be diffuse. Neurophysiological response to the geomagnetic field would thus only be apparent within, or near to, coordinating centres in the brain. Demonstration of the mechanism of magnetoreception would be very difficult.

The task will be a little easier if magnetoreception is an additional, previously unknown, attribute of a sense organ that has some other better-known function. In such a case, there will still be no separate and discrete magnetoreceptor to isolate and identify. Nevertheless, neurophysiological study of the nerves leading from that sense organ would show a response to changes in the ambient geomagnetic field. This

would at least identify a site for magnetoreception, even if 'the' magnetoreceptor *per se* cannot be isolated.

The unfortunate fact is that only if there is a discrete and separate
magnetoreceptor will biologists ever have the satisfaction of pointing
the finger at some specialised tissue with its own, independent, nerve
supply. Of all the hypotheses described in the previous section, only
the magnetic hypothesis offers such a hope. As biologists scour the
animal kingdom in their quest for magnetite, we have to beware that
the undeniable lure of this hypothesis does not cloud our judgement
as to its probability.

3.2.1. *The search for magnetite*

In December 1981 I attended the fall meeting of the American Geophysical Union in San Francisco. No fewer than eleven separate research
projects aimed at finding magnetite and testing its role in magnetoreception were described (abstracts in *EOS*, 1981, **62**, pp. 849–850, and
1982, **63**, p. 156). These contributions were eventually collected together
into a large volume (Kirschvink *et al.* 1985a) devoted to the magnetite
hypothesis.

The initial stage in the search for magnetite in animal tissue usually
involves a combination of magnetometry (Fuller *et al.* 1985) and histo-
logy (Walcott 1985). Ideally, observed deposits of magnetic material are
then extracted and characterised (Walker *et al.* 1985b) by a combination
of Mossbauer spectroscopy (Frankel *et al.* 1985), electron microscopy,
electron diffraction and other analytical techniques (Towe 1985) to check
whether the observed material really is magnetite.

Magnetometry involves placing tissue in a senstitive (usually SQUID)
magnetometer and measuring the level of magnetic remanence (Fuller
et al. 1985). If any magnetic particles in the tissue have strong common
alignment, the natural magnetic remanence may be measurable even
against background magnetic 'noise' (Gould *et al.* 1978). Otherwise, the
tissue must first be exposed to a magnetic field hundreds or thousands
of times stronger than that of the Earth. This induces common alignment in any magnetite particles that are present, and the resultant induced remanence (i.e. saturation Isothermal Remanent Magnetisation
or sIRM) may be measurable by the magnetometer, depending on the
amount of magnetite present. As an example, Gould *et al.* (1978) found
measurable natural remanence in live Honey Bees, but not in dead bees.
There was no increase in remanence when live Honey Bees were exposed to a strong field but there was an increase in remanence in dead
bees. The authors suggested that in live bees the particles were nearly all
aligned whereas in dead bees desiccation had led to misalignment.

Tissue with magnetic remanence may then be sectioned and studied
histologically, using the Perl reaction (Hutchison 1953). Any ferric iron
shows as deep blue coloration.

In addition to chitons (Lowenstam 1962; Nesson & Lowenstam 1985) and magnetotactic bacteria (Frankel *et al*. 1979, 1985; Mann 1985), magnetite, or at least magnetic material, has been reported as found in Honey Bees (Gould *et al*. 1978; Kuterbach *et al*. 1982), butterflies (Jones & MacFadden 1981; MacFadden & Jones 1985), crustaceans (Buskirk & O'Brien 1985), fish (Walker & Dizon 1981; Walker *et al*. 1984, 1985a), reptiles (Perry *et al*. 1981, 1985), birds (Walcott *et al*. 1979; Presti & Pettigrew 1980; Beason & Nichols 1984), bats (Buchler & Wasilewski 1985), mice (Mather & Baker 1981a; Baker & Mather 1982; Mather 1985) and cetaceans (Zoeger *et al*. 1981; Bauer *et al*. 1985). It has also been reported as found in primates, including humans.

The first discovery of magnetic material in primate tissue was by Kirschvink (1981a). The cerebellum, midbrain and corpus callosum, but not the cerebral cortex, of the brain of Rhesus Monkeys (*Macaca mulatta*) was found to have a diffuse sIRM of about 25 picoTeslas, suggesting the presence of between 1 and 5 million single-domain magnetite crystals per gram of tissue.

Kirschvink (1981b) has also examined human adrenal glands for magnetic remanence. He found a measurable amount of high-coercivity ferromagnetic material which appeared to be finely disseminated throughout the tissue. Between 1 and 10 million single-domain magnetite crystals per gram of tissue would be necessary to account for the observed magnetic remanence.

Magnetometric measurements on 'soft' tissues from the human head revealed no areas of significant magnetic remanence (i.e. no readings greater than twice background noise level) (Baker *et al*. 1982, 1983). Specimens of skull, rib and sphenoid bone also gave readings less than twice background levels. In the thin but very hard bones that form the walls of the sphenoid/ethmoid sinus complex (Figs 3.2 and 3.3), however, magnetic remanence was obtained that was consistently greater than twice background. The range of sIRM (emu per gram) for all tissues tested is given by Baker *et al*. (1983). The sIRM of the sinus bones ranged from 3.02 to 31.58 × 10^{-6} emu/g.

Human tissue from all of the regions tested magnetometrically was examined histologically except for the bone of the skull and the sphenoid bone itself. Although a scattering of iron-staining materials was found throughout the soft tissues and in bone marrow, extensive concentrations of ferric iron were found only within the bone of the sphenoid/ethmoid sinus complex (Fig. 3.4). These concentrations are in the form of a continuous layer of iron-staining material roughly 2 μm thick and about 5 μm beneath the surface of the bone. The bone itself is about 200 μm thick.

None of the above examples of magnetic material in primate tissue (i.e. monkey brain, human adrenals, human sinus bones) has positively been identified as magnetite. In the case of the sinus bones, the source

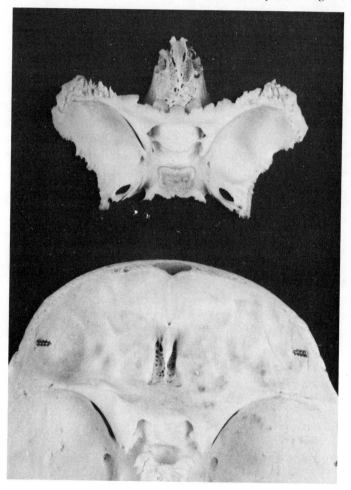

Fig. 3.2. The ethmoid/sphenoid sinus complex in humans, viewed from above. The lower part of the photograph is a view looking down from above into a human skull with the top removed. This view shows the 'floor' of the front part of the brain-case. The central perforated area (between the two screws) is the upper surface of the ethmoid bone. The same area may be seen more clearly in the top part of the photograph which shows the ethmoid and sphenoid bones after removal from the skull. The 'wings' are lateral projections of the sphenoid bone; the forward, perforated section is the ethmoid bone. The ethmoid sinuses are interconnecting cavities within the ethmoid bone and lead posteriorly (Fig. 3.3.) to the sphenoid sinuses which lie centrally and ventrally between the two wings of the sphenoid bone. Photo by Les Lockey.

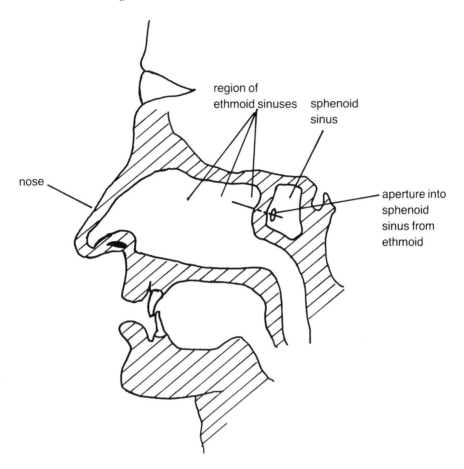

Fig. 3.3. Position of the ethmoid/sphenoid sinus complex in humans, viewed from the side.

of the magnetic remanence was planned to be investigated in collaboration with Joe Kirschvink, at Caltech. The first, and so far only, specimen that became available for testing was contaminated (Kirschvink 1983) through having been specially prepared to be photographed by being trimmed with a band saw.

Studies that involve examination of tissue from recently dead humans are always difficult due to the problem of obtaining suitable material. As a result, it has not yet been possible to study the innervation and other features of human sinus bones by electron microscopy. Instead, the research program into human magnetoreception at Manchester has had to be restricted to making inferences concerning the distribution

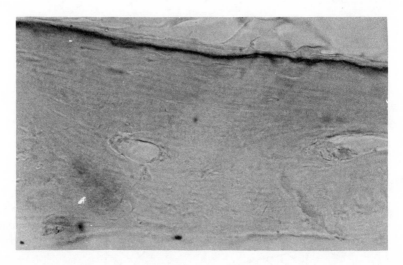

Fig. 3.4. Section through bone from the wall of the sphenoid sinus of a 57-year-old woman. Bones that form the walls of the sphenoid and ethmoid sinuses in the region where the two join are magnetic and appear to contain iron deposits that, after staining, show as a dark line 5 μm or so beneath the bone surface. Photo by Les Lockey from a section by J.H. Kennaugh.

of iron and nerve fibres in human sinus bones from our parallel studies of the analogous ethmoturbinal bones of rodents (Baker 1985a; Mather 1985).

Like humans, woodmice have: (1) a magnetic compass sense (Mather & Baker 1981a); (2) in the head, strongest magnetic remanence in the vicinity of the olfactory region (Mather & Baker 1981a); and (3) a layer that stains positively for ferric iron beneath the surface of the bones of the ethmoturbinal (Mather *et al.* 1982) and other (Mather 1985) regions. At least some of the magnetic material in the woodmouse head seems to be magnetite (J.L. Kirschvink, personal communication).

Electron micrographs of bones from the heads of woodmice show crystal-like structures (Fig. 3.5) ranging in size from 4 × 2 μm, comparable to hydrous iron oxides which could be magnetite precursors, down to 100 nm, within the size range of single-domain magnetite. These structures have so far been found only in the ethmoturbinal bones and are always clustered around nerve fibres (Jorgensen, personal communication). As far as we can tell, however, they are further from the surface of the bone than the layer that we observe histologically.

Presumably, it is pure coincidence that Pre-Columbian sculptures carved 3000–4000 years ago have consistent and distinctive patterns of magnetism. Sculptors in Mexico carved a turtle head with a magnetic

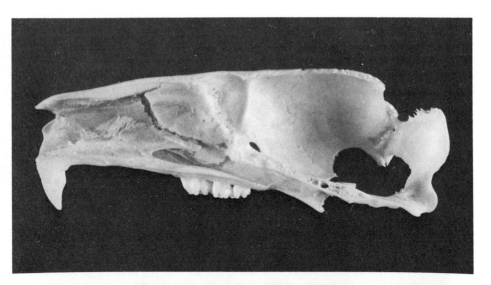

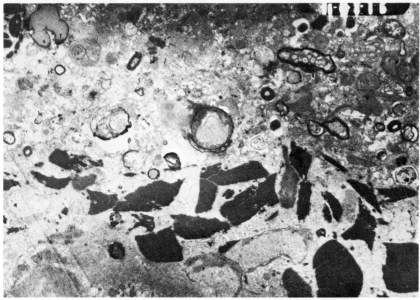

Fig. 3.5. Bones from the ethmoturbinal region of Woodmice contain crystal-like structures that are probably of iron and are associated with bundles of nerve fibres. The upper photograph (a) is of a sagitally sectioned skull of a Wood-mouse (*Apodemus sylvaticus*) to show the region of the ethmoturbinal bones. The lower photograph (b) is a transmission electron micrograph of bone marrow within the ethmoturbinal bones. The largest crystal-like structures are 4 × 2 μm. Rodent skull prepared by J.G. Mather. Electron micrograph by J. Morup Jorgensen (Aarhus, Denmark).

pole located in the snout (Malmstrom 1976), roughly in the region where Perry *et al.* (1985) now report the presence of magnetite. Of similar age in Guatemala are human figures in which the sculptors seem consistently to have located magnetic poles in the temples of the figures' heads and in the region of their midriff (Dunn & Malmstrom, personal communication).

3.2.2. *The sinal magnetite hypothesis*
The search for magnetite in vertebrates seems to have revealed a pattern. In fish (Walker *et al.* 1984), reptiles (Perry *et al.* 1985), cetaceans (Zoeger *et al.* 1981), mice (Mather & Baker 1981a), humans (Baker *et al.* 1983), and perhaps birds (Walcott *et al.* 1979; Walcott & Walcott 1982), magnetic material has been found in or around the region of the ethmoid sinus. In humans, these sinuses are on the mid-line between, behind and slightly below the eyes (Fig. 3.3).

As a result of this coincidence in the different groups, the possibility has been discussed (Kirschvink 1983; Baker 1984a; Walker *et al.* 1984) that there may have been an ancestral, vertebrate magnetoreceptor based in some way on deposits of magnetite in the region of the ancestral ethmoid sinus.

3.3. *From magnetoreceptor to brain*

Earlier, I defined the magnetoreceptor as the site at which the ambient magnetic field is converted into nerve impulses. Most often, we should expect these nerve impulses eventually to reach the central nervous system. There, they should be decoded and integrated both with simultaneous information from other sense organs and with past information from a storage site somewhere in the brain. Whether the conversion of the geomagnetic field into nerve impulses occurs throughout the body, within part of a sense organ that also converts other signals, or within a discrete and separate organ, we might hope that these impulses may be detected and recognised by neurophysiological techniques as they enter the central nervous system.

Our only lead so far comes from the work of Peter Semm and his colleagues (e.g. Semm *et al.* 1982, 1984; Semm 1983, 1988). Nerve cells in the pineal body of pigeons and rodents respond to changes in an earth-strength magnetic field by increasing their rate of firing. Moreover, each cell seems to fire in response to relatively specific changes in the ambient field. Some, for example, respond to changes in intensity, others to changes in direction, and so on. The authors also point out that the pineal gland is known to be a light-sensitive, time-keeping organ and would be an ideal site for the integration of combined magnetic and time-compensated sun compasses. The system also seems to receive input from the vestibular apparatus of the ear such that nerves respond to the geomagnetic field only when the head moves.

3.4. *Storage of spatial information: a mental map*

Information collected from the geomagnetic field, sun, stars, moon, wind, landmarks, etc. during exploration and perhaps integrated in the pineal region is only of future use if it results in the new site being stored within the central nervous system as a location on a 'mental' (Gould & White 1974) or 'cognitive' (Thinus-Blanc 1987) map. The accuracy of navigation is reflected by the accuracy with which the new site is placed on this map; the more accurate was navigation during exploration, the more accurately will the mental map of the familiar area represent the real world.

The study of human mental maps has shown that everybody normally has a more or less adequate imaginary map. Although these are frequently distorted with respect to distance and direction, they are nevertheless functional (Gould & White 1974). Only subjects with damage to particular areas of the brain appear to have grossly distorted maps that may prevent them from finding their way around. The part of the brain most involved with making and storing mental maps is not known with certainty, though the hippocampus is a favourite candidate (Thinus-Blanc 1987).

3.5. *Summary*

A number of authors have argued that magnetoreception is achieved by sensing electric fields or currents generated when the entire body moves through the geomagnetic field. In marine fish, such fields could be sensed by electroreceptors. Other authors have suggested that such induced fields may be detected within the inner ear or eye. Alternatively, molecules in the eye may respond to the geomagnetic field as a by-product of the normal visual process. The most popular hypothesis, however, is that there exists a discrete and separate sense organ that consists of specialised tissue containing deposits of the magnetic iron oxide, magnetite.

Magnetite, or at least magnetic deposits, have been found in animals from throughout the animal kingdom, including Man. Among vertebrates, the most common site for these deposits seems to be in or around the ethmoid sinus region and it is possible that this region contains the site of vertebrate, including human, magnetoreception.

Acuity of magnetoreception may depend on the degree of common alignment of particles in arrays of magnetite. Particles in the magnetorceptor may be in a dynamic state, deposition, absorption, aligment and realignment occurring frequently or even continuously. Alignment of particles may vary from individual to individual and be influenced by orientation within the geomagnetic field when the individual is relatively motionless, as when at rest or asleep.

Geomagnetic information may be integrated with celestial, time and other information in the region of the pineal organ in the general nervous system. A navigation 'estimate' of the location of a new site in relation to previous familiar sites may be entered and stored on a mental map, perhaps located in the hippocampus.

This chapter has provided a picture of the way that the geomagnetic field may be perceived and processed. No major evidence has been presented to support or contradict any one of the hypotheses described. The next five chapters present a variety of experimental data that show magnetoreception in action. Many of the results obtained have inferences for the nature of the magnetoreceptor. The implications of these results and additional data from experiments that aim directly to test the various hypotheses of magnetoreception are brought together in the penultimate chapter of this book, Chapter 8. There an attempt is made to evaluate how much of the picture presented in this chapter is supported by data from experiment.

Experiments have to be designed, and in the study of human magnetoreception, experimental design is paramount if any conclusions are to be drawn and accepted. The next chapter is devoted entirely to a discussion of the design and analysis of experiments and the controversy that has surrounded them.

4

Techniques for experiment and analysis

This is a long chapter. It offers a detailed discussion of the design, execution and analysis of experiments on human orientation and navigation. Such is the contentious nature of human magnetoreception that every fine detail of protocol has to be defended. Sceptics will consider such detail to be essential. Students of the way new scientific findings are treated by the scientific community and how slowly acceptance develops may even find the discussion fascinating. I suspect, however, that the general reader, interested primarily in the role of magnetoreception in navigation, will probably find the whole chapter to be exceptionally tedious. My advice to such a reader is to move straight to the summary section (p.86) at the end and, if necessary later, to use the main body of the chapter for reference rather than as text.

4.1. *Major types of experiment on human navigation*

The usual way to study animal navigation is by means of displacement-release or 'homing' experiments which may be thought of as enforced exploration (Fig. 4.1). Such experiments mimic closely the behaviour of natural exloration in that each animal is taken from its normal home range, displaced to a site it is unlikely to have visited before, then assessed for its ability to: (1) indicate the direction of home from the release site; and/or (2) return home.

In Chapter 2, it was suggested that magnetoreception may be used during exploration in two major ways: (1) to help judge the twists and turns of the exploration route; and (2) to help judge compass direction. In tests on humans, three major types of experiment have been used to evaluate the contribution of magnetoreception to these two aspects of navigation. All three types produce data for ability to judge compass direction, and one, the so-called **chair** experiment, tests only this ability. The other two types, termed **bus** and **walkabout** experiments, are

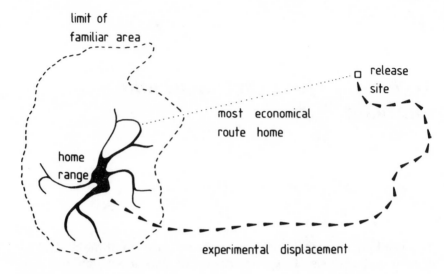

Fig. 4.1. Displacement release experiments mimic natural exploration. From Baker (1981b).

mimics of exploration and allow a direct test of the contribution of magnetoreception to navigation.

4.1.1. *Walkabout experiments*
In walkabout experiments, subjects are led along unfamiliar routes by experienced guides. After a while, at a designated 'test site', they are asked to estimate the direction, distance and compass bearing of the 'home base' from which the walk began.

Forerunners of the walkabout experiments to be described in this section were the tests carried out by Worchel (1951), Juurmaa (1966), Lindberg & Gärling (1978), Gärling *et al.* (1979) and others. For example, Worchel (1951) led blindfolded subjects along two sides of an isosceles triangle in a flat, open yard and then asked them to complete the triangle by returning unaided to the starting point. The real length of the hypotenuse in these experiments was short, usually less than 10 m. Lindberg & Gärling (1978) led blindfolded subjects for 100 m or so through culverts beneath the University Hospital of Umeå. The paths taken had, with one exception, 90° angles of turn and were approximately level throughout. At each stop, the subject was told by the experimenter to estimate direction and air-line distance to the starting point.

Walkabout experiments continue to be performed by experimental psychologists, both at the University of Umeå (Gärling *et al.* 1984) and elsewhere (Golledge *et al.* 1985) in their study of the formation of cognitives maps (see review by Spencer & Blades 1986). Unfortunately, however, from the viewpoint of behavioural ecology and sensory physiology, in none of these other studies are the results analysed with a view to answering the questions that are conventional in studies of animal navigation: (1) does a significant ability for navigation exist; (2) if so, under what range of conditions is it manifest; and (3) which parts of the navigational armoury are most important?

The philosophy behind the walkabout experiments carried out by myself and my collaborators since 1980 is rather different from that of previous workers. Our aim, as reflected in the name we have given this type of experiment, is to study human navigation under conditions that are as near as possible to the situation in which humans, throughout their evolution, will have had to navigate. In our experiments, therefore, subjects are not blindfolded and the walkabouts take place in rural settings, well away from the magnetic and electrostatic jungle that is the modern urban environment. If magnetoreception has had any survival value in human navigation, it should be detectable in walkabouts.

In our experiments, groups of people are taken to an area that they have never before visited, often 100 km or more from their normal home. They spend some time, often overnight, at a home base but are given no opportunity to explore or study maps of the area. At the start of the experiment, they are gathered together for instruction. They are told simply that they are to go on a walk with experienced guides and that, at the end, they will be asked questions. No indication is given of the aim of the experiment, the types of questions to be asked, or even of basic information such as compass directions. Magnetic treatment usually begins when they first aggregate (see Section 4.4.1) and questionnaires are completed (Section 4.3.2). Subjects are told they may talk to each other during the walk but are asked not to discuss anything that relates to where they are or where they are going.

Guides are people who are familiar with the route to be taken. Usually, there is one guide for about every five subjects. The guide leads a group around the route and listens to their conversation, censoring anything that may reduce individual differences in performance at the test site. Often, the guides are biologists, either university lecturers, postgraduates or schoolteachers and the subjects are students attending a biology field course. Guides and subjects quickly become engrossed in biological pursuits, such as collecting, identifying or counting plants and animals and the experimental aspect of the walk is forgotten until they reach the test site.

Walkabout experiments have so far only been carried out by myself and my collaborators (Baker 1985c, 1987b, 1988). Four locations have been used: (1) Woodchester Park Field Centre, Gloucestershire, UK; (2) Delamere Forest, Cheshire, UK; (3) Burnt Wood, Staffordshire, UK; and (4) Lucaya, Grand Bahama.

Fig. 4.2. Locations of British walkabout sites and origin of subjects. WP, Wood-chester Park (subjects from Manchester, Liverpool, Nottingham and Leicester); BW, Burnt Wood (subjects from University of Keele); DF, Delamere Forest (subjects from Manchester).

Most walkabout experiments in the United Kingdom (Fig. 4.2) have been carried out at Woodchester Park and have involved groups of subjects from Manchester (150 km distant), Liverpool (180 km), Nottingham (100 km), and Leicester (100 km). Experiments at Delamere Forest involved subjects from Manchester (30 km) and experiments at Burnt Wood, from Keele (30 km).

Walkabout experiments on Grand Bahama were carried out in collaboration with 'Operation Raleigh', a round-the-world expedition organised by the Scientific Exploration Society. Subjects had arrived simultaneously from: USA, Canada, Scotland, Ireland, Wales, England,

Channel Island, Oman, Hong Kong, Japan, Australia and New Zealand (Fig. 4.3). All were tested within 30 hours of arriving in the Bahamas and within 60 hours of leaving their country of origin.

Walkabout routes have so far been 2–4 km in length and have ended at a test site about 1 km from the home base where the journey began. Details are shown in Fig. 4.4. All have been through woodland with no view of distant landmarks. When skies are clear, sunlight or moonlight, although dappled for parts of all journeys, has been clearly visible at the test site on all routes. Star patterns, although obscured for parts of the route, have been visible at the test site on all routes. Dates and times of experiments along with prevailing weather conditions are given in Table 4.1.

Guides halt their group of subjects about 50 m short of the test site. At the test site, between one and five experimenters are waiting. Subjects then go singly to one of the experimenters (Fig. 4.5). When there is more than one experimenter, so that more than one subject may be tested simultaneously to reduce waiting time, the experimenters are at least 10 m apart to prevent adjacent subjects from seeing each other's response.

The experimenter holds a clip-board and printed sheet (Fig. 4.6) on which the subject first signs their name. Subject and experimenter face each other (Fig. 4.5), the experimenter holding the clip-board in a fixed orientation so that the compass bearing of the long axis of the sheet of paper is known. The experimenter then asks the subject for the following three estimates, pausing after each instruction until the subject has responded:

'From the centre of the circle, draw an arrow pointing towards [home base], the place from where the walk began. If you were a bird and could fly straight to [home base], which direction would you set off in?'

'You see those compass directions listed beneath the circle. I want you to circle one of them, the one that you think best describes the compass direction of the arrow you have just drawn. In other words, is your arrow pointing North, South, East, West or what? Now remember, that's not necessarily North at the top of the page; it could be any direction. I want to know the *real* compass direction of the arrow you have just drawn.'

'Now, finally, I want you to write down the straight-line distance from here to [home base]. Use any units you like: yards, metres, miles, kilometres. But the *straight-line* distance, not the distance you've walked; again, if you were a bird and could fly straight back to the [home base], how far would you have to fly?'

These questions have sometimes then been followed by others, such as 'draw an arrow toward north'; 'draw an arrow pointing to

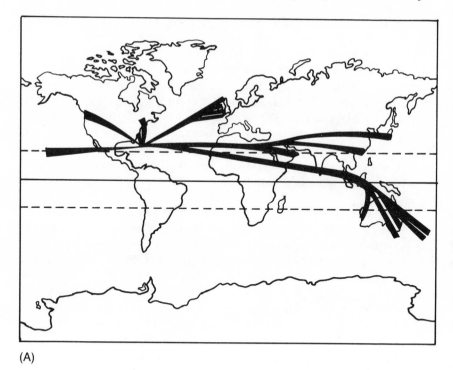

(A)

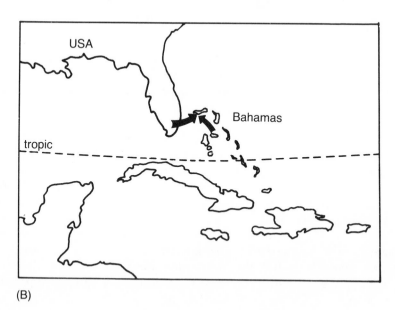

(B)

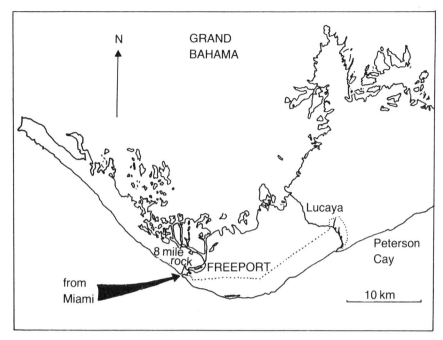

(C)

Fig. 4.3. Origin of subjects and journey to Bahama walkabout site.

(A) Subjects (18–24 years old) flew to the Caribbean from: Hawaii (1), Florida (3), Canada (4), Scotland (8), Ireland (1), Wales (12), England (59), Channel Islands (2), Oman (10), Hong Kong (3) and Japan (3) in the Northern Hemisphere; and from: mainland Australia (11), Tasmania (5), and New Zealand (3) in the Southern Hemisphere.

(B) Most flew to Miami, Florida (except those from Oman and Hong Kong who flew to Nassau, New Providence), then travelled by boat to Freeport, Grand Bahama.

(C) From Freeport, transport was by minibus to the camp site by the side of the Lucayan waterway. In addition to subjects from homes over 1000 km distant, 60 local Bahamians (16–18 years old) were tested from Eight Mile Rock High School. These were taken to Lucaya by minibus.

Manchester/Liverpool/Nottingham, etc.', 'draw a sketch map to show the twists and turns of the journey that you took from [home base] to here', but these data are not discussed further in this book.

The imagery of a bird flying back to the home base is used to give subjects subtle encouragement: (a) not to be too biased by the last leg of the journey (which they would be if they were simply to retrace their steps); and (b) to discount any up-and-down element of topography when they judge distance.

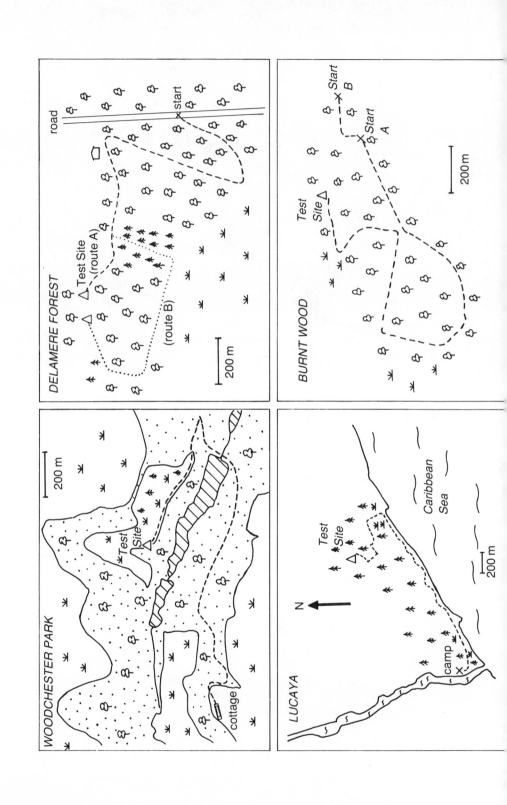

WOODCHESTER PARK

200 m

Test Site

cottage

DELAMERE FOREST

road

start

Test Site
(route A)

(route B)

200 m

LUCAYA

N

Test Site

camp

Caribbean Sea

200 m

BURNT WOOD

Start B

Start A

Test Site

200 m

Table 4.1. Walkabout experiments: dates and other details

Date	Place	Subjects			Treatment		Time	Cloud (/4)	
		M	F	Age (y)			h (D/N)	Walk	Test
1980									
24 June	WP	20	17	20	helmets	worn	09.30 (D)	3	3
10 July	WP	11	22	20	helmets	worn	09.30 (D)	2	2
7 September	WP	14	16	8	helmets	worn	16.00 (D)	0	0
21 September	WP	17	20	20	helmets	worn	09.30 (D)	3	3
21 October	DF	10	8	20	helmets	worn	15.30 (D)	3	3
1981									
23 June	WP	16	15	20	helmets	worn	09.30 (D)	2	2
9 July	WP	15	15	20	helmets	worn	09.30 (D)	4	4
1982									
22 June	WP	17	15	20	bars (V)	worn	09.30 (D)	3	3
8 July	WP	12	19	20	bars (V)	worn	09.30 (D)	0	0
1983									
21 June	WP	18	14	20	bars (V)	pre-	09.30 (D)	4	2
8 July	WP	8	16	20	bars (V)	pre-	09.30 (D)	0	0
4 September	WP	23	16	8	bars (V)	pre-	20.15 (N)	4	4
18 September	WP	23	14	20	bars (V)	pre-	09.30 (D)	1	1
1984									
14 March	DF	12	9	20	bars (V&H)	pre-	15.40 (D)	1	1
12 April	WP	9	16	19	bars (V&H)	pre-	09.10 (D)	0	0
26 June	WP	9	19	20	bars (H)	pre-	09.30 (D)	0	0
13 July	WP	7	21	20	bars (H)	pre-	09.30 (D)	2	2
2 September	WP	26	25	8	bars (V)	pre-	19.30 (N)	1	1

Table 4.1. (continued)

Date	Place	Subjects			Treatment		Time	Cloud (/4)	
		M	F	Age (y)			h (D/N)	Walk	Test
23 September	WP	16	17	20	bars (V)	pre-	09.15 (D)	1	1
8 October	WP	15	22	20	bars (V)	pre-	09.15 (D)	4	4
5 November	DF	6	17	20	bars (V)	pre-	15.05 (D)	0	0
21 November	BW	16	20	19	bars (V)	pre-	15.15 (D)	4	4
22 November	BW	16	24	19	bars (V)	pre-	15.15 (D)	4	3
20 December	LY	10	2	20	bars (V)	pre-	15.20 (D)	0	0
22 December	LY	28	6	20	bars (V)	pre-	08.20 (D)	0	0
22 December	LY	17	11	20	bars (V)	pre-	11.15 (D)	0	0
22 December	LY	26	11	20	bars (V)	pre-	17.20 (N)	0	0
23 December	LY	7	2	22	bars (V)	pre-	08.30 (D)	0	0
24 December	LY	1	1	20	bars (V)	pre-	17.45 (N)	0	0
1985									
14 January	LY	14	16	17	bars (V)	pre-	13.10 (D)	2	2
15 January	LY	6	22	17	bars (V)	pre-	13.10 (D)	0	0
13 April	WP	15	6	19	bars (V)	pre-	09.00 (D)	0	0
25 June	WP	15	19	20	bars (V)	pre-	09.50 (D)	4	1
12 July	WP	12	21	20	bars (V)	pre-	09.30 (D)	4	4
8 September	WP	14	12	8	bars (V)	pre-	19.30 (N)	0	0
16 September	WP	18	23	8	bars (V)	pre-	09.15 (D)	4	4
22 September	WP	12	16	20	bars (V)	pre-	08.55 (D)	2	2
20 November	BW	13	30	20	bars (V)	pre-	14.55 (D)	4	4
21 November	BW	20	29	20	bars (V)	pre-	14.40 (D)	4	4

1986									
12 April	WP	11	14	19	bars (V)	pre-	09.00 (D)	4	4
6 June	DF	16	24	20	bars (V)	pre-	10.20 (D)	2	1
24 June	WP	10	10	20	bars (V)	pre-	10.00 (D)	3	2
7 September	WP	23	25	9	bars (V)	pre-	19.30 (N)	0	0
19 November	BW	11	26	20	bars (V)	pre-	15.00 (D)	4	4
20 November	BW	10	27	20	bars (V)	pre-	14.45 (D)	1	1
1987									
9 April	WP	18	14	20	bars (V)	pre-	09.05 (D)	3	0
12 June	DF	15	15	20	bars (V)	pre-	10.00 (D)	4	3
23 June	WP	9	13	20	bars (V)	pre-	09.40 (D)	4	3
18 November	BW	11	23	20	bars (V)	pre-	14.45 (D)	4	4
19 November	BW	10	22	20	bars (V)	pre-	14.50 (D)	4	4
1988									
1 May	WP	16	7	19	bars (V)	pre-	08.30 (D)	2	2

WP, Woodchester Park; BW, Burnt Wood; DF, Delamere Forest; LY, Lucaya.

Age = median age of subjects (years).

Time = h GMT (Britain) or h EST (Bahamas) that walk began plus whether it was still day (D) or night (N).

Treatment = helmets or bars (V, vertical; H, horizontal), either 'worn' during walk or used for 'pre-'treatment.

Cloud = cover in quarters during walk and at test site.

Fig. 4.5. Subject being processed at walkabout test site at Delamere Forest. Photo by Les Lockey.

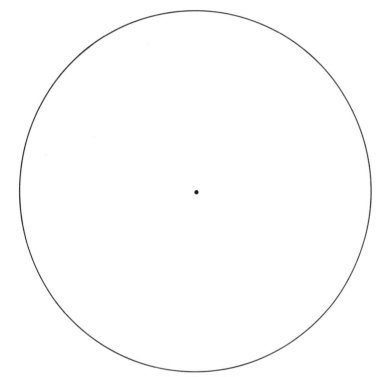

Directions: N NNE NE ENE E ESE SE SSE S SSW SW WSW W WNW NW NNW

Fig. 4.6. Test sheet used in walkabout experiments.

The sheet is removed from the clip-board and stored out of sight. The subject just tested moves to a site at least 50 m beyond the experimenters and thus at least 100 m from the subjects still to be tested. This avoids any interaction between tested subjects and those being tested or waiting to be tested. Departure from the home base by the different guides with their groups is staggered to avoid too large a build-up of untested subjects at the test site.

4.1.2. *Bus experiments*

Bus experiments are similar to walkabout experiments in so far as groups of subjects travel away from a home base to a test site at which they estimate the direction, distance and compass bearing of the home base. The experiments differ, however, in a number of ways. The key difference is that in bus experiments subjects are transported: they do not walk. This has the advantage that 'exploration routes' may be over greater distances and also that subjects may be blindfolded. It has the disadvantage that magnetic and electric anomalies association with vehicles, roads and the urban environment cannot be avoided.

An early, perhaps even the first, description of navigation during passive displacement was given by Forster (1778). It concerned Tupaia, a dispossessed high chief and navigator from Raiatea, about 150 km WNW of Tahiti in the Pacific. Tupaia was encountered by Captain James Cook and accompanied the Captain on board the *Endeavour* to Batavia, a distance of nearly 10 000 km. Despite the distance involved and despite the ship's circuitous route between latitudes 48°S and 4°N, Tupaia was able to point towards Tahiti at any position throughout the journey.

The first 'bus' experiment seems to have been carried out by Lord (1941) who displaced schoolchildren along a 3-km course through Ann Arbor, Michigan. As with the early walkabout experiments, however, the results were not analysed with a view to answering the questions that are of most interest in this book: (1) does a significant navigational ability exist; and (2) if so, under that range of conditions is it manifest? Published bus experiments aimed specifically at answering these questions are those of Baker (1980d, 1981b, 1985a, b, c, 1987b, c, 1988), Gould (1980, 1985), Gould & Able (1981), Able & Gergits (1985), Adler & Pelkie (1985), Judge (1985) and Westby & Partridge (1986).

The protocol of bus experiments at Machester from their inception in 1976 through 1979 has been described in some detail (Baker 1980d, 1981b). Since then, the Manchester protocol has evolved, both through changes in the hypotheses being tested and in response to the comments of other scientists. Modifications to the Manchester protocol have also been introduced by other workers in their own bus experiments. In this section, I shall describe the Manchester protocol as it was in 1987. Changes in experimental design since 1976 and differences in the protocol adopted by other authors are noted only where such procedures have become particular areas of contention or are known to influence results.

Most of my bus experiments have begun from Manchester University, which therefore constitutes 'home' in these navigation tests. Outside one of the main doors of the University, subjects board a bus while still sighted (Fig. 4.7). In some experiments, subjects have completed the questionnaire (Section 4.3) and begun the magnetic treatment (Section 4.4) before boarding the bus; in others, neither begins before the subjects are actually seated on the bus. After a period of between 1 and 20 minutes on the stationary bus, subjects put on their blindfolds. If subjects are to be instructed on compass bearings (only pre-1985 experiments) and told the initial compass heading of the bus, this is done just before they put on their blindfolds or just before magnetic treatment

Fig. 4.7. Since June 1979, all bus experiments have involved displacement by coach. Photo by Les Lockey.

begins, whichever is first. Before the journey begins, subjects are told they will be allowed to talk but are asked not to discuss anything relating to location or direction. Conversations are then monitored by the experimenter and assistants, and anything that may tend to aid or mislead is interrupted. The consequence of any deliberate or inadvertent communication of relevant information is that differences between treatment groups may be reduced. Therefore, while it is in the interest of the experiment to reduce communication, any breach is conservative (i.e. will interfere with, not spuriously enhance, the success of the experiment).

In 1979, bus windows were curtained on some journeys (Baker 1981b). Since then, windows have never been curtained or blacked out in any way. Pre-1983, single cloth blindfolds (from British Airways) were used (Fig. 4.8); since 1983, double blindfolds have been used (Fig. 4.9). These consist of the original cloth blindfold with a second layer consisting of swimming goggles lined with plasticine. This second layer not only reduces light penetration but also, by pinching the cloth against the nose, closes the light channel down the side of the nose that is always a problem when cloth blindfolds are used alone. Occasional journeys (1977, 1985, 1986, 1987) involved sighted people, not wearing blindfolds, and in 1985 and 1987 two extensive series were carried out in which

Fig. 4.8. In bus experiments at Manchester, subjects face the direction of travel and sit in pairs, side by side. In two series of experiments (March 1985; March 1987), sighted and blindfolded subjects sat side by side, alternating between window seat and aisle seat along the length of the bus. Curtains were used only in 1979. Photo by Les Lockey.

Fig. 4.9. Since 1983, blindfolded subjects at Manchester have worn a double blindfold: an inner cloth and outer swimming goggles lined with plasticine. Photo by Les Lockey.

half of the subjects were blindfolded and half sighted. On these journeys, blindfolded and sighted subjects sat side by side and alternated window/aisle along the length of the bus.

Routes used (Fig. 4.10) are the same as, or similar to, those described previously (Baker 1980d, 1981b). Details of some additional routes are given in Chapter 5. In particular, routes continue to be of a 'dog-leg' form, to avoid subjects simply extrapolating from the first part of the journey. Otherwise, the trend since 1979 has been to simplify the route to make it more similar to an envisaged exploratory foray (e.g. Fig. 4.1). A roundabout manoeuvre is still used (in which the bus goes round a roundabout two or three times; Baker 1981b), but, since 1983, only once per journey and then only within the first kilometre to aid initial disorientation. Care was taken to avoid complex manoeuvres near to the test site. In particular, since 1979, the bus never backtracked nor reversed to its parking position.

Before 1979, subjects faced at right angles to the direction of travel. Once, in 1979, four subjects faced backwards as they travelled. On all other occasions, subjects faced forwards in the direction of travel.

From 1976 to 1979, subjects left the vehicle to make their estimates individually by pointing and stating their compass estimates aloud. They then removed their blindfolds and made a second set of estimates while sighted (Baker 1981b). From 1981 onwards, each subject has on his/her lap during the journey a clip-board (clip at the top of the board,

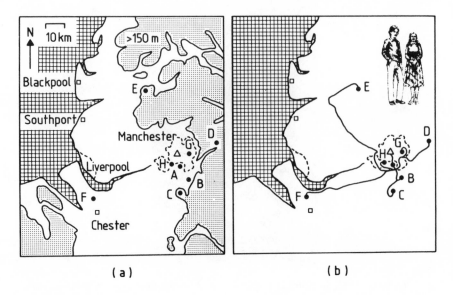

(a)   (b)

Fig. 4.10. Examples of routes taken in bus experiments at Manchester. For further examples, see Fig. 5.1. From Baker (1981b).

away from the subject), paper and pencil. All estimates are then made in writing without leaving the coach. Second, sighted, estimates are not made. During the change-over period in method of testing, some experiments employed one system, some the other.

At the test site, subjects are asked three questions (blindfolded subjects write down their answers *without* removing their blindfolds) (wording as in 1987):

(1) 'Make sure the clip-board is parallel to the bus, with the clip away from you. Draw an arrow pointing towards the [university/start of the journey]'.
(2) 'Write down the compass direction in which the arrow you have just drawn is pointing. Is it pointing North, South, East, West or what? Don't think of the sheet as a map, with North at the top. North may be in any direction. We want to know the real compass direction of the arrow you've just drawn. You may find it best first to work out the true direction of North, then work out the direction of your arrow from that'.
(3) 'Now, finally, write down the distance from here to the [university/start of the journey]. Use any units you like: yards; metres; miles; kilometres; whatever. But remember, we want the straight-line distance from here to the [university/start of the journey], not the distance the bus has travelled'.

These questions show only one major change from those asked in earlier experiments (Baker 1980d, 1981b). When written answers were introduced in 1979, question 2 was a direct replacement for the earlier, verbally answered, question which required the compass direction that subjects were from the university/start of the journey. Subjects therefore estimated the compass direction of 'home'. Consequently, their estimate may have used assessment of the compass direction of travel throughout the journey. In 1983, the question was changed to the above format to obtain consistency with the question that had been asked in walkabout experiments since their inception in 1980. By asking the subjects to judge the compass direction of their arrow, the question placed greater emphasis on an instantaneous assessment of compass direction at the test site, rather than over a period during the journey. All estimates of compass direction on bus and walkabout experiments were then comparable to those made during chair experiments (Section 4.1.3).

Early bus experiments at Manchester (1976–1983) used more than one test site on each journey. Such multiple stops were introduced as a means of: (1) studying the way navigational accuracy changed with time and distance; and (2) testing whether orientation used primarily a sense of rotation or direction (Baker 1981b). Able & Gergits (1985) make a similar use of such data. From 1984 onwards, however, the use of multiple stops has been abandoned and only one test site is used per journey. The reasons for this change emerge from the discussion in Sections 4.2 and 4.3.

Adler & Pelkie (1985) were under the erroneous assumption that, on journeys with multiple stops, my protocol at Manchester involved subjects removing their blindfolds at each stop before replacing them once more for the next stage of the journey. This was the procedure in the first four journeys in 1976, but not since. Instead, subjects wore their blindfolds until the last blindfolded estimate had been taken. Much of the discussion in Adler & Pelkie (1985), including virtually all of their note 8, is therefore inapplicable. This has been pointed out elsewhere (Baker 1985b) and the misunderstanding acknowledged (Adler & Pelkie 1985, p. 592).

Bus experiments have not only been carried out at Manchester by myself and my students. Virtually identical experiments have been carried out in the USA (Gould 1980, 1985; Gould & Able 1981; Able & Gergits 1985; Adler & Pelkie 1985; Judge 1985) and elsewhere in Britain (Westby & Partridge 1986). In addition to these published accounts, a number of authors have circulated unpublished results of bus experiments. Table 4.2 summarises all of the experiments carried out by myself, Table 4.3 all of those carried out by other authors. In some of those carried out by other authors, I was present as an observer or collaborator. This is also indicated in Table 4.3.

Table 4.2. Bus experiments carried out by author: dates and other details

Date	Journey			Subjects				Treatment	
	Start		Test	M	F	Median age (y)	No. naive	No. blindfolded	Magnetic
	Place	Time (h)	Distance (km)						
1976									
11 October	M/c	13.30	7.0	3	5	20	8	8*	none
18 October	M/c	13.15	7.0	5	3	20	8	8*	none
20 October	M/c	13.15	7.0	3	3	20	6	6*	none
1 November	M/c	14.15	7.0	7	0	20	7	7*	none
17 November	M/c	14.15	21.5	1	4	20	0	5*	none
22 November	M/c	14.30	40.0	7	4	20	1	11*	none
6 December	M/c	14.30	51.5	8	0	20	0	8*	none
1977									
24 October	M/c	14.15	6.0	6	5	20	11	6*	none
31 October	M/c	14.15	6.0	5	7	20	12	6*	none
1978									
4 December	M/c	14.30	6.0	6	5	20	11	11*	none
1979									
29 June	BC	09.00	21.5	26	16	16	42	42	none
29 June	BC	13.30	5.0	16	15	16	0	31	bars (V) worn
15 October	M/c	13.15	15.8**	18	13	20	31	31*	helmets worn
22 October	M/c	14.15	18.0**	17	12	20	2	29*	helmets worn
29 October	M/c	14.15	12.6**	18	14	20	0	32*	helmets worn
5 November	M/c	14.15	12.7**	17	15	20	0	32*	helmets worn
1980									
3 October	M/c	13.50	1.5	13	10	18	23	23	helmets worn
13 October	M/c	13.00	3.0	17	12	20	29	29	helmets worn
20 October	M/c	14.15	2.0	17	13	20	1	30	helmets worn
27 October	M/c	14.15	3.0	18	11	20	1	29	helmets worn

10 November	M/c	14.15	11.5	6	3	20	0	9*	none
10 November	M/c	15.15	0.2	6	3	20	0	9	helmets worn
17 November	M/c	14.15	11.5	5	5	20	0	10*	none
17 November	M/c	15.15	0.2	5	5	20	0	10	helmets worn
24 November	M/c	14.15	11.5	6	3	20	0	9*	none
24 November	M/c	15.15	0.2	6	3	20	0	9	helmets worn
1981									
19 October	M/c	13.25	2.5	14	11	20	25	25	bars (V) worn
26 October	M/c	14.20	2.7	14	8	20	0	22	bars (V) worn
2 November	M/c	14.20	3.1	14	11	20	1	25	bars (V) worn
9 November	M/c	14.15	2.4	12	11	20	0	23	bars (V) worn
1982									
25 October	M/c	14.20	1.5	16	12	20	28	28	bars (V) worn
1 November	M/c	14.15	2.5	13	11	20	0	24	bars (V) worn
8 November	M/c	14.15	3.0	15	13	20	2	28	bars (V) worn
1983									
14 November	M/c	14.32	5.1	11	12	20	23	23	bars (V) pre-
21 November	M/c	14.30	1.4	10	12	20	0	22	bars (V) pre-
28 November	M/c	14.25	3.2	10	12	20	0	22	bars (V) pre-
1984									
14 March	M/c	14.40	39.0	12	9	19	21	21	barsV&H pre-
29 October	M/c	14.27	17.1	4	16	20	20	20*	bars (V) pre-
1985									
28 March	M/c	11.00	2.5	22	28	17	50	26	bars (V) pre-
28 March	M/c	12.00	2.3	24	26	17	50	26	bars (V) pre-
28 March	M/c	14.00	2.4	13	37	17	50	24	bars (V) pre-
28 March	M/c	15.00	2.6	15	35	17	50	25	bars (V) pre-
29 March	M/c	10.55	2.5	20	30	17	50	26	bars (V) pre-
29 March	M/c	12.00	2.3	26	24	17	50	26	bars (V) pre-
29 March	M/c	14.00	2.4	17	33	17	50	24	bars (V) pre-
29 March	M/c	14.58	2.6	18	32	17	50	24	bars (V) pre-
14 June	M/c	13.30	3.4	13	29	20	42	22	bars (V) pre-
2 July	Aix	14.15	52.0	19	10	40?	30	0	none

Table 4.2. (continued)

Date	Journey			Subjects					Treatment
	Start		Test	M	F	Median age (y)	No. naive	No. blindfolded	Magnetic
	Place	Time (h)	Distance (km)						
1986									
6 June	DF	14.10	35.0	16	24	20	40	0	none–alcohol
1987									
26 March	M/c	10.30	2.5	24	26	17	50	24	bars (V) pre-
26 March	M/c	11.15	2.3	25	25	17	50	26	bars (V) pre-
26 March	M/c	13.30	2.4	25	25	17	50	26	bars (V) pre-
26 March	M/c	14.40	2.6	24	26	17	50	25	bars (V) pre-
27 March	M/c	10.15	2.5	25	25	17	50	25	bars (V) pre-
27 March	M/c	11.45	2.3	25	25	17	50	24	bars (V) pre-
27 March	M/c	13.40	2.4	22	28	17	50	25	bars (V) pre-
27 March	M/c	14.30	2.6	13	21	17	34	18	bars (V) pre-
12 June	DF	14.00	35.0	15	15	20	30	0	none–alcohol

M/c, Manchester; BC, Barnard Castle; Aix, Aix-en-Provence (France); DF, Delamere Forest.

Time, h GMT (Britain) or CEDST (France).

Distance = air-line distance from start to first test site (except ** when full data were only collected at last test site).

Naïve subject = subject on first bus experiment.

Treatment: number blindfolded (* indicates that, after making a blindfolded estimate, subjects then removed blindfolds and made a sighted estimate); and type of magnetic manipulation (either none or subjects wore or were pretreated with helmets or bars (V = vertically aligned; H = horizontally aligned)).

Table 4.3. Some details of bus experiments by workers other than author

Year	Place	Main worker	RRB present (Y/N)	Published (Y/N)
British experiments				
1980–82	Sheffield	Westby	N	Y
1981	Durham	Greenwood	N	N
1983–84	Keele	Campion	Y	N
American experiments				
1980	Cornell	Keeton	N	N
1980	Princeton	Gould	N	Y
1980	Albany	Able	N	Y
1981	Princeton	Gould	Y	Y
1981	Cornell	Pelkie	Y	Y
1981	Swarthmore	Leitner	N	N
1981	New Jersey	Rosenthal	N	N
1981	Albany	Judge	N	Y
1981–82	Cornell	Adler	N	Y

Further details in Gould (1980); Gould & Able (1981); Able & Gergits (1985); Adler & Pelkie (1985); Baker (1985b, 1987c); Gould (1985); Judge (1985).

4.1.3. *Chair experiments*

At first sight, the simplest test for a sense of geographical direction is to sit someone on a rotatable chair, deprive them of all useful cues except the ambient magnetic field, turn the chair, and ask them to estimate the compass direction in which they are facing each time the chair stops. If an ability to judge direction under such conditions is shown, some means of changing the magnetic field then checks whether the subject is using magnetoreception or some other, non-magnetic, mechanism.

Since December 1980, over 1000 different subjects have taken part in such chair experiments carried out by myself and my students from Manchester University. The equipment used is illustrated in Fig. 4.11.

The chair is made of wood with brass and aluminium fittings. Approximately 50% of tests have taken place in a magnetically 'quiet' environment: a hut specially constructed from wood, brass and aluminium on the edge of woodland in rural Gloucestershire, 100 m from the only building within nearly a 1-km radius. One series took place in open woodland (without a hut) near the Lucayan Waterway, Grand Bahama. In both of these locations, the ambient magnetic field is a normal geomagnetic field. Remaining experiments have taken place in rooms at the University of Manchester and elsewhere in Britain. In these, electromagnetic noise and magnetic anomalies could not be avoided. Rooms were only considered if the ambient magnetic field fell within the range: intensity, 40 000 to 60 000 nT; inclination, 55° to 85°; declination, 345° to

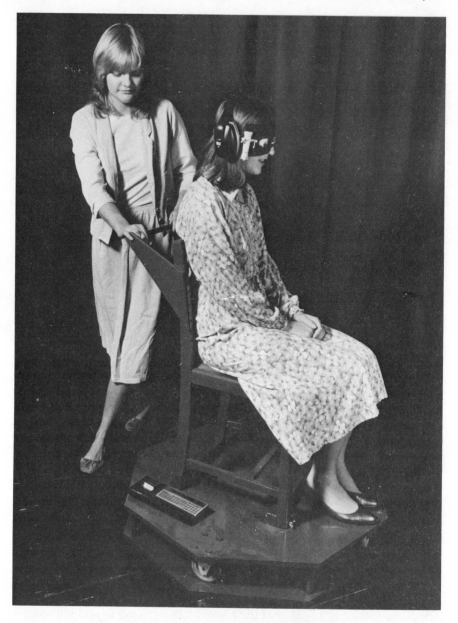

Fig. 4.11. Experimental set-up for chair experiments. The TRS 80 computer that runs the experiment is normally behind the subject and carried by the experimenter, but has been placed to the side for illustration. Photo by Les Lockey.

15°. Even then, only if a pilot series of 10 female subjects, aged 18–22 years, were able to orient significantly ($P < 0.05$) better than could be expected from guesswork (Section 4.2) was the room finally adopted for further experiments.

At each test run, a subject enters the testing room and sits on the chair while still sighted. The chair is then turned and the subject is shown the eight different directions (N, NE, E, etc.) that the experimenter may use. The subject is then double-blindfolded (an inner, heavy-cotton, blindfold and an outer pair of swimming goggles lined with plasticine) and fitted with ear-muffs (Fig. 4.11).

At present (1988) a test run involves the subject making nine (as opposed to 20 or 12 for tests in 1980; eight from 1980 to 1983) estimates of compass direction during which time the experimenter does not speak. Each estimate is preceded by the experimenter rotating the chair clockwise (270–540°) and then anticlockwise (angle ≤ 360°). Whenever the chair stops, the subject says aloud the compass direction he or she thinks they are facing.

The sequences of directions in which the subject is to be faced are determined by a TRS 80 'pocket' computer and printer (Fig. 4.11). A random number program produces directions that are printed by the computer, one at a time, during the experiment. The computer accepts and prints each estimate as it is made and has the facility at the end of the test to compute and print out the mean vector ($e°$, r) of the nine angular errors associated with the nine estimates of compass direction (see Section 4.2). Murphy (1987) analysed 11 511 directions output by this program to check that the directions really were being selected randomly. The mean direction (where North = 0°) was −113° (i.e. approximately WSW) with a mean vector length (r) of 0.007. The probability of these occurring by chance (Rayleigh z-test; Batschelet 1981) is 0.569. We can accept, therefore, that there was no bias to the directions in which the subjects were faced.

An extensive series of chair experiments, involving over 2000 schoolchildren, has also been carried out at Manchester by Murphy (1987). Gai Murphy carried out research for a PhD under my supervision from October 1982 to September 1986. The subject of her research was the development of compass orientation in children. However, an equally important and mutually understood aim of her work at the outset was to determine whether chair experiments would provide evidence for magnetoreception when performed by someone other than myself. Naturally, in order for this aspect of her research to be meaningful, it was necessary for her to work as independently and as 'blind' as was compatible with postgraduate research. Consequently, whereas the protocol and equipment she used were identical to mine, the study was otherwise her own. The points of similarity and difference between our two studies are therefore important pointers to the replicability of results when as many aspects of the techniques used are as similar as possible.

The study by Murphy (1987) is the only true repeat of my chair experiments. However, a number of other authors have performed their own versions (Zusne & Allen 1981; Fildes *et al.* 1984; Kirschvink *et al.* 1985b). In addition to these published studies, Dr Mary Campion of the University of Keele, UK, has carried out an extensive series of chair experiments (Campion, in preparation). The studies at Tulsa, USA (Zusne & Allen 1981), near Melbourne, Australia (Fildes *et al.* 1984), and at Keele (Campion, in preparation) all involved leading blindfolded subjects on tortuous walks to an unfamiliar test site where the subjects were rotated and then asked to judge compass direction. The study by Kirschvink *et al.* (1985b) at Caltech, USA, involved testing subjects in an artificial magnetic field that changed between each estimate.

RAW DATA

predicted direction

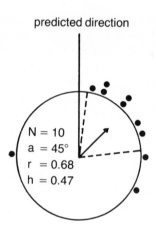

Fig.4.12. Circular statistics and the conventions used in this book.

Raw data: The vertical line indicates the direction to be estimated by the subject. Each dot is an individual's estimate of this direction. The *mean vector* for the ten estimates shown is represented by the oblique arrow. The mean vector has angle $a°$ and length r. If all estimates were in precisely the same direction, $r = 1.0$. If the estimates are distributed uniformly around 360°, $r = 0.0$. The arrow is drawn proportional to the radius of the circle: when $r = 1$, the length of the arrow = the radius; when $r = 0$, the arrow has no length and is not shown. The component of the mean vector in the predicted direction is the *homeward component*. When $a = 0°$, $h = r$. When all estimates are in precisely the predicted direction, $h = +1.0$. When all estimates are in precisely the opposite direction, $h = -1.0$. When the distribution is uniform or when the mean angle is at right angles to the home direction. $h = 0.0$. The probability of obtaining the observed homeward component by chance (*V*-test) may be placed as an exact *P*-value inside the circle (not shown).

4.2. *Statistical analysis of estimates of direction and distance*

4.2.1. *Estimates of direction: circular statistics*

Data for estimates of direction such as are generated by experiments on orientation and navigation are usually analysed by a branch of statistics known as circular statistics. The tests used in this book are those conventional in the study of navigation by non-human animals and are all described by Batschelet (1981). (See Fig. 4.12.)

Vector analysis Essentially, estimates of direction are treated as vectors and subjected to a form of vector analysis. A mean vector is calculated which has both direction ($a°$) and length (r). Most often, estimates of direction are expressed relative to some predicted direction (e.g. 'home'

MEAN VECTOR + 95% CONFIDENCE LIMITS   N = 10

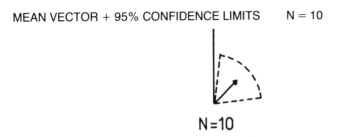

N =10

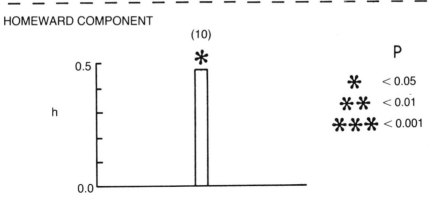

Fig. 4.12. cont.

Mean vector +95% confidence limits: As long as the scatter of estimates is not too great, 95% confidence limits may be attached to the mean vector. When (as shown) the confidence limits of the mean vector do not include the predicted direction, the mean vector is significantly different from the predicted direction at the 5% level.

Homeward component: A convenient way of expressing the strength of orientation is to show the homeward component as a bar. The taller the bar (up the page), the stronger the orientation in the predicted direction. Sample size is shown in brackets above the bar. The probability of obtaining an *h*-value so much greater than zero (*V*-test) may be indicated by asterisk code, as shown.

direction; true compass direction) as an error, clockwise errors having a positive sign, counter-clockwise errors a negative sign. Thus, the mean direction ($a°$) of a set of estimates is usually presented as a mean error ($e°$) relative to the predicted direction (0°). The length (r) of the mean vector takes a value between limits of 0.0, when estimates are completely uniform, and 1.0, when estimates show complete agreement. As long as the scatter of estimates is not too great, 95% confidence limits to the mean vector may be calculated (or, as in this book, obtained from the graphs presented by Batschelet 1981).

Homeward component   The often-called 'homeward component' (h) of the mean vector (i.e. the component in the 'home' or other predicted direction) takes a value between limits of +1.0, when all estimates are 0° in error, and −1.0, when all estimates are 180° in error. The homeward component is the most convenient measure by which to describe the level of performance of groups of people in their attempts to estimate direction.

Tests of significance   The probability that a given value of r is greater than 0.0 by chance is determined by Rayleigh's z-test; the probability that a given homeward component is greater than (i.e. more positive than) 0.0 by chance is determined by the V-test. Normally, significance levels attached to particular values of z and V are determined from tables (e.g. in Batschelet 1981). However, in this book, exact probabilities are used. The BASIC program for the algorithm used to calculate these from mean vectors was written and provided by the orientation research group at Cornell University (Pelkie, personal communication).

In 1981, Aneshansley & Larkin published an article on the use and interpretation of the V-test that has proved to be widely influential. They pointed out that it was possible for mean vectors to be significantly non-uniform by the V-test, yet could still have confidence intervals that excluded the predicted direction (e.g. a mean error of 10° ± 9°). In other words, a mean direction could be significantly different from the predicted direction, yet still be significant by the V-test. As a result, they laid down two ground rules that most authors have since followed: (1) data should not be described as *significantly clustered about the predicted direction* simply because the V-test yields a P-value less than 0.05; and (2) homeward orientation should only be accepted as occurring if both the V-test (or z-test) yields significance *and* the confidence intervals of the mean vector include the home direction.

Whereas there are no problems associated with following the first rule, the second often produces anomalies equally as disconcerting as those Aneshansley & Larkin (1981) sought to avoid. To illustrate this anomaly, suppose that two groups of 100 people each estimate the direction of home. Every single person in the first group points just $1°$ clockwise of the true direction; the mean vector is given by: $e = 1 \pm 0°$; $r = 1.000$. The second group is much more scattered in its estimates, producing a mean vector of $e = 40 \pm 60°$; $r = 0.160$. Both are significant by the *V*-test, but the strength of homeward orientation is clearly and significantly different, the homeward component for the first group being effectively 1.000, that for the second being only 0.123. Yet, according to Aneshansley & Larkin's second rule, we can accept homeward orientation only for the second group, not for the first!

The situation is clearly unsatisfactory. Moreover, a neat solution is probably unattainable. In this book, if I use the phrase 'homeward orientation' (or 'compass orientation'), it is only when Aneshansley & Larkin's criteria are not violated. Most often, however, I avoid the concept and centre discussion on the *strength* of homeward orientation as reflected by the homeward component (and tested for significance by the *V*-test).

Two-sample tests   When subjects are exposed to two or more different treatments or sets of conditions, it is necessary to compare the two groups to determine the probability that observed differences could have arisen by chance. In this book, two tests are used for the comparison of estimates of direction. Most commonly, the null hypothesis is that the strength of homeward (or compass) orientation does not differ between the two treatment groups (e.g. sighted versus blindfolded). On such occasions, Wallraff's modification of the Mann–Whitney *U*-test is used (Batschelet 1981), with estimates ranked in order of size of angular error (ignoring sign) relative to the predicted direction. Occasionally, however, the important question is whether errors are clockwise or anticlockwise (e.g. morning versus afternoon estimates of compass direction by sighted subjects with the sun shining), rather than simple accuracy of orientation. On these occasions, Watson's $U^2_{m,n}$ test is used instead (Batschelet 1981).

The test statistic of the Mann–Whitney *U*-test is *U*. The probability that a given value of *U* could occur by chance, given the sizes of the two samples, may then be checked in the appropriate table from a set covering a range of sample sizes (e.g. in Siegel 1956). When one of the samples is larger than 20, however, the *U*-value may be converted to the *z*-parameter of the normal distribution and an exact probability obtained from an appropriate table of *z* (e.g. Table A, Siegel 1956). Such exact probabilities are particularly useful when a series of experiments are to be checked for replicability using Fisher's method for combining probabilities (see Section 4.2.4).

Occasionally, it is useful to compare *z*-values calculated from two applications of the Mann–Whitney *U*-test to determine if apparent differences in observed differences are greater than expected from chance (e.g. is the difference in performance of blindfolded and sighted males significantly different from the difference in performance of blindfolded and sighted females?). As long as sample sizes are comparable, this can be done by comparing the z-values calculated from application of Mann–Whitney U-tests (or Wallraff's modification). The two values of z obtained from the Mann–Whitney test may be summated (if the direction of response is opposite; e.g. males better when sighted, females better when blindfolded) or subtracted (if the direction of response is the same; e.g. both males and females better when sighted). Dividing the sum or difference obtained by the square root of 2, to restore unit degrees of freedom, gives a new z-value which is a measure of the difference in the differences. This value of z may then be checked against the usual tables.

One problem with this procedure arises when one of the two comparisons has sample sizes less than 20. To calculate z from U under such circumstances gives a falsely inflated value. On these rare occasions in the chapters that follow, the following procedure has been adopted. An 'approximately exact' probability of obtaining a particular value of U is obtained by interpolation or extrapolation from the critical values presented in standard U-tables. This P-value is then converted to a z-value under the normal distribution from a table of z-values (Siegel 1956, Table A). This z-value is then used, both for convenience in the presentation of results (Chapters 5–8) and in any comparison of differences.

4.2.2. *Estimates of distance*

At the test site that marks the end of a bus or walkabout journey, subjects are asked to: (1) draw an arrow pointing towards 'home' (the starting point of the journey); (2) estimate the compass direction of the arrow they have just drawn; and (3) estimate the air-line distance between the test site and 'home' (Section 4.1). Estimate (3) can be used in its own right to assess and compare ability to judge distance. In addition (see Fig. 4.13), estimates (1) and (3) may be combined to produce measures of both the accuracy of map-building and the accuracy with which the subject could return home from these enforced 'explorations'.

Air-line distance   Throughout this book, medians and inter-quartile ranges are used, rather than means and standard errors. Estimates from different tests are often combined by expressing errors as a percentage of the actual air-line distance to home. Thus, if a person estimates the distance to home to be 200 m when the true distance is 500 m, the actual error of -300 m would become a relative error of -60%. However, although some use is made of such actual or relative errors (where underestimates have negative values, overestimates have positive),

estimated direction
and distance

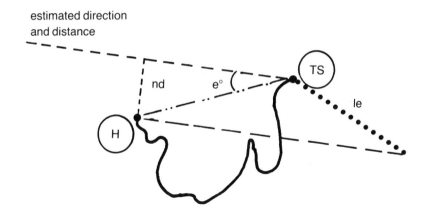

Fig. 4.13. Facets of navigational performance in walkabout and bus experiments. Subjects are taken from 'home' (H) along a tortuous route (heavy line) to a test site (TS) where they estimate the direction and distance of H. Their estimate has a directional error ($e°$). It is also possible to calculate their error at judging their location (le) and also the nearest distance (nd) to home that they would pass if they travelled their estimated distance in their estimated direction.

much more use is made of absolute errors. Thus, in the above example, an estimate of 200 m and an estimate of 800 m would both become 60% errors. Finally, the probability that an observed difference between two sets of estimates, such as by different treatment groups, occurred by chance is calculated using the Mann–Whitney U-test (Siegel 1956).

Location-error In many ways, the most sensitive measure of navigational accuracy during exploration is of ability to pinpoint position in two-dimensional space, as on a map. Such a measure reflects ability to monitor both distance and direction in combination. In bus and walkabout experiments, people estimate both the direction and air-line distance of home from the test site. These estimates are, in effect, a vector that allows the coordinates of the person's estimated location in space to be calculated by simple trigonometry (Fig. 4.13). The distance between this point and the actual location of the test site may then also be calculated. Expressed as percentage of the distance walked, this 'location-error' measures accuracy of map-building (Baker 1987b). Manipulation of location-errors uses the same statistical techniques as estimates of air-line distance.

Nearest distance to home This is a measure of the accuracy with which a person could return to the start of their journey after bus and walkabout experiments. It is less sensitive as a measure of performance than the 'location-error' for any, even a gross, overestimation of the distance to home is relatively unimportant. An explorer needs simply to identify home direction with sufficient accuracy to pass near enough to recognise familiar landmarks. Naturally, the nearer to home the person passes, the greater the chance of recognising such landmarks and the shorter the total distance of the return journey. A functional measure of navigational accuracy, therefore, is to measure or calculate the nearest distance to home that will be achieved by travelling a particular distance in a particular direction. Suppose, in a bus or walkabout experiment, the subject were to attempt to return home by walking in the direction he or she has pointed. Let $e°$ be the angular error (i.e. the difference between the direction the person points and the true direction of home). When $e > 90°$, the subject never gets nearer to home than the distance (T) of the test site. If, on the other hand, $e < 90°$, at first the subject approaches nearer to home and, after a certain distance, (D), reaches the nearest distance (ND). Thereafter, if the subject continues in a straight line, he or she will pass further and further away from home. Given that T and $e°$ are both known, the distances D and ND may be calculated by simple trigonometry ($D = T (\cos e°)$; $ND = T (\sin e°)$). When $e \geqslant 90°$, $ND = T$. Now, suppose A is the subject's estimate of the air-line distance to home. If $A < D$, then a person attempting to return home by walking the estimated distance in the estimated direction would stop before being as near to home as if they had continued further. For such people, the nearest distance to home is given by:

$$ND = ((D-A)^2 + (D^*\tan e°)^2)^{0.5}$$

Measures of nearest distance may be handled in the same way as estimates of air-line distance. When expressed as a percentage of the actual distance between home and test site, such measures may also be combined across tests.

4.2.3. *Statistical problems*
The probability values calculated from the application of the above statistical techniques are only meaningul if a number of rules are not violated (Siegel 1956; Sokal & Rohlf 1969; Batschelet 1981). Orientation and navigation experiments are particularly prone to violate two of these rules because: (1) they often generate non-independent data; and (2) the particular range of statistics available can seduce authors into testing more than one hypothesis with each set of data. In addition, students of navigation are as prone as any other scientists to succumb to the temptation of post-hoc anaylsis and the inappropriate application of one-tailed probabilities.

Gould and Able (1981), in their Table 1, present data from three bus experiments. These data are subdivided into 17 subsets, each relating to a single test site. To each of these 17 subsets, the authors apply both the z- and V-tests. The analysis is then summarised (Gould and Able, 1981; p. 1063) by the sentence: 'The one instance of orientation at the 5 per cent level out of the 34 statistical tests in Table 1 is about what ought to turn up by chance.'

This example illustrates two of the statistical abuses that are commonplace in the orientation literature: (1) the use of non-independent data; and (2) multiple hypothesis testing. First, the 17 subsets are not independent samples. Within any journey, estimation of home direction at one site must build upon, and be influenced by, estimates of home direction at previous sites. The 17 subsets, therefore, derive in fact from only three independent data sets. Secondly, z- and V-tests address different null hypotheses. Application of both constitutes multiple hypothesis testing.

Independence of data   Orientation and navigation experiments produce data that may lack independence for two major reasons. First, in a single test, each subject may make more than one estimate. Secondly, subjects may be tested on more than one occasion. the problems raised in the handling of such data have been the target for much discussion (Adler & Pelkie 1985; Baker 1985a, b; Dayton 1985; Gould 1985).

Most authors (Able & Gergits 1985; Adler & Pelkie 1985; Baker 1985a; Dayton 1985) agree that, when a single test run (e.g. a single bus journey) obtains a succession of estimates from each subject, the correct procedure is to use second-order statistics as described by Batschelet (1981). First, a mean vector ($e°$, r) is calculated for each subject. Individual mean errors ($e°$) are then subjected to higher-order analysis (individual r-values being ignored) to calculate a mean vector for the group. Probability calculations are then made on the basis of this higher-order mean vector. However, Gould (1985) argues that successive estimates on a single journey may be relatively independent. If so, second-order analysis would be less necessary and the lumping of data from several stops may sometimes be justified. In support of his suggestion he shows that at Princeton the mean difference between successive estimates is 83° rather than 0°. The analysis, however, is inappropriate.

On journeys with multiple stops, subjects undoubtedly make a direct attempt to estimate home direction at the first stop. At subsequent stops, however, an individual often compromises between making navigational judgements and 'playing percentages' in the hope that at least one estimate during the journey will be absolutely correct. To this end, many people deliberately err to one side or other of their previous estimate. A mean difference of 83° as calculated by Gould is consistent with this practice and is in no way evidence for a lack of dependence of one estimate on another. Indeed, the possibility that subjects may use such a 'percentage' strategy emphasises the importance of second-order analysis as a means of isolating the element of navigational ability from other factors when each subject makes more than one estimate. Further evidence that successive estimates are not independent is illustrated in Fig. 4.14.

Whereas there is general agreement on how to handle data from journeys with multiple stops, there is less agreement on how to handle data from subjects who make more than one journey. Adler & Pelkie (1985) feel that such subjects should contribute only one data point to higher-order analysis. Dayton (1985) sometimes uses only one data point per subject and sometimes more than one, depending on some subjective assessment of the influence of the time interval between suc-

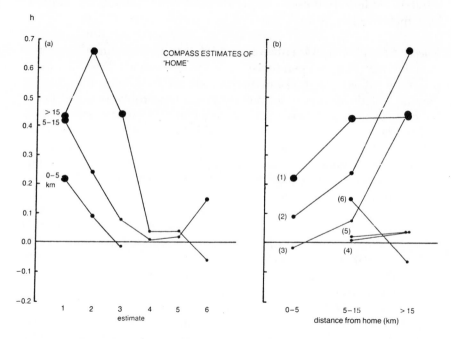

Fig. 4.14. Variation in homeward components in bus experiments according to distance travelled and number of previous estimates already made on that journey. Large dots, $P < 0.05$ (V-test); small dots, ns (V-test).

(a) Strength of homeward orientation at different distances from home declines according to how many previous estimates have been made on that journey.

(b) The first estimate on a journey is significant at all distances; the second and third only at longer distances; the fourth, fifth and sixth are no better than guesswork at all distances.

NB: Estimates are of compass direction of home, not arrow (pointing) estimates.

cessive journeys. Researchers on pigeon navigation regularly allow individual birds to contribute more than one data point to specific analyses.

I have no strong feelings either way on this matter, have offered no guidelines (Baker 1985a) and, as pointed out by Adler & Pelkie (1985, note 3), have in the past combined results from experiments in which subjects were tested on more than one journey (Baker 1985a, Table III). Re-analysis (Baker 1985b) of the data in question, using only subjects on their first trip, changed no conclusions. Indeed, homeward components were improved.

In contrast to my lack of strong feelings on this matter for bus experiments, I feel more concerned that chair experiments should generate for higher-order analysis only one data point per person (Baker 1985a, Section 3.2.2). Otherwise, there is a temptation to make more frequent use of 'good' or 'bad' subjects, depending on prejudice. Thus, I should accept for higher-order analysis only the seven individual mean errors shown under each category in Kirschvink *et al.* (1985b, Table I), not the 68 mean errors shown in their Fig. 1 (see Chapter 6).

Adler & Pelkie (1985) accept the correctness of second-order analysis in bus experiments. At the same time they see a danger that such an analytical technique may exaggerate the actual level of homeward orientation. They illustrate their point by means of a Monte Carlo simulation. The reader should beware, however, of Adler & Pelkie's use of the word 'random' in describing this simulation. Just once in their paper, Adler & Pelkie warn that their data are not random but designed to model a bias in the correct direction. In their introduction, however, they give no such warning. Second-order analysis cannot spuriously produce homeward orientation unless something causes a bias in the correct direction: a bias that may be due to a variety of factors, *including* magnetoreception.

Despite general support for the use and validity of second-order analysis, I feel we should consider seriously the suggestion by Adler and Pelkie (1985) that future bus experiments should make just one stop per journey. This would not only remove one area of dissent but also have the benefit that measured levels of navigational performance by humans and other animals would be more comparable. It is for this reason that, since 1983, bus experiments at Manchester have used only one test site per journey.

Multiple hypothesis testing Published probabilities for particular statistical tests are based on the assumption that only that test is applied. If data are subjected to more than one test, the chance of obtaining an apparently 'significant' probability value is increased, and published probability values for the particular statistic should be modified accordingly. However, the appropriate correction factor is never obvious and is usually unkown. The only safe procedure, therefore, if spurious probability statements based on the testing of multiple hypotheses are to be avoided, is to apply only one statistical test to each set of data. This test should be appropriate, should be decided in advance, and preferably should be adopted by all workers in the field.

A widespread statistical abuse in the orientation literature, as in the example above (Gould & Able 1981), is the application of *both* z- and V-tests to the same data. These tests address different null hypotheses. The z-test is appropriate when a unimodal departure from uniformity in any direction is predicted; the V-test when the mean vector is expected to have a significant component in a particular direction (Batschelet 1981). Published probabilities for these tests assume that only one of the two tests has been applied. Probability levels change if both are used. On independent data sets, application of both tests illegitimately improves the chance of obtaining a 'significant' result; on non-independent data sets the effect is problematic.

This form of multiple hypothesis testing should not be the problem it has been in the orientation literature. As far as chair, bus and walkabout experiments on humans are concerned, there is always a clear prediction that orientation should produce an error of 0° and that treatments should influence the strength of homeward or compass orientation. Only the V-test (against $e = 0°$) for single samples and Wallraff's non-parametric two-sample test for the strength of homeward orientation would seem to be appropriate unless there is a clear alternative prediction before the experiment is carried out (e.g. morning versus afternoon errors at judging compass direction when the sun is shining). These are the tests used throughout this book.

Post-hoc analysis   Gould (1985) correctly warns of the dangers of post-hoc analysis but incorrectly implies that conclusions in my earlier review of the Manchester experiments (Baker 1985a) derive from such a procedure. For example, hypotheses concerning the influence of bed orientation and clothing were first presented publicly in 1981 at conferences at Pisa in September (Baker & Mather 1982) and San Francisco in December (Baker *et al.* 1982). Subsequent experiments have been designed to test specific predictions (e.g. N–S sleepers orient better than E–W sleepers; subjects not wearing polyester material orient better than subjects wearing such material). Thus, the procedure used is precisely that advocated by Gould (1985).

The only gross example of post-hoc analysis in the literature on human navigation, acknowledged by the authors themselves, is that by Adler & Pelkie (1985). However, there are other, more subtle, examples that are not acknowledged. When Dayton (1985) states that the American compass data show significant homeward orientation only because of the collaborative experiment at Cornell, he is performing post-hoc analysis.

Similarly, when Able & Gergits (1985) suggest that significant homeward orientation at Albany is heavily influenced by good orientation at one site on one journey, they too are carrying out post-hoc analysis. They are also showing bias. For example, their results are also heavily influenced in the opposite direction by poor homeward orientation at other stops on other journeys (e.g. sites 4 and 5, 16 April 1981, their Fig. 2), but the authors choose not to mention this in the same context.

One-tailed and two-tailed tests When research hypotheses (*sensu* Siegel 1956) are clearly directional, I see no violation in applying one-tailed tests of probability. For example, several years ago, Larkin & Keeton (1976) showed that a previously demonstrated influence of magnetic storms on the orientation of homing pigeons was masked by magnets on or near the birds' heads. In consequence, the research hypothesis adopted in my later study of the possibility of interactive effects of magnetic storms and magnets on human navigation (Baker 1984b, 1985a) was that an artificial magnetic field through the head would similarly mask any influence of magnetic storms. Statistically, such a masking effect should emerge as a weaker correlation between homeward orientation and magnetic storm activity for subjects wearing magnets than for controls. A one-tailed test would seem to be totally justified (see Chapter 8).

Policy over the use of one-tailed and two-tailed tests in the face of directional research hypotheses remains a matter for discussion rather than dogma. What is obviously important, however, but is not always followed, is to make absolutely clear when presenting the results of statistical tests whether one- or two-tailed probabilities are being applied. It should be noted that, of the tests applied in this book, the *V*-test is automatically one-tailed and requires no further clarification. The Mann–Whitney *U*-test, however, and Wallraff's modification thereof, may be one- or two-tailed and need appropriate qualification. Watson's $U_{m,n}^2$ test is automatically two-tailed.

4.2.4. *The statistics of replicability*
It is part of the scientific process that before a claimed discovery is granted proven status it has to be shown to be replicable, not only by the original claimant, but also by other workers in other places. Few scientists, if any, would argue against the necessity for this yardstick. However, few rules have been laid down over what constitutes successful replication and what does not.

The problem is that in any series of experiments (by the same or other authors) some tests of a particular phenomenon will produce significant results, some will produce nearly significant results, and some will produce non-significant results. Moreover, chance is such that, even if a phenomenon does not exist, some tests will give 'significant' results. Equally contrarily, even if a phenomenon does exist, some tests will inevitably give non-significant results. Some *objective* guideline is needed by which a series of repeat experiments may be evaluated to decide whether they constitute successful replicaton or not.

The ultimate aim for any series of replicates of a particular experiment by different authors is to make a statement of the form: 'repeats of the experiment by other authors have produced results with a probability of occurring by chance that is (?).' On this probability value will depend the confidence that may be felt in the original claim or conclusion. The question is how to calculate this probability when a number of authors have performed a variety of relevant experiments and obtained a variety of results.

One solution, of course, would be simply to summate the data, such as mean vectors, from all replicates, and test the total data for significance. However, Adler & Pelkie (1985) have rightly warned for human orientation that results from different experiments should only be combined with care. Obviously, when, for example, some authors measure orientation ability by taking the mean of nine errors per subject in chair experiments while others use a single error per person in bus experiments, it would be dangerous to lump the data. Even when a single type of experiment, such as bus, is used, there is still danger of statistical artefact if mean vectors from different authors, working in different places, using different protocols and equipment, and analysing their data in different ways, are simply summated.

I have suggested (Baker 1987c) that one way to overcome this problem is to use a method based on Fisher's suggested procedure for combining probabilities from tests of significance (Sokal & Rohlf 1969).

Imagine that three authors (A, B and C) each carry out a series of experiments to test the claim that humans have a non-visual ability for solving problems of orientation and navigation. Using the V-test (Section 4.2.1), author A finds that his data show a significant ability for non-visual orientation for which $P = 0.040$. Authors B and C, on the other hand, obtain data for which $P = 0.212$ and 0.844, respectively. Fisher's method tells us that these three probabilities (0.040, 0.212, 0.844) themselves have a probability of occurring by chance of 0.130 ($\chi^2 = 9.879$; df = 6). Even though one of the authors obtained 'significant' results, therefore, the total series of replications do not warrant acceptance of the existence of non-visual orientation ability. In contrast, suppose that none of the authors obtained significant results, but all three were near to the 0.05 level (say, 0.055, 0.060, 0.080). The probability of these three probabilities being obtained by chance is 0.012 ($\chi^2 = 16.479$; df = 6). In which case, the replications warrant acceptance of non-visual orientation ability, even though none of the replications themselves was significant.

It should be stressed that this procedure for combining the results of tests is valid only as long as two conditions are met: (1) the data on which different tests are based are independent (under the null hypothesis); and (2) *all* relevant data are included. The problems surrounding condition (1) have already been described (Section 4.2.3). Throughout this book, condition (2) has been met by including *all* of the data of which I am aware. In my own replicates of my own experiments, it has been met by using every single *independent* data point I have obtained (to August 1987). In evaluating work by other authors, I have included all experiments of which I am aware, either from the published literature or through written personal communications. This includes every student project that has ever been carried out in my own and related departments. Difficulties in meeting condition (2) sometimes arise such as when experiments are mentioned in the literature but detailed results are not given (e.g. the late W.T. Keeton's experiments at Cornell, mentioned by Gould 1980). In such instances, condition (2) prohibits exclusion of the experiment (in case unpublished data are more or less likely to be 'successful' or 'unsuccessful') and thus forces allocation of some token probability value. In all such cases, any token values are deliberately conservative to avoid any danger of spurious bias in favour of successful replication.

One exception is the set of results of chair experiments reported by Bayliss *et al.* (1985). These authors claimed that humans with non-calcified pineal glands showed good non-visual ability to orient whereas humans with calcified pineal glands were significantly less able to orient. The entire paper, however, was a hoax (Bayliss, personal communication) aimed at entertaining the readers of the Christmas issue of the *British Medical Journal*. The orientation data were entirely fictitious as were the data on the relationship between age of subjects and percent with calcified pineals (Bayliss, personal communication).

The convention used in this book is that mean vectors are summated only as long as the results come from the same type of experiment by the same author under similar conditions in the same general location. Otherwise, Fisher's procedure for combining probabilities is used.

Perhaps this is a suitable moment to point out that the evidence that humans possess a non-visual ability to orient and navigate based, at least in part, on magnetoreception has been replicated successfully: (1) by myself in Britain (Chapters 5–7); (2) by myself in the United States (Baker 1985a, b, c, 1987c); and (3) by other authors working in Britain, the United States and Australia (Baker 1987c).

4.3. *Measuring levels of ability*

4.3.1. *Potential causes of spurious levels of performance*
Only during the first few bus experiments (1976–1978) were experi-

ments at Manchester concerned simply with measuring the level of people's ability to orient and navigate. Every experiment at Manchester ever since has been concerned with *differences* in level between treatment groups (Nup vs Sup magnets; sighted vs blindfolded; under sunny vs under overcast skies; smokers vs non-smokers; dyslexics vs non-dyslexics; etc.). The primary criterion in these latter experiments is that treatment groups differ only with respect to the treatment, all other factors being controlled. However, most other authors (Gould & Able 1981; Zusne & Allen 1981; Fildes *et al.* 1984; Able & Gergits 1985; Adler & Pelkie 1985; Judge 1985; Westby & Partridge 1986; even Kirschvink *et al.* 1985b) have, in effect, been concerned largely with measuring the level of non-visual orientation in single-treatment groups. Essentially, they have tried to design experiments that ruled out the use of all orientation cues except the ambient magnetic field. Levels of orientation are then tested statistically for their probability of having been achieved by pure guesswork. Naturally, with such an experimental design, the main worry is that the experimental protocol has been inadequate to exclude non-magnetic information, or that some quirk of the experiment led to subjects spuriously guessing the correct answer. Alternatively, there is the danger that, in their zeal to exclude all sensory information other than magnetoreception, the authors so stress their subjects that either the magnetoreceptor does not function or the information is not processed in the central nervous system.

Factors that may spuriously enhance performance   As the Manchester experiments since 1979 have been concerned with the influence of specific factors, based on comparison of different treatment groups, they are immune from worries concerning factors that may influence general level of performance. Nevertheless, other authors (e.g. Gould 1980, 1985; Adler & Pelkie 1985) have expressed concern that various features of the Manchester protocol for bus experiments may spuriously raise the general level of performance and thus exaggerate any apparent ability due to magnetoreception. This concern derives in part from their interpretation of (and evidently confusion from: Adler & Pelkie 1985) my published accounts but primarily from first-hand observation of the collaborative experiments I ran with Gould at Princeton and with Adler's colleagues Chris Pelkie and Irene Brown at Cornell. The points of concern are all important and deserve scientific evaluation.

Gould (1985) questions the efficacy of the blindfolds used at Manchester, and both Gould (1985) and Adler & Pelkie (1985) suggest the Manchester routes may be too simple. The same authors suspect that verbal instructions from an experimenter who knows the route about to be taken may give unconscious information to the subjects in accordance with some 'Clever Hans' effect (i.e. subjects may, consciously or subconsciously, pick up useful information from the intonation or demeanour of the experimenter). Adler & Pelkie (1985) are further concerned that olfactory, acoustic and topographic cues may be useful, and Able & Gergits (1985) are 'suspicious' that inertial navigation may be employed. Any of these factors could aid orientation and produce levels of performance better than could be achieved by guesswork. Such performance, however, could owe nothing to magnetoreception.

All of the American experiments took elaborate precautions to prevent the use of visual information, often at the cost of considerable discomfort to their subjects (Gould 1980; plus my own personal experience as a subject at Princeton). Various combinations of double blindfolds and hoods plus blacked-out windows were used. Despite these precautions, homeward orientation still occurred (summaries in Baker 1985b, 1987c). It is a safe conclusion that some non-visual ability for orientation and navigation is available to subjects on bus experiments.

Able & Gergits (1985) 'suspect' that this non-visual ability may be based on inertial navigation, presumably using some form of internal gyroscope as suggested by Barlow (1964). Gould (1985) also implies such a mechanism when he suggests I carry out bus experiments over routes that are too simple. Able & Gergits see support for their suspicion in a tendency for homeward orientation to deteriorate as the journey progresses. They suggest this would not happen if magnetoreception were involved.

Analogy with what is known for pigeons makes such an argument surprising. First, there is no *a priori* reason for magnetoreception to prevent deterioration in homeward orientation with increasing distance. Secondly, pigeons are known to use magnetoreception during displacement (e.g. R. Wiltschko & Wiltschko 1978) yet pigeons from many, if not the majority, of lofts show just such a deterioration with distance (Schmidt-Koenig 1979). Thirdly, despite this observed deterioration, no recent reviewers argue that pigeons use inertial rather than magnetic information in navigations. There is an inconsistency here.

The influence of distance and complexity of route on navigational performance by blindfolded people is discussed further in Chapter 5.

So far, the most elaborate precautions to prevent non-magnetic orientation during bus experiments were those taken by Adler & Pelkie (1985) at Cornell. Routes were complex and there was stringent care to prevent the use of visual cues. In addition, verbal instructions were given by tape recorder, compass directions were displayed by signpost, and all aspects of the execution of experiments and transcription of results were double blind. Olfactory cues were masked by sprays; acoustic cues by playing the sound of surf. Experimental protocol was admirable and contrasts with the much less stringent design of the earlier collaborative experiment at Cornell.

Having gone to such lengths to control all of these factors, Adler & Pelkie (1985) might have been expected to present a direct comparison between results from the collaborative and subsequent experiments. Instead, the results are presented in such a way that comparison is difficult. No second-order calculations are made and data are presented separately for each site. The important question of whether stringent experimental protocol reduces homeward orientation is lost in a maze of post-hoc analysis. We are told only that the number of stops showing significant compass estimates of home is lower for the stringent tests than for the collaborative test. As Adler & Pelkie (1985) stress that the only truly independent estimates of home direction at Cornell are those at the first stop (on each of the single collaborative and four subsequent journeys), one generally acceptable measure of the effect of stringent protocol on homeward orientation should be to summate estimates at all first stops on the Cornell-2 experiments and compare the homeward component with that at the first stop on the collaborative journey. Even when this is done (Baker 1985b), the stringent experimental protocol has no clear effect, reducing the homeward component for compass estimates from 0.295 to 0.202 but actually increasing that for pointing estimates from 0.272 to 0.287. Moreover, despite the larger sample size for the more stringent tests, the length of the mean vector increases with greater stringency in both cases (compass: 0.296 to 0.317; pointing: 0.274 to 0.300).

As yet, there is no clear evidence that marginally inefficient blindfolds, simple routes, familiar sounds and smells, or instructions delivered by a live experimenter (rather than tape) lead to spuriously elevated measures of performance. An important factor that did emerge from the study by Adler & Pelkie (1985), however, was the psychological impact on blindfolded subjects of sitting on a bus, facing forward, and writing answers on a sheet of paper on their lap. In the Cornell experiments, subjects had a clear tendency to suppose that: (a) home was behind them; and (b) the top of the sheet on their lap was North, as on a map.

I can confirm that in my own tests the tendency for subjects to be biased toward assuming they are facing North is found in both bus and walkabout experiments. It is for this reason that walkabout experiments, since 1983 (Baker 1985c), have tested subjects while they were facing either East or West. Bus experiments since 1983 have either followed the same convention (stopping with the bus facing East or West) or, over a series, have ensured that the directions faced by the bus are uniformly spread through 360°. Failure to do this may lead to spuriously high levels of compass orientation if the bus happened to face North more often than South. Any tendency for subjects to assume they are facing North in chair experiments is controlled by the uniform scatter of directions in which they are faced (Section 4.1.3).

I can also confirm that, over short bus journeys (15 km or so), subjects in my own tests tend to judge that 'home' is behind them, as in the experiments by Adler & Pelkie (1985). Over longer journeys, this tendency disappears and may even be replaced by the opposite tendency: subjects judging home to be ahead of them, as if the bus were heading back towards home. There is no evidence in my data of any such spurious tendency in walkabout experiments. Even so, since 1983, both bus and walkabout experiments have been controlled so that either: (1) 'home' is either to the right or left; and/or (2) occasions when 'home' is behind the subject at the test site are balanced by occasions when 'home' is ahead of the subject. Failure to control the experiments in this way may lead to spuriously high levels of navigation being recorded.

Factors that may spuriously reduce performance   It is a natural corollary to the discussion of the previous few paragraphs that failure to control the direction subjects face relative to compass bearing and home may spuriously reduce performance, as well as enhance it. Too many tests in which subjects face South and/or (on short bus journeys) towards home will give measured levels of performance that are spuriously low due to dilution by subjects who, rather than orient by the geomagnetic field, employ the simple 'North is ahead; home is behind' rule.

Another factor that spuriously lowers performance is to ask subjects to make too many estimates. The probability that successive estimates in bus experiments lack independence when several test sites on a single journey are used has already been discussed (Section 4.2.3). Figure 4.14 analyses estimates of the compass direction of home in bus experiments at Manchester from 1976 to 1982. Estimates are divided according to distance from home and whether it is the first, second, third, etc. (to sixth) estimate on that particular journey. Although there is a general trend for an improvement in judgement of direction with distance, this is completely masked by the deterioration with number of previous estimates. This is an obvious reduction in performance over the first few estimates, independently of actual distance. Whether this deterioration is attributable to boredom or fatigue, or to the 'playing percentages' technique described earlier, is unknown. Two things are clear, however: (1) successive estimates on a journey are not independent; and (2) multiple stops give spuriously low measures of navigation ability. Figure 4.14 gives strong support for the suggestion (Adler & Pelkie 1985; Baker 1985b) that navigation experiments should use only one test site per journey.

In Chapter 8, a number of features of the physiology of magnetoreception are discussed. A by-product of this discussion is that a number of features of people's everyday lives and behaviour are found to influence level of performance in experiments on orientation and navigation. People are unable to judge compass direction when wearing a robe made of 100% polyester. Cigarettes, nasal spray and stereo headphones all influence performances; so too does time of day. The best performance is produced by non-smokers, who have not used nose sprays or stereo headphones for at least 48 hours, who are tested wearing 100% cotton (or nothing!) at around midday. Female subjects tend to perform better in the mid-part of their oestrous cycle rather than premenstrually, though the differences are not significant.

Chair experiments have been particularly valuable in unravelling various of these confounding factors (Baker 1984b), but themselves are sensitive to a number of artefacts. Not the least important factor is the experimenter him- or herself. So many of my students have carried out projects using chair experiments that it has been possible to make some inferences concerning the role of the experimenter. Over the years, there have been differences in the results obtained by different experimenters, even when using the same equipment and protocol in the same place at more or less the same times. Some experimenters obtain consistently good compass orientation from all their subjects; others from only one of the sexes (Chapter 5); and yet others consistently obtain orientation performances that are no better than guesswork. For example, in summer 1985, when two student experimenters (Roz Brian and Karen Perchard) carried out chair experiments on the same group of subjects, the relative performance of male and female subjects measured by the two experimenters was significantly different. Males were significantly worse than females at compass orientation when tested by Brian, but marginally better when tested by Perchard. We have been unable to identify the critical characteristics of different experimenters, though some feature of the speed and smoothness with which the chair is turned and the subject is treated is perhaps the most likely.

The extensive series of chair experiments carried out by Murphy (1987) has shown (Chapter 5) that performance is not even throughout a test. One consequence of this is that the number of estimates made in a test is important: tests involving one, two, eight or nine estimates of direction may yield higher levels of performance than tests involving, say, four, five or six estimates.

4.3.2. *Background data: questionnaires*
Much of the above information to identify the confounding influence of particular variables emerged in the first instance from background information obtained from questionnaires which subjects completed. A typical questionnaire is illustrated in Fig. 4.15.

Such questionnaires were first introduced in the Manchester experiments in 1981. Prior to this, subjects wrote down only their name, age and gender. Since 1981, questionnaires have evolved and the one illus-

NAME

AGE

Answer the following by circling or ticking:

SEX | Male | | Female |

RIGHT or LEFT-HANDED | Right | | Left |

HAVE YOU EVER VISITED THE SOUTHERN HEMISPHERE | Yes | | No |

IF YES, WHERE | S. Africa | | S. America | | Australia | | New Zeland | | Oceania |

WHEN | less 1 y ago | | 1–5 y ago | | more 5 y ago |

BED ORIENTATION

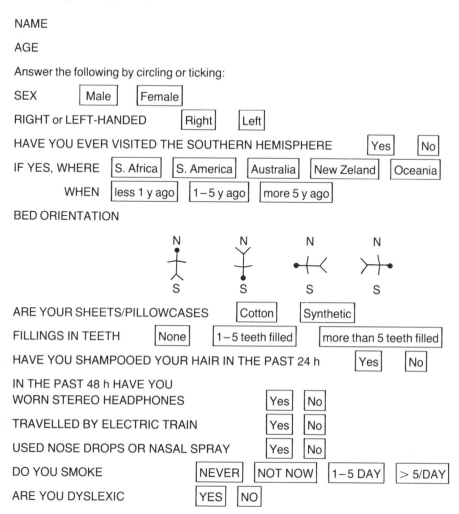

ARE YOUR SHEETS/PILLOWCASES | Cotton | | Synthetic |

FILLINGS IN TEETH | None | | 1–5 teeth filled | | more than 5 teeth filled |

HAVE YOU SHAMPOOED YOUR HAIR IN THE PAST 24 h | Yes | | No |

IN THE PAST 48 h HAVE YOU
WORN STEREO HEADPHONES | Yes | No |

TRAVELLED BY ELECTRIC TRAIN | Yes | No |

USED NOSE DROPS OR NASAL SPRAY | Yes | No |

DO YOU SMOKE | NEVER | | NOT NOW | | 1–5 DAY | | > 5/DAY |

ARE YOU DYSLEXIC | YES | | NO |

Fig. 4.15. Example of background questionnaire used for all subjects in bus, chair and walkabout experiments at Manchester since 1982.

trated is as used in 1987. Most of the questions are self-explanatory; only the question concerning bed orientation requires further comment.

We have three different methods for determining the direction of alignment of a person's bed: (1) the subject decides (as in Fig. 4.15); (2) the subject draws a diagram with themselves (as a 'matchstick' person) in bed, in their bedroom, relative to their bedroom window, with the time of day that the sun shines in classified as early morning, morning, noon, afternoon, evening, late evening, or never; or (3) the subject draws a diagram with themselves in bed, in their bedroom, relative to two major named streets in their city of residence.

In all three cases, the aim is to classify the person as a North, South, East or West sleeper; intermediate categories are not used. A North sleeper is a person the foot of whose bed points North (i.e. if the person were to sit up in bed, they would be facing North). When the subject decides their own normal bed orientation (as in Fig. 4.15), they are urged to put themselves into one of the four categories. If they really feel their bed lies exactly on the NW–SE or NE–SW axis, they are asked to choose in some arbitrary manner (e.g. by tossing a coin) which side of that axis they lie. When subjects draw diagrams and the experimenter decides in which category the subject should be placed, the same arbitrary mechanism is used for intermediate cases. In all such cases the decision is made either before the navigation data are processed or by a naive experimenter not knowing the expected corollaries of bed orientation (Chapter 6).

Bed orientation data were first collected in 1981. From 1981 to 1983, the person was asked for the alignment of the bed in which they last slept for two consecutive nights. Since 1983, the criterion for 'normal bed' has been extended. We now ask for the alignment of the bed in which the person last spent 14 consecutive nights. When no such bed qualifies, the subject is asked to give the alignment of the bed that they consider to be their 'normal' bed.

Questionnaires are completed before the experiment begins, often while the subjects are undergoing magnetic treatment. After completion, these questionnaires are collected and kept and collated separately from the sheets containing orientation and navigation data collected during the experiment itself.

4.4. *Testing for the role of magnetoreception*

As in experiments on other animals, a role for magnetoreception in human orientation and navigation may be studied by comparing the performance of either: (a) 'experimentals' (subjects exposed to an altered ambient magnetic field) and 'controls' (subjects exposed to an unaltered ambient field); or (b) groups of subjects exposed to different altered fields (e.g. 'enhancing' and 'disruptive'; Baker 1984a, b, 1987b, 1988). If magnetoreception is involved, experimental manipulation of the magnetic field should influence the strength of homeward orientation. Experiments at Manchester have used large electromagnetic coils, electromagnetic helmets and bar magnets to alter the ambient field, though, since 1981, electromagnetic helmets have not been used. Elsewhere, magnets were used at Princeton (Gould 1980; Gould & Able 1981), Tulsa (Zusne & Allen 1981), Cornell (Adler & Pelkie 1985) and Keele (M. Campion, personal communication) and large electromagnetic coils at Caltech (Kirschvink *et al.* 1985b). In all experiments involving bar magnets, bars are sealed inside either the blindfolds, or opaque cotton or brown paper envelopes that are then placed somewhere on the head. Precautions are taken to ensure that neither subjects nor experimenters know which subjects receive which treatment. Use of enhancing and disruptive magnets is particularly powerful in this respect for, even if subjects or experimenters do accidently detect that a magnet is being used, they have no possibility of knowing whether it is expected to enhance or disrupt.

Differences in the strength of homeward orientation by subjects given different treatments are tested for significance by Wallraff's modification of the Mann–Whitney *U*-test (Batschelet 1981, pp. 126–8).

4.4.1. *Types of magnetic treatment*

Large electromagnetic coils (radius 40 cm, 50 cm, or 1 m) have been used to alter the magnetic field around a person's whole body or part of their body (Chapter 6). Other coils have been fitted to PVC structures to form helmets (Fig. 6.4). These different coils are described in more detail in relation to particular experiments (Chapters 6 and 8).

Electromagnetic coils may be used to alter particular features of the ambient magnetic field (inclination, declination, intensity) in different ways for different treatment groups. Alternatively, the coils may be activated or deactivated and performance in the altered and unaltered fields compared. In all experiments at Manchester, only dc fields have been used; no experiments have yet been carried out with ac fields. However, when coils are powered by transformed mains electricity, a certain level of field fluctuation has always been present and may yet prove to have some influence on performance.

The most common way to alter the ambient magnetic field, however, is to use bar magnets. Except where indicated otherwise, magnets at Manchester have always been aligned vertically and located just behind the eye on the right temple (Fig. 4.16). In most experiments, some subjects have worn magnets, others brass bars of the same dimensions. Of the subjects wearing magnets, some have worn the magnets with the N pole uppermost (Nup), half with the S pole uppermost (Sup) (Fig. 4.17).

Two types of bar magnet have been used in experiments at Manchester: type-A magnets are made from chrome steel, measure 77 × 15 × 6 mm and had a pole strength when leaving the manufacturer of about 20 mT; type-B magnets are made from cobalt steel, measure 75 × 8 × 3 mm and had a pole strength when leaving the manufacturer of about 18 mT (not 30 mT as stated by Baker 1987b). Only one batch of type-A magnets has been used, compared with two batches of type-B magnets. Median pole strength of each batch of magnets deteriorated with time since

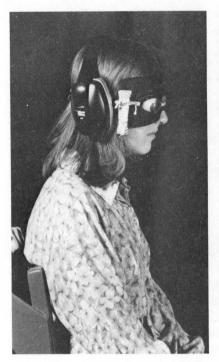 

Fig. 4.16. Most common position for magnet or brass bar in all Manchester experiments since 1981: vertically aligned on right temple. Note that the bar is enclosed in an opaque envelope, either cotton (a) or brown paper (b). During the 15 minutes of pretreatment (b), when the magnet is clipped on to an adjustable PVC helmet, subjects are usually occupied by completing the background questionnaire (see Fig. 4.15). Photo by Les Lockey.

purchase (Fig. 4.18). Matching sets of brass bars of appropriate physical dimensions are used accordingly.

In a few experiments (1979; 1981–1982), subjects have worn the bars on their heads throughout bus or walkabout journeys. Since June 1983, however, bus and walkabout experiments have used almost entirely *pretreatment*.

The rationale behind pretreatment emerges from the data presented in Chapter 6. Briefly, subjects wear a bar on the right temple for 10–15 minutes (10 minutes in 1983 and 1984; 15 minutes ever since) *before* setting off on a journey. Often this treatment time is used for completion of a questionnaire (Section 4.3.2). The bars are then removed and collected and the subjects set off on their journey, unencumbered by bars or helmets.

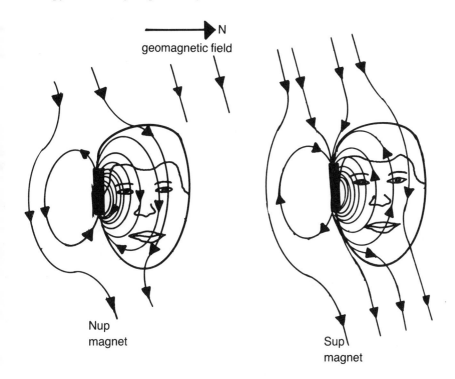

Fig. 4.17. Approximate magnetic field through the head of a person wearing a bar magnet on the right temple as in (or preceding) most chair, bus and walk-about experiments carried out by the author. Diagram is drawn for a person facing east at middle latitudes in the Northern Hemisphere. Magnets worn in Nup alignment reinforce the Earth's magnetic field through both eyes and the sphenoid/ethmoid sinus region. Magnets worn in Sup alignment reverse the Earth's field through the right eye and sphenoid/ethmoid sinus region. How far this reversal also affects the left side of the head will depend on magnet strength. Magnets of 15 mT almost certainly weakly reverse the field through the left eye but weaker magnets may not.

Whether the bars are worn throughout the journey, or used for pretreatment, the envelope in which the bar is wrapped has an identification number which the subject writes on their questionnaire. Alternatively, subjects sign the envelope.

4.4.2. Double-blind protocol
It is absolutely essential in all experiments on human magnetoreception to avoid any possibility that subjects exposed to different magnetic treat- ' ments are treated in any way differently by the experimenters. Failure to achieve this runs the risk of generating differences between treatment

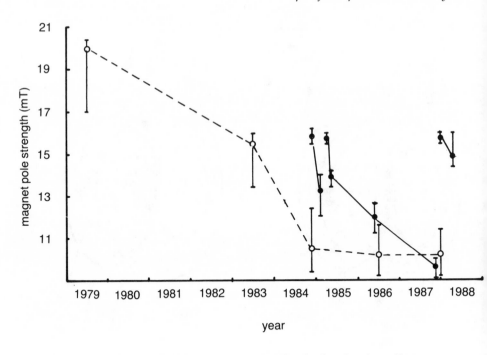

Fig. 4.18. Variation in pole strength with age for the four batches of bar magnets so far used in chair, bus and walkabout experiments by the author. Open circles, type-A (chrome steel) magnets; solid circles, type-B (cobalt steel) magnets. Dots show medians; vertical bars show range. Type-B magnets leave the manufacturers with a pole strength of 18 ± 2 mT.

groups that are due not to differences in magnetic treatment but to some other difference in experience or attitude. 'Double-blind' protocol such that neither subject nor experimenter knows, understands or misunderstands the treatment the subject has received is vital. The only factor that must differ between the treatment groups is the treatment itself.

Influence of experimenter   The scope for experimenters to influence individual subjects differently, according to treatment, varies according to the type of experiment. Throughout bus experiments and, at least during the preliminary instruction phase of walkabout experiments, subjects are addressed en masse. There is no possibility, therefore, that subjects with different magnetic exposures are treated differently by the experimenters. At the walkabout test site, however, subjects are tested individually and there is then a risk that individual subjects could be treated differently. In chair experiments, the experimenter–subject interaction is on a one-to-one level throughout the test.

In all cases, any danger that the field experimenters (those that have direct contact with the subjects) may prejudice the subject in the way expected from the treatment is removed by not allowing these experimenters to know which subjects receive each treatment. Conditions are set (e.g. bars are placed in envelopes and numbered) by a 'coordinator' (a person who does not have direct contact with the subjects).

In a similar way, any danger that the field data (arrows, compass estimates, etc.) may be transcribed, measured, collated or tabulated in a biased way is avoided. Such tabulators are unaware of the treatment received by each subject. Field sheets show only the subject's name, not their treatment. Only at the last minute, when tabulations of questionnaires and field data are brought together, can any connection between the two be made. Since 1985, the field data and questionnaires are entered directly on to computer file, the computer then printing out the final combined tabulation.

In chair experiments, with the exception of the pilot series run by Mike Meharg in 1980–81, the magnetic treatment is implemented by a third party.

In none of the experiments, therefore, is there any possibility of the experimenter introducing any form of spurious difference between the different treatment groups.

Influence of subject   Any subject that successfully identifies the treatment he or she is receiving could, consciously or subconsciously, bias their estimates in the direction predicted by the experimenter (or, depending on prejudice, in the direction opposite to that predicted by the experimenter). Subjects from different treatment groups could therefore produce different results, not because of the different magnetic fields, but because of their different psychological response to knowledge of the fields they have experienced.

For this danger to be real, it is necessary both for: (1) the subject to identify the treatment; and (2) for subjects to respond to knowledge of their particular treatment in a consistent manner, as, for example, when they know the predicted result of such treatment.

Although unlikely, subjects could conceivably identify whether electromagnetic coils are activated or not. To the initiated subject, clues such as heat, sound or vibration may all just conceivably be discernible. I have no evidence that any such identification has ever taken place, but cannot totally exclude that possibility.

Similarly, it is just possible that, by accident or design, subjects may identify whether they are wearing a bar magnet or a magnetically inert bar, such as brass. That this is not as easy as it might appear, even to the determined subject, may be illustrated by one of my favourite anecdotes.

James (the Amazing) Randi is a well known investigator of any scientist or non-scientist who makes claims that some might consider to verge on the 'paranormal'. He is best known for his investigation of Uri Geller (Randi 1982). On 19 February 1981, James Gould and I were due to carry out a bus experiment on pupils from a school near Princeton, New Jersey, USA (Gould & Able 1981), the only one of our three 'collaborative' experiments that was to use magnets. In addition to the main subjects, various American scientists involved in navigation research also took part, invited by Gould. Randi also arrived to take part, apparently uninvited, and throughout the test proceeded to judge direction (but not distance) with great accuracy. In a subsequent interview with the *Los Angeles Times* (Jacobs 1982), Randi is reported to have said that the blindfolds were 'adequate' but that 'he also noted that he could feel the magnet on his head sticking to the metal walls of the van', thereby destroying the double-blind protocol. In fact, Randi had not been wearing a magnet but a magnetically inert lead bar!

Despite the enormous satisfaction Randi's error has given me ever since, the danger still remains that, intentionally (as in Randi's case) or accidentally, the occasional subject may correctly identify whether they are wearing a magnet or an inert bar of brass or lead, etc.

In view of the danger that subjects may be able to tell whether the magnetic field they experience is altered or not, the most powerful experiments are designed, not around a control versus experimental comparison, but around two different types of altered field. Unless subjects come equipped with a compass or magnet of their own, even if they do discover they are wearing a magnet, there is no way that they can tell if it is a Nup or Sup magnet. Equally, unless a subject brings their own dip needle, there is no way they can tell what type of field is being generated by a particular set of electromagnetic coils.

In view of the strength of designing experiments around different magnetic treatments, rather than experimental versus controls, one of the priorities in the Manchester series of experiments was to discover a protocol by which the same magnet might give different results depending solely on the polarity of alignment. With the success of this search, described in Chapter 6, it was then possible to design experiments in the most powerful way. Since 1983, therefore, there has not been the remotest possibility that subjects could bias their estimates as a result of discovering their treatment.

4.4.3. *Interpretation of results*
On the face of it, the interpretation of results in experiments involving magnets is straightforward: if different treatment groups produce significantly different strengths of homeward or compass orientation, magnetoreception is demonstrated; if not, it is discredited. Such an interpretation suffers from two flaws.

First, suppose that a control group, treated with inert brass bars, produces good orientation, whereas a second experimental group, treated with magnets, is disorientated (i.e. produces random orientation, no better than could be achieved by guesswork). It does not follow, automatically, that the treatment was interfering with magnetoreception. Other interpretations are possible. First, there is the remote possibility that enough subjects identified their treatment and consciously or subconsciously biased their estimates to produce the difference observed. Secondly, it is possible that the treatment interfered, not with magnetoreception, but with general physiology. Suppose magnets make a person feel ill, perhaps give them a headache, or stress them in some way, whereas brass bars do not. The results would be exactly as described, yet owe nothing to magnetoreception.

This particular problem is largely avoided by comparison of different magnetic treatments (e.g. Nup vs Sup). Not only does such comparison remove the danger that subjects might identify their treatment, it also makes the idea of a general effect on physiology much less plausible. It seems most unlikely that the same magnet should be differentially stressful depending on alignment (especially when, as in Chapter 6, the effect is found to interact with normal bed orientation). Nevertheless, although unlikely, the possibility of general physiological trauma from a magnet in one alignment, but not another, still exists, no matter how remote. Magnetoreception can only really be established if at least some treatments lead, not to disorientation (i.e. guesswork) but misorientation (e.g. misinterpreting North as South, East as West, etc.) in a consistent and, eventually predictable way.

In the same way that significant differences between treatment groups cannot necessarily be interpreted as support for magnetoreception unless they meet the above, most rigorous, criterion, a lack of significant difference between treatment groups cannot necessarily be interpreted as evidence that magnetoreception is unavailable. This is particularly the case when some feature of the design, protocol, location, equipment, or even the attitude of the experimenter, forces or seduces the subjects into the use of simple guesswork (or some inappropriate strategy such as 'home is always behind me'). If the subjects are guessing, magnetic treatment will not be effective. The first step in any experimental series is to check that competent, untreated subjects can perform better than they could achieve by guesswork. Only when this is established does a lack of influence of *appropriate* magnetic treatment offer any evidence that the subjects were not using magnetoreception.

As in many scientific studies, whereas it is possible to demonstrate beyond reasonable doubt that magnetoreception exists, it is not possible to prove that magnetoreception does not exist. When controls perform better than by guesswork, even though a particular magnetic treatment has no effect on performance, it is always possible that the magnetic treatment itself is inappropriate for the particular test. Until all treatments have been shown to be ineffective, magnetoreception as a mechanism that helps to elevate performance above that of guesswork cannot be ruled out. The search for evidence to disprove the existence of magnetoreception could, therefore, be without end. Fortunately, as shown in Chapter 6, such an infinite search will not be necessary.

4.5. *Summary*

The usual way to study animal navigation is to force an animal to explore unfamiliar terrain and then test its ability either to return home or, preferably, to indicate the direction of home. Two types of such displacement-release or 'homing' experiments have been carried out on humans: the so-called 'bus' and 'walkabout' experiments.

Compass orientation has been studied by a variety of techniques on other animals. For humans, in addition to data on compass orientation collected on bus and walkabout experiments, one type of experiment, the chair experiment, has been designed especially to study compass orientation.

Estimates of direction in chair, bus and walkabout experiments are analysed by a branch of statistics known as circular statistics. Essentially, estimates of direction are treated as vectors and subjected to a form of vector analysis. A mean vector is calculated which has both direction ($a°$) and length (r). Usually, estimates are expressed relative to some predicted direction (e.g. 'home' direction; true compass direction) as an angular error ($e°$). The measure of performance at judging direction used throughout this book is the component of the mean vector in the expected direction ($e = 0°$). This component is usually known as the 'homeward' component (h). The probability that a given homeward component is better than could be expected had the subjects simply been guessing is calculated by the V-test. The probability that two sets of orientation data differ in the strength of their homeward orientation by chance is calculated from Wallraff's modification of the Mann–Whitney U-test.

Estimates of distance in bus and walkabout experiments are expressed as median error and inter-quartile range. The probability that two sets of estimates differ in accuracy by chance is calculated by application of the Mann–Whitney U-test.

Orientation and navigation experiments are particularly prone to violate two of the rules of the calculation of meaningful probability values using statistical techniques: (1) they sometimes generate non-independent data; and (2) the range of statistics available may seduce authors into testing more than one hypothesis with each set of data. In addition, students of navigation are as prone as any other scientists to succumb to the temptation of post-hoc analysis and the inappropriate application of one-tailed probabilities. Due care has to be taken not to violate statistical protocol through any of these pitfalls.

The claims made for the ability of humans to use magnetoreception as an aid to orientation and navigation need to pass the test of replicability just as much as any other scientific claim. In this book, the probability that a given set of replicates of a particular experiment (by the same or other workers) could have produced the observed series of results by chance is calculated using Fisher's method for combining probabilities.

Tests have identified a number of features of protocol, particularly in bus experiments, that can lead to measures of performance that are either spuriously high or low. It is important that such factors are controlled in the execution of experiments. Bus and walkabout experiments should have just one test site at which the subjects should be facing either East or West with home lying either North or South (i.e. the subject should not be facing North or South and home should be neither in front nor behind). There is as yet no evidence that sounds, smells, marginally inefficient blindfolds, or 'Clever Hans' effects have a spurious influence on measured levels of performance.

As in experiments on other animals, a role for magnetoreception in human orientation and navigation may be studied by comparing the performance of either: (1) 'experimentals' (subjects exposed to an altered ambient magnetic field) and 'controls' (subjects exposed to an unaltered ambient field); or (2) groups of subjects exposed to different altered fields. Experiments at Manchester have used both electromagnetic coils and bar magnets to alter the ambient field. Sometimes coils or magnets are worn on the head throughout the experiment. Most often, however, subjects are 'pretreated'. Elsewhere, magnets were used at Princeton, Tulsa, Cornell and Keele; electromagnetic coils at Caltech. Elaborate precautions are taken to ensure that neither subjects nor experimenters know which subjects receive which treatment. The results of experiments involving magnetic treatment have to be interpreted with care to identify their implications for a magnetic sense. A significant influence of treatment does not always demonstrate a role for magnetoreception; a lack of influence does not necessarily discredit the role of magnetoreception.

This has been a long chapter, with what may have seemed endless discussion of minutiae. The literature shows, however, that many authors find the claims made for human magnetoreception in this book to be so contentious that, before they will take them at all seriously, they demand an immaculate level of scientific protocol. Nevertheless, a consensus has been reached and ground rules have been established. This should mean that, as long as experiments adhere to the consensus rules, the results they produce should be acceptable.

With this reassurance, we are now in a position to measure the level of performance of people in bus, walkabout and chair experiments.

5

Levels of ability

The aim of this chapter is to quantify people's ability to solve navigational problems under experimental conditions, using information from a number of investigations in Britain, the United States and Australia. Where possible, variation with age, sex, time of day, etc. is also considered.

All of the data presented in this chapter are for people free of exposure to artificial magnetic fields (other than self-imposed exposure through, for example, the wearing of stereo headphones or travelling on subway trains and other normal activities). Nevertheless, the majority of people for whom data are presented were controls in experiments in which some subjects were exposed to artificial magnetic fields (Chapter 4). As such, they were wearing, or had worn, magnetically inert materials (e.g. brass bars; PVC helmets) and therefore may have thought they had been exposed to unusual magnetic fields. Measured levels of performance may in part reflect psychological repercussions of experimental treatment.

The warning is perhaps unnecessary but it should be stressed that this chapter does not describe, and is not intended to describe, the levels of orientation and navigation that can be achieved by humans solely by magnetoreception. Some of the data are for people who are blindfolded but many are for people who can see. Yet, whether subjects could see or not, senses such as smell, hearing, touch and inertia were all intact and could provide useful information. In any particular test, information gleaned through magnetoreception may or may not have been a useful addition. Identification of the contribution made by magnetoreception to the levels of ability described in this chapter is delayed until Chapter 7.

A major problem is how to quantify the normal accuracy with which people judge direction and distance within the context of map-building and navigation during exploration. Ideally, measures need to be simple and intelligible; they also need to be amenable to statistical appraisal and analysis. In deference to this latter requirement, I have opted to quantify directional estimates using the *h*-value described in Chapter 4 and cal-culated by circular statistics (Batschelet 1981). Most readers, I am sure, would have been more comfortable with a more familiar measure, such as median error and inter-quartile range (IQR). However, the *h*-value has two enormous advantages not offered by other, more familiar mea-sures: (1) performance is described by a single number (between +1.0 and −1.0 (Chapter 4)); and (2) application of the *V*-test allows calculation of the probability that such a level of orientation could have occurred by chance. The probability that two sets of directional estimates differ in their strength of orientation only by chance may be calculated using Wallraff's modification of the Mann–Whitney *U*-test (Batschelet 1981).

No such convenient measure is available to summarise estimates of the air-line distance of home (or of the accuracy of map-building or re-turning home, which also use measures of distance (Chapter 4). Con-sequently, estimates of distance by a group of people are summarised by median value and inter-quartile range. Usually the estimate is expressed as an error, calculated by subtracting the true distance from the estimate; most often, this error is then expressed as a proportion of the true dis-tance (e.g. metres error per kilometre of actual distance). As an example, a level of ability to judge distance which is given as 400 m/km (200–800) would show that: 50% of people could judge distance to within 400 metres for every kilometre being judged; 25% could judge to within 200 m/km; and 25% could judge no better than to within 800 m/km. Unlike estimates of direction, the probability that a given set of estimates of distance is purely the result of guesswork cannot usefully be calculated. However, application of the Mann–Whitney *U*-test (Siegel 1956) allows us to calcul-ate the chances that two sets of estimates of distance are different and thus presumably the product of different levels of perception (and/or labelling) by the two groups of people concerned.

5.1. *General ability to discriminate between geographical directions*

A sighted person, standing at a fixed location, can easily recognise dif-ferent geographical directions around the 360° of surrounding space. Few panoramas are so uniform that there are no markers; landmarks that allow accurate and consistent relocation of any direction even after the person has turned round or returned to the site after moving away.

Such visual discrimination between different directions at one site is relatively easy; more difficult is identification of the same geographical direction at different sites. Yet most of the techniques for navigation de-scribed in Chapters 1 and 2 require just such an ability. Landmarks are of limited use for they change their geographical direction as an animal moves. A conspicuous nearby tree in line with the rising sun at one site is a less useful indicator of the direction of the rising sun at another site even if the distance between the two sites is relatively short. Even distant landmarks, such as hills or mountains, are of little use if exploration traverses a comparable distance. The only indicators of geographical direction that are relatively consistent at different sites are either geophysical, such as the Earth's magnetic field, or celestial, such as the sun, moon and stars. Other types of information (e.g. the side of a tree on which moss grows; the direction in which trees are leaning; the orientation of sand dunes and furrows (Gatty 1958)) may sometimes be useful but are often misleading.

First impressions are that chair experiments test an ability to discriminate different directions at one site whereas bus and walkabout experiments test an ability to identify the same direction(s) at different sites. However, this apparent difference is an illusion for all types of experiment (usually) require people to label directions as North, South, East and West, etc. Effectively, therefore, even chair experiments (but see Murphy 1987) require people at a novel test site to recognise geographical directions that they first perceived and learned elsewhere.

As so many of the reliable cues to geographical direction are visual, it might be expected that sighted people would have a striking ability to identify such directions. However, celestial cues are not always visible and, even when they are, subjects in experiments may not use them, may never have learned how to use them, or may use them inaccurately. For example, one male subject in a night-time walkabout experiment on Grand Bahama saw Venus shining conspicuously in the SW sky. He assumed that the brightest object in the sky must be the Pole Star and therefore interpreted the direction of that object as North.

5.1.1. *Compass orientation when sighted*

Few authors have quantified the accuracy with which sighted people can identify georgraphical direction. Murphy (unpublished data), working in Gloucestershire, England, had students (mainly 20–21 years old) sit on a swivel-chair on an open lawn with their head enclosed by an open-topped wooden box; they could see the sky but not the horizon. In all, 35 people were tested, each making eight estimates of direction, and as a group produced an h-value of 0.514, a performance much better ($P < 0.001$; $N = 35$; V-test) than could be expected from guesswork or chance but nowhere near the level of perfect orientation for which h would be 1.0. Of the 35 people tested, only one (the author!) was absolutely correct ($0°$ error) on all eight of his estimates.

Two other series of chair experiments have been carried out but in which subjects had only one opportunity to estimate direction while sighted. First, Fildes *et al.* (1984), working near Melbourne, obtained an h-value of 0.539 ($P < 0.001$) when they asked their 103 sighted Australian subjects to point North. Secondly, I obtained an h-value of 0.350 ($P =$

0.002) in chair experiments at a woodland site on Grand Bahama in January 1985. The group tested consisted of 33 subjects of Northern Hemisphere origin (USA, Canada, Britain, Channel Islands, Oman, Hong Kong, Japan) who had been in residence on Grand Bahama for 2–4 weeks. While blindfolded and ear-muffed, subjects were rotated, asked to estimate direction when the chair stopped, and then rotated again. When the chair stopped a second time, ear-muffs and blindfolds were removed. Subjects were required to estimate the compass direction in which they were facing before the experimenter reached a count of 5.

Not only chair but also bus and walkabout experiments have been used to quantify the ability of sighted subjects to estimate geographical direction. In these experiments, subjects are taken or walk to a test site where they are asked first to point, or draw an arrow, towards 'home' (the starting point of the journey). They are then asked to estimate the compass direction of the arrow they have just drawn. This task is similar to that required in chair experiments except that the estimate is preceded by travel rather than by 'on the spot' rotation.

Eighteen bus experiments have now been performed in which some or all of the subjects could see throughout the journey. These include (Baker 1987b) an impromptu test on delegates at the NATO Advanced Study Institute on spatial orientation at Aix-en-Provence, southern France, in July 1985. In total, 208 people have been tested for ability at compass orientation while sighted in bus experiments; h-value is 0.160 ($P < 0.001$).

Perhaps surprisingly, the weakest level of compass orientation by sighted people has been obtained on walkabout experiments. The 554 people tested between June 1980 and August 1987 produced an h-value for compass orientation of 0.087 ($P = 0.002$).

Table 5.1 summarises the levels of ability of sighted subjects to estimate geographical direction as obtained in the different experiments described above. In all cases, estimates are better than should be obtained purely by guesswork or chance. Nevertheless, even the best performance ($h = 0.539$) is far from perfect, and the worst ($h = 0.087$) is so weak that it can only be distinguished from guesswork ($h = 0.000$) by virtue of the large sample of people that has been tested.

5.1.2. *Compass orientation when blindfolded*
The obvious expectation is that judgement of geographical direction will be even less accurate when people are blindfolded than when they can see. Two series of bus experiments were carried out at Manchester in 1985 and 1987 which allowed this expectation to be tested.

Sixteen journeys were carried out over four days (28/29 March 1985; 26/27 March 1987). Each journey was between 5.3 and 7.7 km in length and ended at a site 2.3 to 2.6 km from the start at the University of

Table 5.1. Ability of sighted people to judge geographical direction in chair, bus and walkabout experiments

	n	$e \pm$ CI	r	h	P (V-test)	Author
		Mean vector				
Chair						
England	35	$-1 \pm 27°$	0.514	0.514	<0.001	Murphy
Australia	103	$-3 \pm 13°$	0.540	0.539	<0.001	Fildes *et al.*
Bahamas	33	$36 \pm 32°$	0.431	0.350	0.002	Baker
Bus						
England/France	208	$-12 \pm 38°$	0.164	0.160	<0.001	Baker
Walkabout						
England/Bahamas	554	$-50 \pm 22°$	0.134	0.087	0.002	Baker

Significant orientation (V-test) underlined.

Compiled from: Fildes *et al.* (1984); Baker (1987b); Baker (unpublished data); Murphy (unpublished data).

Manchester. Four sites were used, one in each of the cardinal directions (Fig. 5.1). Orientation of the bus at the four sites was chosen so that overall the direction faced by the subjects while being tested was uniform (i.e. North as often as South; towards the University as often as away). This controlled for the danger of spurious orientations of the type described in Chapter 4. Subjects were schoolchildren (16–18 years) from Yorkshire, Lancashire and Cheshire and were unfamiliar with the area of Manchester through which the bus travelled. On each journey, half the subjects were blindfolded and half were sighted. Sighted and blindfolded subjects sat side by side and alternated (window, aisle) along the length of the bus. Occupants of a given seat were alternated (blindfolded, sighted) on successive journeys. There were no curtains on the bus but throughout all four days the weather was continuously overcast with intermittent rain and drizzle.

Of the 784 people that took part in this experiment, 379 were pretreated (Chapters 4 and 6) with magnetically inert brass bars. As usual, ability to recognise geographical direction was tested by asking subjects to write down the compass direction of the arrow towards home they had a moment earlier drawn on paper. Results are given in Table 5.2. Sighted subjects judged compass direction better than could have been expected by guesswork ($h = 0.118$; $P = 0.012$) but blindfolded subjects did not ($h = 0.046$; $P = 0.179$). The apparent superiority of sighted subjects, however, was not significant (P (one-tailed) = 0.125).

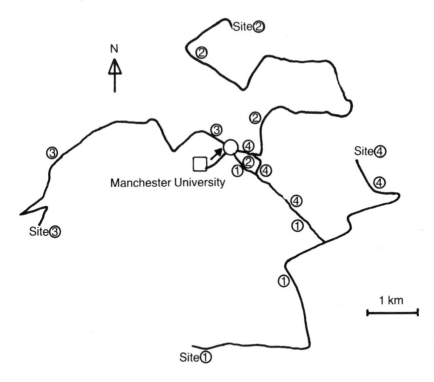

Fig 5.1. Four routes taken on bus experiments in which sighted and blindfolded subjects sat side by side, 28 and 29 March 1985, 26 and 27 March 1987. 1–4, Sites and routes in order visited.

Table 5.2 Compass orientation under total overcast by sighted and blindfolded subjects side by side on bus experiments (1985/1987)

	n	Mean vector $e \pm CI$	r	h	P (V-test)	Wallraff's test z	P (1-tailed)
Sighted	183	$3 \pm 55°$	0.118	<u>0.118</u>	<u>0.012</u>		
Blindfolded	196	-10	0.047	0.046	0.179	1.156	0.125

Significant orientation (V-test) <u>underlined</u>.
Data from Baker & Murphy (unpublished).

Chair experiments properly controlled to test how much sense of direction deteriorates when people are blindfolded have not been carried out, though Fildes *et al.* (1984), Murphy (1987) and myself in my Bahama chair experiments all obtained h-values for blindfolded subjects that were lower than for sighted subjects in comparable tasks. However, formal comparison of performances would be dangerous for in no case were all relevant factors controlled (e.g. the sequence in which blindfolded and sighted estimates were made).

Although formal verification is not yet available, the signs are that blindfolded subjects do show the expected deterioration in ability to judge geographical direction. Even so, data collected in chair and bus experiments by various authors working in Britain, the United States and Australia now show clearly that blindfolded subjects are still able to judge geographical direction better than expected from guesswork alone (Table 5.3).

My initial series of chair experiments on blindfolded subjects between 1980 and 1983 suggested that people with different backgrounds and activities varied in their ability to judge direction without sight (Baker 1985a). Worst performances were by 22 members of the British National Orienteering Squad ($h = 0.065$; $P = 0.334$) and 122 dyslexics and their families from Watford ($h = 0.071$; $P = 0.135$); best were by 17 people

Table 5.3. Chair and bus experiments (1976–1986) to test for non-visual ability to judge geographical direction

Starting year	n	Mean vector		h	P (V-test)	Main author
		$e \pm$ CI	r			
Chair experiments						
1980 UK	397	$14 \pm 33°$	0.098	0.095	0.004	Baker
1981 USA	25	$(90°)$	no data	0.000	(0.500)	Zusne
1982 UK	1279	$-17 \pm 18°$	0.116	0.111	<0.001	Murphy
1982 USA	7	$-170 \pm 80°$	0.558	-0.550	0.979	Kirschvink
1983 Australia	103	$-52 \pm 75°$	0.144	0.089	0.101	Fildes
1983 UK	335	$-28 \pm 30°$	0.138	0.122	<0.001	Campion
Bus experiments						
1976 UK	354	$4 \pm 32°$	0.107	0.107	0.002	Baker
1981 USA	86	$21 \pm 51°$	0.191	0.179	0.009	Adler
1983 UK	64	$155 \pm 52°$	0.219	-0.198	0.987	Campion

Significant orientation (V-test) underlined.

Modified from: Baker (1987c), after Zusne & Allen (1981); Fildes *et al.* (1984); Adler & Pelkie (1985); Kirschvink *et al.* (1985b); Murphy (1987); Baker (1988); Campion (unpublished data); Baker (unpublished data).

from a Manchester suburb ($h = 0.656$; $P < 0.001$) and 39 members of a group of naturists ($h = 0.548$; $P < 0.001$). The total sample of 397 blind-folded people (i.e. subjects tested without any exposure to artificial magnetic fields; many more subjects have been tested (Chapter 6)) I had tested in chair experiments by August 1986 produced an h-value of 0.095 ($P = 0.004$).

All repeats of my chair experiments by other authors are summarised in Table 5.3. Combined probability analyses of these experiments show that my original data have been replicated successfully, the probability of other authors having obtained their results by chance being <0.001 (Baker 1987c). Only Zusne & Allen (1981) and Kirschvink *et al.* (1985b) failed to find an ability to judge geographical direction. In both cases, however, sample sizes were small (25 and 7 respectively) and the experimental protocol followed by Kirschvink and his colleagues may have been inappropriate (Baker 1985b).

Fildes *et al.* (1984) went to great lengths to prevent their test subjects from using directional cues other than the geomagnetic field. Subjects wore surgical overalls, boots and aprons as well as black velour mittens and face masks. Industrial noise protectors were placed over their ears, and after-shave perfume was dabbed on the upper lip beneath the nostrils. A wicker basket was then placed over the head and a black scrim cover encased the basket and shoulders. Finally, throughout the trials, 'pink noise' was played from a portable cassette player worn by the experimenter. Thus, no part of the subject's body was exposed to the sun or air and directional sounds and smells were also unavailable. Over 100 people were tested but interpretation of the data was complicated because each person was asked to estimate direction in six different ways while blindfolded and once while sighted. Inexplicably, Fildes *et al.* did not subject their data to conventional V-test analysis. Apparently, therefore, they were unaware that one of the six estimates produced better orientation ($h = 0.148$; $P = 0.017$) than expected by chance. The full set of V-test probabilities for the six estimates while blindfolded was 0.017, 0.096, 0.101, 0.162, 0.287 and 0.750 (see Baker 1987c). Combined probability analysis of this set gives $P = 0.020$ ($\chi^2 = 24.133$; df $= 12$). It follows that, despite undoubtedly extreme discomfort, these Australian subjects were nevertheless able to judge geographical direction better than expected from guesswork. The authors' statement that 'In statistical terms, subjects were not able to orientate towards any target...' (Fildes *et al.* 1984, p. 229) is made in spite of, rather than on the basis of, the data they present.

The experimental protocol used by Fildes *et al.* (1984), Kirschvink *et al.* (1985b) and Zusne & Allen (1981) were all different, both from each others' and from my own. Campion (in Baker 1987c), working at the University of Keele, UK, used a protocol similar to that of Zusne & Allen but with a larger sample size (335 as opposed to 25). Judgement of direction was significantly better than chance ($h = 0.122$; $P < 0.001$). Campion (in preparation) has since extended this work. Orientation is still significant ($P < 0.001$).

The series of chair experiments with protocol most comparable to my own was that by Murphy (1987) who tested 1279 British schoolchildren (aged 4–18). the major difference between our two experiments was that, instead of using compass directions, Murphy's subjects estimated the direction they were facing relative to memorised key objects in the test room. Judgement of direction was again significant ($h = 0.111$; $P < 0.001$).

The way in which subjects are asked to indicate direction may well affect the measure of apparent ability at judging direction. Thus, the 103 subjects for which Fildes *et al.* (1984) present data, although unable to point towards their own house from the test site ($h = -0.047$; $P = 0.750$), were able to indicate the direction of Melbourne ($h = 0.148$; $P = 0.017$). At Keele, blindfolded students were more accurate at pointing towards a familiar building on the university campus ($h = 0.271$; $P < 0.001$) than at pointing towards North ($h = 0.122$; $P < 0.001$). In contrast, Murphy (1987) found no difference in the ability of blindfolded children to describe the direction in which they were facing in terms of compass direction or relative to memorised key features in the test room.

Blindfolded subjects on bus experiments have shown a significant ability to judge compass direction at Manchester ($h = 0.107$; $P = 0.002$; Baker 1988a) and Cornell ($h = 0.179$; $P = 0.009$; Adler & Pelkie 1985) but not at Keele ($h = -0.198$; $P = 0.987$; Campion, unpublished data) (Table 5.3).

5.1.3. *Discussion*

The summated data in Tables 5.1 and 5.3 give *h*-values for ability to judge compass direction of 0.196 for 824 subjects tested while sighted and 0.101 for 2625 people tested while blindfolded. Neither value is likely to have been obtained by chance ($P < 0.001$; combined probability). Thus, to a person standing in one position, whether sighted or blindfolded, different geographical directions are perceived differently. Moreover, as most experiments involved the use of compass directions, it seems that the same direction (e.g. North) is perceived as the same direction from different locations. It follows that people's explorations take place through space within which geographical directions form a continuous frame of reference.

The data presented in this section show clearly that people have an ability to perceive and indicate geographical direction as required by the models of navigation described in Chapter 2. Nevertheless, the most striking features of this ability are, first, its weakness when subjects are blindfolded and, secondly, how little accuracy improves when subjects can see. Sighted subjects on walkabout experiments ($h = 0.096$) judge direction no better than blindfolded subjects in chair or bus experiments ($h = 0.101$). Only in chair experiments do people perform noticeably better when they can see.

Still unclear is whether the apparent weakness of perception is an experimental artefact of the use of compass 'labels' (N, NE, E, etc.) compounded by the primarily urban background of the vast majority of test subjects. Many complain they have never learned to use compass terms, particularly East and West. Suggestively, both Fildes *et al.* (1984) and Campion (personal communication) obtained their best performances when their subjects were asked to use reference systems other than compass directions. However, in a direct comparison of estimates, Murphy (1987) obtained a higher h-value (0.119) for 90 children asked to use compass directions in chair experiments than for 322 age-matched subjects who referred instead to the directions of memorised key objects in the test room ($h = 0.019$). However, the difference was not significant ($P = 0.224$; Wallraff's test).

Comparable studies on hunter-gatherers, nomads, and other subjects from regions less industrialised than Britain, the United States and South–East Australia have not been carried out. Such studies would be particularly interesting and might help to establish whether weakness of ability to judge geographical direction is a general human characteristic or a feature only of subjects from a primarily urban or industrial background.

5.2. *Accuracy of map-building and navigation*

The previous section has established that humans are able to perceive a stable reference system of geographical directions. In experiments, however, performance at judging direction is weak, even when sighted. Such results could indicate that actual perception of direction is weak. Aternatively, perception itself may be acute but could be seriously disrupted or masked by experimental protocols (e.g. rotation or displacement; the use of labels such as North, South, East and West), or even by the psychological effects of simply taking part in an experiment.

Of these two possibilities, it seems the more likely that perception of geographical direction is weak; it does not follow, however, as suggested by Turner (1988), that the perceived reference system is of marginal value in navigation. In the same way that, averaged over many people, mean errors approach 0° (Tables 5.1 and 5.3), one person, averaging weak perceptions over a long enough period of time, may also be able to sense direction with usable accuracy.

The aim of this section is to quantify the accuracy with which people build-up their mental map and pioneer direct routes back to home on their *very first* exploration through an unfamiliar area. It should not be assumed, however, that the levels of ability described here are attributable solely to perception of the geographical reference system established in the previous section. Other useful information is available in the experiments described. During walkabout experiments, for example, landmarks offer a reference system that could be used independently of compass directions. Rotational information derived from internal gyroscopes (Barlow 1964; Mittlestaedt & Mittlestaedt 1982; Etienne 1987) or from visual assessment of bends, twists and turns would also be useful navigational aids. Indeed, on occasion, such information may be so useful that more global reference systems, such as compass directions, become redundant. In fact, the data suggest (Chapter 7) that this rarely, if ever, happens.

As described in Chapters 1 and 2, the essential function of navigation during exploration is to build-up a mental map of the expanding familiar area. This mental map is then used to pioneer direct and economical routes between important sites. Everything begins, however, with estimation of the direction and distance of familiar sites that cannot be perceived from the person's current location.

5.2.1. *Navigation while sighted*
Of all the experiments carried out on human navigation, walkabouts must come the nearest to mimicking the situation in response to which navigational mechanisms evolved. Setting out from a familiar base, people explore unfamiliar terrain, then estimate the direction and distance back to the base (or 'home'). En route, in many walkabouts, their attention is continually being distracted by observation of plants and animals.

Asking a person to indicate the direction of a distant site by pointing towards it is probably the 'purest' available test of their ability to judge and use directions. Unlike measures that involve familiarity with compass labels or units of distance, a request to point requires only that the person understands the question. Occasionally, when there are language difficulties or when testing young children, this may be a problem. Otherwise, the test involves no form of abstraction other than the spatial awareness that is under investigation. So far (to August 1987), 554 people (controls) have been asked to point towards the start of their journey ('home') in walkabout experiments. Performance is significantly better than chance ($h = 0.404$; $P < 0.001$). Sighted people in bus experiments are also able to point towards home significantly better than expected by chance ($h = 0.404$; $P < 0.001$) (Table 5.4).

In contrast to pointing, asking a person to estimate the distance to home produces data less easy to interpret. For example, a person may

Table 5.4. Ability of sighted subjects to point towards home on bus and walkabout experiments (1980–1987)

| | n | Mean vector | | h | P |
		$e \pm$ CI	r		(V-test)
Bus	183	$7 \pm 14°$	0.407	<u>0.404</u>	<0.001
Walkabout	554	$17 \pm 10°$	0.423	<u>0.404</u>	<0.001

Significant orientation (V-test) <u>underlined</u>.

Data from Baker (unpublished) for walkabouts; Baker & Murphy for bus.

appreciate such a distance perfectly yet be unable to convert that appreciation into descriptive units such as kilometres or metres. The experimenter can only assume that the subject's appreciation of such units is accurate. Nevertheless, as with tests of compass orientation, this potential problem of inaccurate labelling of distances should be borne in mind.

Data collected for 278 subjects on walkabout experiments show that, when estimating air-line distance to home from the test site, people in general have a marked tendency to overestimate (Baker 1987b), median value being an overestimation of 791 m/km (Table 5.5). In other words, after about an hour of walking through novel woodland over distances of just a few kilometres, people on average judge the start to be 1.79 times further away than it is. If we consider absolute errors (i.e. ignoring whether they are under- or overestimates), accuracy at judging *and describing* air-line distance emerges as relatively weak. Median error is 791 m/km and even the most accurate 25% of people judge distance to

Table 5.5. Error (m/km*) at judging air-line distance to home by sighted subjects on bus and walkabout experiments (1980–1986)

| | n | Error (m/km) | | |
		Lower quartile	Median	Upper quartile
Walkabout				
actual error	278	−86	+791	+1667
absolute error	278	403	791	1667
Bus				
actual error	106	−519	−580	+440
absolute error	106	294	500	826

* Error expressed as metres per kilometre of true distance from home. Negative errors = underestimates; positive errors = overestimates.

within only 403 m/km. The least accurate quarter misjudge distance by 1667 m/km, i.e. by 2.67 times the actual distance (Table 5.5).

In contrast to the overestimation of distance that occurs when people explore by walking, people displaced through unfamiliar areas by bus tend, if anything, to underestimate distance. A quarter of sighted people tested underestimated air-line distance to home by at least 519 m/km (Table 5.5). On average people underestimated by 58 m/km. Ignoring whether errors are under- or overestimates, median error was 500 m/km, with the most accurate quarter of people in error by less than 294 m/km (Table 5.5). The least accurate quarter misjudged distance by at least 826 m/km.

Errors at judging the direction and distance of home combine to determine the accuracy of the mental map built up while exploring. Figure 5.2 shows the level of accuracy with which new sites are placed on the mental map when an area is explored for the very first time. Errors are expressed as metres per kilometre travelled (i.e. actual length of journey) and are very similar whether people walk or are taken by bus. Median errors are 401 m/km (IQR = 257–676) on walkabouts and 450 m/km (283–681) on bus experiments.

Errors at judging the direction and distance of home also combine to influence the accuracy with which people could pioneer a direct route back to home the first time they visit a new site. Assuming that subjects in experiments, if 'released', would walk in the direction they point for

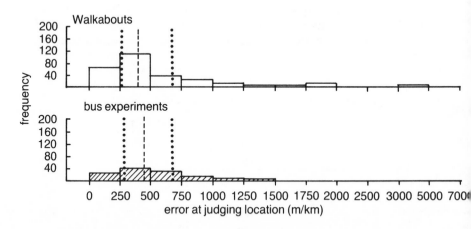

Fig 5.2. Frequency distribution of errors made by sighted subjects at judging location on bus and walkabout experiments Frequency shows number of subjects whose error fell within the category shown. Vertical lines show median and inter-quartile range. The difference in estimates is not significant ($z = 0.848$; $P = 0.395$; Mann-Whitney U-test).

the distance they state, it is possible to calculate the nearest distance to home that they would reach (Chapter 4). As long as this distance brings the person within perceptual range of familiar landmarks, they will eventually find their way back. The nearer to home the estimated direct route passes, the more economical the total return path in terms of both time and energy. The data thus allow us to identify how far from home a person can explore and still be able to return home by a direct route rather than being forced to try to retrace their steps.

Walkabout experiments have so far involved treks through woodland of between 2 and 4 km, have lasted about one hour, and have ended at a test site 0.3 to 1.75 km from home. At all locations, distant landmarks cannot be perceived and estimates are made without any assistance from familiar landmarks. Results show that, over all ages and conditions, people would return to within 717 m/km (407–969) of the starting point of their walk. In other words, from a novel site 1 km from home, 25% of people would arrive to within 407 m of home while 25% would arrive no nearer than 969 m. Half will navigate to within 717 m of home. The implication is that, whereas a quarter of people can perhaps safely explore for sites up to 2.5 (= 1000/407) times the radius of their familiar map, on average people cannot safely explore areas further from home than 1.4 (= 1000/717) times this radius.

One possible explanation for this, at first sight weak, performance is that people are not making as conscious an effort to navigate during their walk as they might in real exploration. Certainly, in almost all walkabout experiments, subjects have not known (until actually at the test site) either the questions to be asked or even the aims of the experiment. Most groups have, in fact, been students on biology field courses and have been engaged in other tasks (e.g. collecting insects; identifying bird songs) during the walk. Moreover, as the subjects were in the presence of guides familiar with the area, they would never have expected they might need to find their way back to base themselves. Consequently, it is a safe assumption for most subjects that any navigation and map-building that took place during their walks was more or less entirely subconscious. However, in six recent experiments (four at Burnt Wood, 1985–86, two at Woodchester Park, 1986–87), subjects were divided into two groups. Half were told in advance the questions to be asked and were requested each to concentrate on solving these questions throughout the journey. The other half were given no advance information. As usual, guides ensured that subjects did not discuss anything of relevance to the test during their walk. The assumption, supported by questioning after the experiment, was that half of the subjects would attempt consciously to navigate; the other half, as in all previous walkabouts, would navigate subconsciously (or not at all). The combined results for brass-pretreated controls in these six experiments are given in Table 5.6. There

Table 5.6. Accuracy of conscious and subconscious map-building, navigation and compass orientation on walkabout experiments (1985–1987)

	Conscious ($n = 43$)	Subconscious ($n = 44$)	Mann-Whitney U-test	
	Error (m/km)			
	median (IQR)	median (IQR)	z	P (1-tailed)
Map-building	318 (164–676)	215 (129–356)	−2.004	0.978
Returning home	884 (473–990)	718 (337–978)	−0.652	0.742
Air-line distance	791 (254–2265)	490 (184–796)	−2.403	0.992

Homeward component

	h	P (V-test)	h	P (V-test)	z	P (1-tailed)
Pointing to 'home'	0.427	<0.001	0.490	<0.001	−0.577	0.716
Compass direction	0.117	0.139	−0.082	0.780	1.486	0.069

Significant orientation (V-test) underlined.
Negative z-values indicate tendency for subconscious estimates to be the more accurate.

is no indication that conscious navigation is in any way more accurate than subconscious, at least under the overcast conditions that prevailed throughout four of the six walks (Table 4.1).

Walkabout experiments have shown that sighted subjects do have a real ability to navigate the *first time* they explore through unfamiliar woodland. Presumably the accuracy of the mental map and the directness of the route back to home will improve on future acquaintance with the area (Golledge *et al.* 1985). As with perception of geographical direction, however, the initial impression is of a weak and imprecise ability. Even so, it should be stressed that, without this ability, people could never explore beyond the range of perceptual contact with familiar landmarks; with it, the area through which they can explore and still return home is, on average, 96% larger (i.e. area of a circle, radius 1.4 units, relative to the area of a circle, radius 1.0 units).

5.2.2. *Navigation while blindfolded*

As for judgement of geographical direction, it would be expected that navigation and map-building would be less accurate when people are blindfolded than when they can see. The extent of deterioration can be quantified from results for the series of bus experiments (described in Section 5.1) in which sighted and blindfolded subjects sat side by side. Unlike the judgement of compass direction (Table 5.2), all aspects of navigation and map-building are significantly worse for blindfolded subjects (Table 5.7). Estimates of both the direction and distance of home are affected and thus so too are the judgement of location and the accuracy of pioneering a direct route back to home.

Although blindfolded subjects do not navigate or build maps as accurately as sighted subjects under the same conditions, their navigational performance is better than could be expected by chance (Baker 1980d, 1981b, 1985a, 1987c; see also Table 5.8). The conclusion is that humans possess some form of non-visual ability that contributes towards the solution of navigational problems. This conclusion, however, has been the centre of some controversy.

A complete set of data from my own bus experiments at Manchester and Barnard Castle between 1976 and 1982 was published by Baker (1985a). Adler & Pelkie (1985) criticised certain aspects of the presentation and analysis of these data, which were subsequently reanalysed (Baker 1985b). However, both versions of the data supported the original claim (Baker 1980d) that blindfolded humans, in bus experiments, are able to: (1) describe the compass direction of home; and (2) point (or draw an arrow) towards home, with an accuracy better than could be accounted for by guesswork or chance alone ($P < 0.001$; V-test). My data are brought up to date (August 1986) in Table 5.8. Data are presented by year and only the first estimate ever made by each person is used.

Table 5.7. Influence of blindfolds on accuracy of map-building and navigation in controlled bus experiments (1985 and 1987)

	Sighted ($n = 183$)		Blindfolded ($n = 196$)		Mann-Whitney U-test	
	median (IQR)		median (IQR)		z	P (1-tailed)
	Error (m/km)					
Map-building	420 (261–642)		488 (352–701)		2.043	0.020
Returning home	743 (439–1000)		968 (720–1000)		2.828	0.002
Air-line distance	500 (280–840)		692 (360–956)		3.705	<0.001
	Homeward component					
	h	P (V-test)	h	P (V-test)		
Pointing to 'home'	0.404	<0.001	0.054	0.141	5.046	<0.001

Significant values of h and z are underlined.

Table 5.8. Summary of estimates of home direction by blindfolded subjects in all bus experiments from Manchester and Barnard Castle (1976–1987)

Year	Pointing to home					Compass estimate of home				
	n	Mean vector		h	P (V-test)	n	Mean vector		h	P (V-test)
		e ± CI	r				e ± CI	r		
1976	29	12 ± 40°	0.381	0.372	0.003	13	−4 ± 25°	0.777	0.775	<0.001
1977	12	116 ± 90°	0.402	−0.176	0.809	12	25 ± 46°	0.542	0.490	0.009
1978	11	86°	0.397	0.024	0.454	11	71 ± 58°	0.491	0.156	0.229
1979	34	−63 ± 31°	0.444	0.024	0.046	76	−6 ± 21°	0.447	0.445	<0.001
1980	41	11 ± 20°	0.480	0.472	<0.001	41	54°	0.036	0.021	0.424
1981	25	−3 ± 31°	0.515	0.514	<0.001	25	64 ± 38°	0.419	0.181	0.100
1982	27	−24 ± 23°	0.633	0.579	<0.001	27	26 ± 34°	0.466	0.421	0.001
1983	13	46 ± 32°	0.649	0.453	0.011	0				
1984	16	33°	0.154	0.129	0.230	0				
1985	92	3°	0.102	0.102	0.083	0				
1986	0					0				
1987	104	−85 ± 85°	0.133	0.012	0.431	0				
Total	404	−9 ± 17°	0.206	0.203	<0.001	205	16 ± 15°	0.347	0.333	<0.001

Significant orientation (V-test) underlined.

Results are thus for only the first test site on a journey (see Chapter 4), and each person contributes no more than one estimate of each type. Table 5.8 thus satisfies the most stringent requirements laid down by Adler & Pelkie (1985). Note that, since 1983, subjects have not been asked to estimate the compass direction of home. Instead, for consistency with walkabout experiments, they have been asked to estimate the compass direction of the arrow they have drawn. Measured homeward components currently stand at 0.270 ($P < 0.001$) for pointing to home and 0.333 ($P < 0.001$) for estimating the compass direction of home (Table 5.8).

The controversy surrounding my claim for human (non-visual) navigational ability based on these data has involved several arenas. Discussions over experimental protocol and statistics (Adler & Pelkie 1985; Baker 1985a, b; Dayton 1985; Gould 1985) have now established clear and valuable guidelines for the design of experiments and analysis of data (see Chapter 4). Westby & Partridge (1986) violated just about all of these guidelines but undoubtedly were unaware that guidelines existed. However, it is to be hoped that future authors follow the consensus opinion over what is and what is not required for data to be generally acceptable. Valuable though the points raised by these discussions have been, however, their adoption has failed to erode the evidence for non-visual navigation provided by the Manchester bus experiments (Baker 1985b). As such, therefore, discussions of statistics and methodology are mere diversions from the issue that is really at the centre of the controversy: replicability.

Gould & Able (1981) claimed not only that they were unable to replicate the results of my bus experiments but that, in collaborative experiments at Princeton and Cornell in February 1981, I also was unable to replicate my results. Gould (1985), with support from Dayton (1985) has repeated these claims which have also been perpetuated uncritically by other workers (Fildes *et al.* 1984; Westby & Partridge 1986) and commentators (Moore 1986). Yet, even from these early bus experiments, it was always quite clear (Baker 1985a, b, c) that the evidence for non-visual navigation ability was being replicated satisfactorily. With more data from more authors, the question now seems to be resolved beyond reasonable doubt (Baker 1987c).

Table 5.9 lists the results of all bus experiments by authors other than myself. Homeward orientation is significant ($P < 0.050$) or highly significant ($P < 0.001$) in some experiments, nearly significant ($P = 0.050$–0.100) in others, and far from significant ($P > 0.500$) in yet others. Combined probability analysis of the list of replicates shows that the probability of getting such a list of probabilities by chance is 0.001 both for pointing to home and judging the compass direction of home (Baker

Table 5.9. All replicate bus experiments to test for the existence of non-visual navigational ability in blindfolded humans

Start			Mean vector				Main author
Date	Place	n	$e \pm$ CI	r	h	P (*V*-test)	
Pointing to home							
1980	Cornell	?	data not given			(0.500)	Keeton
1980	Princeton	20	−78°	0.140	0.029	0.426	Gould
1980	Albany	67	−178°	0.080	−0.080	0.822	Able
1980	Sheffield	45	−176°	0.020	−0.020	0.575	Westby
1981	Princeton	20	−45°	0.281	0.199	0.102	Gould
1981	Cornell	30	56 ± 55°	0.310	0.173	0.087	Pelkie
1981	Durham	17	3°	0.204	0.204	0.116	Greenwood
1981	Swarthmore	27	20 ± 53°	0.340	0.319	0.010	Leitner
1981	New Jersey	19	39 ± 85°	0.328	0.255	0.059	Rosenthal
1981	Albany	9	121°	0.159	−0.082	0.638	Judge
1981	Cornell	56	−40 ± 31°	0.342	0.262	0.003	Adler
1983	Keele	66	−59 ± 31°	0.311	0.160	0.032	Campion
	Total	376	−25 ± 27°	0.132	0.120	0.001	
Compass estimate of home							
1980	Cornell	?	data not given			(0.050)	Keeton
1980	Princeton	50	−107 ± 55°	0.223	−0.068	0.758	Gould
1980	Albany	45	38 ± 42°	0.289	0.228	0.016	Able
1981	Princeton	45	19°	0.144	0.136	0.098	Gould
1981	Cornell	30	20 ± 26°	0.541	0.508	<0.001	Pelkie
1981	Durham	17	64 ± 32°	0.601	0.263	0.059	Greenwood
1981	Swarthmore	?	data not given			(1.000)	Leitner
1981	Albany	8	106°	0.168	−0.046	0.575	Judge
1981	Cornell	56	−46°	0.179	0.124	0.094	Adler
1983	Keele	64	104°	0.092	−0.022	0.602	Campion
	Total	315	20 ± 34°	0.128	0.121	<0.001	

P-values in brackets are token and conservative.

Significant orientation (*V*-test) underlined.

Modified from Baker (1987c) based on data by: Gould (1980); Gould & Able (1981); Rosenthal (unpublished); Greenwood (unpublished); Leitner, Weitzman & Williams (unpublished); Campion (unpublished); Able & Gergits (1985); Adler & Pelkie (1985); Baker (1985a, b); Dayton (1985); Judge (1985); Westby & Partridge (1986).

1987c). The only reasonable conclusion, therefore, is that other authors have successfully replicated the evidence for a non-visual element in the navigational armoury of humans.

Although bus experiments by other authors have produced levels of homeward orientation by blindfolded people that are much better than could be expected by chance, h-values are nevertheless lower than obtained in my experiments at Manchester (Table 5.10). Using the total available data, it seems that blindfolded people in bus experiments produce h-values of 0.186 for pointing to home and 0.200 for describing the compass direction of home (Table 5.10).

In a few of my bus experiments at Manchester (Baker 1981b, 1988a) and in the bus experiments by Westby & Partridge (1986) at Sheffield, UK, people were displaced while blindfolded but finally, outside of the bus, were asked to remove their blindfolds before pointing towards home. More than any described so far, the results from these tests invite comparison with results from experiments on homing pigeons; birds normally allowed to see their surroundings upon release. In the Sheffield experiments, the h-value for the 420 estimates made by sighted subjects after blindfolded displacement was 0.105. Although a V-test on these data yields apparent significance ($P = 0.001$), its application is unfortunately invalid as the estimates were not all independent. In my own experiments around Manchester, 166 subjects produced an h-value of 0.205 ($P < 0.001$) (Baker 1988). These levels of performance by the inexperienced human navigators that took part are comparable to the h-values of between 0.15 and 0.25 obtained for inexperienced homing pigeons over similar distances in Germany (Foà *et al.* 1982).

5.3. *Variation in ability*

Humans have a real ability both to perceive geographical direction and to navigate. Moreover, the sensory battery on which these abilities is based has at least one non-visual element. These conclusions derive from the data presented in Sections 5.1 and 5.2; sections which have also quantified, in the most general of ways, the levels of ability involved. It is obvious, however, that performance must vary both between individuals and with changes in ambient conditions. The aim of this section is to identify the influence of some of the more obvious factors: sex; age; cloud cover; height of sun; time of day; and, to begin, the distance and complexity of exploration.

5.3.1. *Influence of distance and complexity of the outward journey*
In bus and walkabout experiments, subjects estimate the air-line distance and direction of home. Journeys differ in at least three different ways: (1) their length; (2) their complexity; and (3) the final distance between the test site and 'home'. Each one of these could influence people's accuracy at map-building and navigation, a possibility that has been analysed.

The unit for analysis for my own data was a single journey, either bus or walkabout. Sample size therefore equals the number of journeys

Table 5.10. Bus experiments: comparison of total data for blindfolded subjects from Manchester and elsewhere (data from Tables 5.8 and 5.9)

| | | Pointing to home | | | | | Compass estimate of home | | | |
| | | Mean vector | | | | | Mean vector | | | |
	n	$e \pm$ CI	r	h	P (V-test)	n	$e \pm$ CI	r	h	P (V-test)
Manchester	404	$-9 \pm 17°$	0.206	0.203	<0.001	205	$16 \pm 15°$	0.347	0.333	<0.001
Replicates	376	$-25 \pm 27°$	0.132	0.120	<0.001	315	$20 \pm 34°$	0.128	0.121	<0.001
Total	780	$-15 \pm 15°$	0.169	0.163	<0.001	520	$17 \pm 14°$	0.210	0.200	<0.001

Significant orientation (V-test) underlined.

Table 5.11. Influence of distance and complexity of journey on navigational performance by sighted and blindfolded subjects in bus and walkabout experiments

| | Distance | | | | Complexity (km travelled/km to home) | |
| | To home | | Travelled | | | |
	Sighted r_s	Blindfolded r_s	Sighted r_s	Blindfolded r_s	Sighted r_s	Blindfolded r_s
Direction (pointing)						
Median error (°)	0.003	0.221	-0.002	0.341*	-0.033	0.146
Distance						
Actual estimate (km)	0.574**	0.744**	0.524**	0.672**		
Error: actual (km)						
Over/under	-0.354*	0.331	-0.342	0.375		
Absolute	0.699**	0.700**	0.706**	0.690**		
Error: proportional (m/km)						
Over/under	-0.550**	0.193	-0.395*	0.179	0.638**	-0.221
Absolute	-0.420	-0.408*	-0.230	-0.264	0.489**	0.200
No. experiments						
Direction	39	38	39	38	39	38
Distance	33	26	33	26	33	26

Proportional error = (estimated minus true distance to home)/true distance to home.

2-tailed probabilities: * <0.05; ** <0.01.

Over-/underestimates: negative Spearman correlation coefficients indicate that increasing distance or complexity is associated with decreasing tendency to overestimate or increasing tendency to underestimate air-line distance to home.

(i.e. experiments). To reduce variation due to other factors, only experiments on people aged between 19 and 24 years are used. Level of performance during the journey was taken to be the median estimate for the group being tested. Distance travelled (T km) and air-line distance (A km) between the test site and home were measured directly from a map, as usual. An index of complexity for the journey was obtained from T/A (thus, a value of 1.0 indicates a straight outward journey; otherwise, the larger the index, the more tortuous or circular the route. Spearman's rank order correlation coefficient (r_s) was calculated for all journeys for which a particular measure of performance was available. Results are summarised in Table 5.11.

The ability of sighted subjects to point towards home was uninfluenced by either the distance or the complexity of the journey. Blindfolded subjects, however, became increasingly inaccurate at pointing on longer journeys (this contrasts with the tendency towards increased accuracy at judging the compass direction of home with increased distance from home suggested by Fig. 4.14). Variation in homeward component with length of journey in my own experiments around Manchester is summarised in Table 5.12; comparable data from experiments by other authors are summarised in Table 5.13. On the whole, there is good agreement between the results obtained at Manchester and elsewhere, and the data are combined in Table 5.14. Performance deteriorates markedly on journeys longer than 10 km and there is no indication from my own or other data that on journeys longer than about 40 km blindfolded people can point towards home any better than they could achieve by guesswork.

As the length of journey and distance from home increase, so too do the estimates of air-line distance to home (Table 5.11). Inevitably, also,

Table 5.12. Influence of length of outward journey on accuracy of pointing to home: bus and walkabout experiments (1976–1986)

Distance travelled		Mean vector				
(km)	n	$e \pm$ CI	r	h	P (*V*-test)
Sighted subjects (bus + walkabout)					
0–10	399	19 ± 9°	0.496	0.468	<0.001
80–160	27	46 ± 42°	0.393	0.272	0.023
Blindfolded subjects (bus only)					
0–10	199	4 ± 18°	0.325	0.325	<0.001
10–20	56	44 ± 41°	0.274	0.198	0.018
20–40	89	−22°	0.103	0.096	0.101
40–80	28	30°	0.065	0.056	0.336

Data from Baker (unpublished).

Table 5.13. Influence of length of outward journey on accuracy of pointing to home: blindfolded subjects on all bus experiments by other authors

Distance travelled (km)	n	Mean vector e ± CI	r	h	P (V-test)	Main author (see Table 5.9)
0–10						
New Jersey	19	39 ± 85°	0.328	0.225	0.059	Rosenthal
Keele	29	−67 ± 31°	0.480	0.188	0.075	Campion
10–20						
Albany	41	131°	0.180	−0.117	0.856	Able
Durham	17	3°	0.204	0.204	0.116	Greenwood
Cornell	56	−40 ± 31°	0.342	0.262	0.003	Adler
Keele	37	43°	0.189	0.139	0.115	Campion
20–40						
Sheffield	45	−176°	0.020	−0.020	0.575	Westby
Princeton	20	−45°	0.281	0.199	0.102	Gould
Cornell	30	56 ± 55°	0.310	0.173	0.087	Pelkie
Swarthmore	27	20 ± 53°	0.340	0.319	0.010	Leitner
40–80						
Princeton	20	−78°	0.140	0.029	0.426	Gould
Albany	26	−100°	0.223	−0.040	0.613	Able
Albany	9	121°	0.159	−0.082	0.638	Judge
Totals						
0–10	48	−41 ± 43°	0.283	0.214	0.018	
10–20	151	−32 ± 50°	0.143	0.122	0.017	
20–40	122	22 ± 56°	0.149	0.139	0.015	
40–80	55	−99°	0.133	−0.021	0.588	

Table 5.14. Influence of length of outward journey on accuracy of pointing to home: blindfolded subjects on bus experiments by all authors

Distance travelled (km)	n	Mean vector e ± CI	r	h	P (V-test)
Totals (Manchester + elsewhere)					
0–10	247	−3 ± 15°	0.303	0.303	<0.001
10–20	207	−2 ± 43°	0.142	0.142	0.002
20–40	211	8 ± 49°	0.121	0.120	0.007
40–80	83	−86°	0.076	0.005	0.473

Data from Tables 5.12 and 5.13.

Significant orientation (V-test) underlined.

as actual distance increases, the magnitude of the error at estimating distance also increases, no matter whether subjects are blindfolded or can see. However, whereas sighted subjects show an increasing tendency to underestimate distance the further from home they go (Table 5.11; Fig. 5.3), the same may not be true for blindfolded subjects, though more experiments over different distances are needed (see Fig. 5.3). Both sighted and blindfolded subjects become proportionately (i.e. errors expressed as metres per kilometre of actual distance) more accurate at judging distance the further from home they go (Table 5.11; Fig. 5.3).

Complexity of journey influences the estimates of distance to home made by sighted subjects (Table 5.11; Fig. 5.4): the more complex the journey the less accurate the estimate and the greater the tendency to overestimate. Blindfolded subjects, however, are unaffected, largely because they are less accurate than sighted subjects over the longer journeys which inevitably tend to be straighter and less complex (Fig. 5.4).

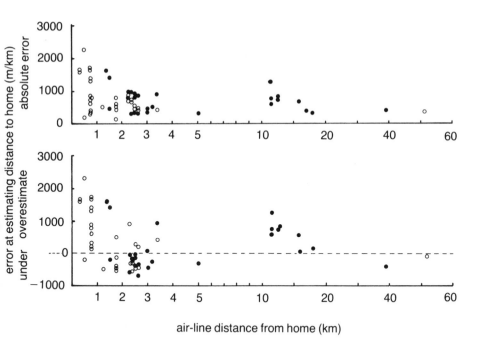

Fig. 5.3. Error at judging air-line distance to home in relation to distance in bus and walkabout experiments: comparison of sighted and blindfolded estimates. Each dot shows the median error for a single experiment. ○, Sighted subjects; ●, blindfolded subjects. Errors expressed as metres per kilometre of true distance (NB scale on *x*-axis is not linear).

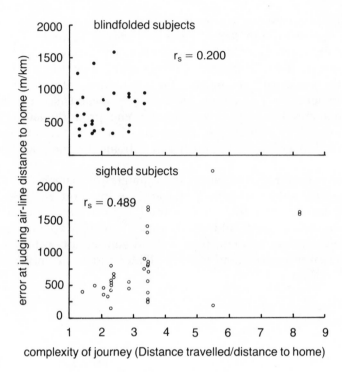

Fig. 5.4. Error at judging air-line distance to home in relation to complexity of journey for sighted and blindfolded subjects on bus and walkabout experiments.

In summary, therefore, the non-visual component of the navigational armoury is an aid to navigation over short distances, but after about 40 km (or, perhaps, after a certain time blindfolded) it no longer helps to raise performance at pointing towards home above guesswork level. Vision continues to aid assessment of the direction of home over much longer distances. Over short and complex journeys, sighted people tend to overestimate the air-line distance to home; thus erring on the 'safe' side for attempting to return (Bovet 1987). Over longer, straighter journeys estimates are proportionally more accurate.

5.3.2. *Relative performance of males and females*
The relative performance of males and females in all of my chair, bus and walkabout experiments (1976–August 1986) is summarised in Table 5.15. Individual errors in two of the more interesting comparisons are given in Fig. 5.5. Table 5.15 also includes data for chair experiments taken from Murphy (1987).

Judgement of geographical direction Previously, Lord (1941) had shown that, among schoolchildren in the city of Ann Arbor, males were better

CHAIR EXPERIMENTS (judging compass direction)

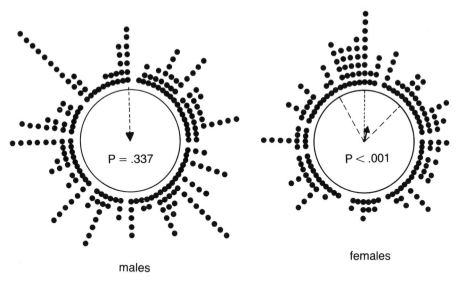

WALKABOUTS (Pointing to 'home')

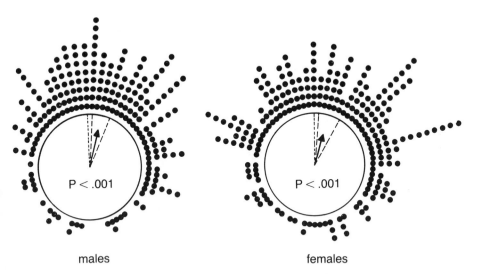

Fig. 5.5 Relative performance of males and females at: (a) judging compass direction while blindfolded in chair experiments; and (b) pointing to home while sighted a walkabout experiments. Each dot is one person's estimate of direction relative to the true direction shown by the vertical dotted line. Arrows and dashed lines show mean vectors and 95% confidence limits.

Table 5.15. Comparison of performance by males and females in chair, walkabout and bus experiments (1976–1986)

| | Males | | | | Females | | | | Mann–Whitney U-test | |
| | n | Mean error | | | n | Mean error | | | | |
		e ± CI	h	P (V-test)		e ± CI	h	P (V-test)	z	P
Compass direction										
Chair										
sighted*	23	6 ± 27°	0.593	<0.001	12	−23°	0.361	0.039	+0.800	0.212
blindfolded*	704	−36 ± 70°	0.051	0.029	575	−9 ± 18°	0.184	<0.001	−3.875	<0.001
blindfolded	218	46°	0.020	0.337	179	9 ± 36°	0.185	<0.001	−2.553	0.005
Walkabout										
sighted	211	−17 ± 55°	0.112	0.010	234	−44 ± 62°	0.080	0.041	+0.198	0.421
Bus										
sighted	44	−32 ± 30°	0.349	<0.001	63	−12 ± 79°	0.164	0.033	+1.608	0.054
blindfolded	143	21 ± 80°	0.108	0.034	140	32 ± 42°	0.148	0.007	−0.474	0.317
Pointing to home										
Walkabout										
sighted	211	15 ± 10°	0.535	<0.001	234	18 ± 12°	0.397	<0.001	+3.093	0.001
Bus										
sighted	45	40 ± 29°	0.308	0.002	64	1 ± 27°	0.353	<0.001	−0.012	0.504
blindfolded	152	11 ± 21°	0.312	<0.001	148	−13 ± 31°	0.227	<0.001	+1.016	0.310
Air-line distance to home (error as m/km)		Median (inter-quartile)				Median (inter-quartile)				
Walkabout										
sighted	144	771	(371–1597)		158	791	(403–1985)		+1.304	0.303
Bus										
sighted	42	510	(304–840)		62	489	(280–739)		−0.766	0.441
blindfolded	100	600	(360–1000)		111	565	(333–920)		−1.035	0.303

* Data from Murphy (1987).

Negative z-values indicate female performance better than male. Positive z-values indicate male performance better than female.

Significant h- and z-values underlined.

at indicating compass direction than females when both could see. Murphy (personal communication) found a similar, but non-significant ($P = 0.212$; one-tailed), trend in chair experiments in which a wooden box around the head allowed full view of the sky but not of the horizon. I found similar trends in both bus and walkabout experiments, but in neither case was the trend significant (P (one-tailed) = 0.054, 0.421, respectively). Although these three trends are all in the same direction as that found by Lord, combined probability analysis shows that they are not significantly different from chance ($\chi^2 = 10.67$; df = 6; $P = 0.099$). Thus, there is as yet no support for Lord's suggestion that males are significantly better than females at judging compass direction when sighted.

Conversely, when subjects were blindfolded, Murphy (1987) found that female children (between 4 and 18 years old) judged geographical direction significantly better than males (P (two-tailed) < 0.001). My own chair experiments, using a wider age range (6–71 years old), produce the same result (P (one-tailed) = 0.005) (Fig. 5.5). The only difference between Murphy's and my results is that, whereas the males in Murphy's experiments were able to judge compass direction better than they could have achieved by guesswork ($P = 0.029$; V-test), in mine they did not ($P = 0.337$). The tendency for blindfolded females to judge compass direction better than males is also found in bus experiments, but in this case the difference is not significant (P (one-tailed) = 0.317). Nevertheless, combined probability analysis of my two sets of results ($\chi^2 = 12.77$; df = 4; $P = 0.013$) supports Murphy's suggestion that females are significantly better than males at judging compass direction when blindfolded.

The possibility that blindfolding alters the relative performance of males and females at judging compass direction has been checked both statistically and by experiment. The Mann–Whitney z-values calculated for sexual differences when males and females are sighted and blindfolded (Table 5.15) may themselves be compared for difference. For example, adopting a convention that a minus sign shows female superiority, a positive sign male superiority, we may ask for Murphy's chair experiments whether a z-value of -3.875 (for blindfolded subjects) is significantly different from a z-value of $+0.800$ (for sighted subjects). First, we calculate a z-value for the difference in z-values ($z = z_1 - z_2/\mathrm{sqr}2$). This gives a value for z of 3.305 (P (one-tailed) < 0.001). The same calculation for my bus data (Table 5.15) gives $z = 1.472$ (P (one-tailed) = 0.071). Combined probability analysis of Murphy's and my results ($\chi^2 = 20.49$; df = 4; $P < 0.001$) thus supports the hypothesis that blindfolding alters the relative performance of males and females at judging compass direction in bus and chair experiments.

This statistical conclusion is reinforced by the 1985 series of bus experiments already described in which sighted and blindfolded males and females sat side by side on the same journeys. Comparison of the interaction of visual state and gender could therefore be made with all other factors controlled. Results are given in Murphy (1987). The change in relative performance of males and females from males being better when sighted to females having the edge when blindfolded appears to be confirmed ($z = 1.854$; P (one-tailed) $= 0.032$). It is noticeable in this series of experiments that, whereas being able to see significantly improved the judgement of compass direction by males, the performance of females showed no improvement at all. Unfortunately, a second series of bus experiments in which sighted and blindfolded males and females sat side by side on the same journeys failed to confirm the 1985 results. When the two series (1985 and 1987) are combined (Table 5.16), there is no significant difference in influence of blindfolds on the performance of males and females. More such controlled experiments are needed to resolve the question.

The differential influence of blindfolds indicated by some of the experiments implies, as suggested earlier (Baker 1981b, Chapter 10), that males and females may use different strategies in solving problems of orientation. Support for this view may be taken from the extensive and important analysis by Murphy (1987) who compared the performance of males and females throughout the course of a chair experiment.

In Murphy's tests, each person made nine estimates of direction between the donning and removal of blindfolds and ear-muffs. As usual (Chapter 4), the chair was rotated between each estimate. Murphy compared performance for each of these nine estimates to determine if there were any particular stages of the test in which females excelled relative to males. Her results are shown in Fig. 5.6. Both sexes begin well, the first estimate being better than guesswork (*V*-test). If either sex has the edge, it is males. Both sexes then go through a phase of increasing disorientation, a state which then persists for males for the remainder of the test. Halfway through the test, however, females begin to improve once more and end the test as, if not better, able to judge direction as at the beginning.

Murphy (1987) interprets her data as follows. Both sexes begin by trying continuously to follow the rotation of the chair. Although this is adequate up to the first estimate, errors accumulate and disorientation ensues. Males persist with this 'continuous rotation' strategy and remain disoriented but females eventually regain orientation by switching to an alternative method involving an external reference system, such as geographical direction.

If Murphy's interpretation of her data is correct, it follows that tests with only one, limited, bout of disorientation will find no sexual difference in ability to judge geographical direction whereas tests with several

Table 5.16 Comparison of performance by males and females in controlled bus experiments in which sighted and blindfolded subjects sat side by side (1985 and 1987)

	Males				Females				Mann–Whitney U-test	
	Mean error				Mean error					
	n	$e \pm$ CI	h	P (V-test)	n	$e \pm$ CI	h	P (V-test)	z	P (2-tailed)
Compass direction										
sighted	85	$-91°$	0.098	0.099	98	$30 \pm 61°$	<u>0.135</u>	<u>0.029</u>	-0.132	0.896
blindfolded	85	$91°$	-0.001	0.507	111	$-39°$	0.083	0.108	-0.910	0.362
Pointing to home										
sighted	85	$13 \pm 24°$	<u>0.356</u>	<u><0.001</u>	98	$2 \pm 18°$	<u>0.445</u>	<u><0.001</u>	-0.452	0.652
blindfolded	85	$-26°$	0.059	0.220	111	$-62°$	0.051	0.224	$+0.067$	0.952
Air-line distance to home (error as m/km)										
		Median (inter-quartile)				Median (inter-quartile)				
sighted	85	478 (231–846)			98	520 (280–833)			$+0.120$	0.904
blindfolded	84	763 (375–1000)			111	692 (330–940)			-0.820	0.412

Significant h-values underlined.

Negative z-values indicate female performance better than male. Positive z-values indicate male performance better than female.

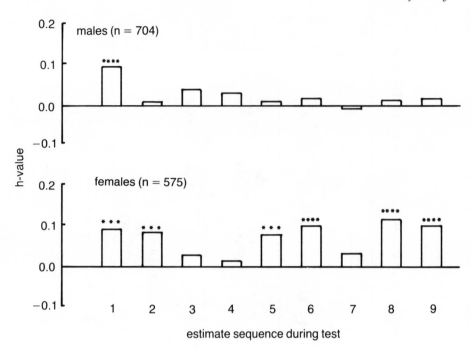

Fig. 5.6. Variation in ability of blindfolded males and females to judge geographical direction during the course of a chair experiment involving nine estimates. Histograms show h-values for the first to ninth estimates of direction in a series of chair experiments on 4- to 18-years-old schoolchildren. The chair is rotated between each estimate. V-test: * $P < 0.05$; ** $P < 0.02$; *** $P < 0.01$; **** $P < 0.001$. Data for 704 males and 575 females from Murphy (1987).

bouts may well find a difference. Thus, in my major series of chair experiments with eight or nine rotation bouts, females were significantly better than males (Fig. 5.5). In my series with a chair in woodland in the Bahamas described earlier, however, with only one bout of rotation, there was no difference. Fildes *et al.* (1984), with only one bout, also found no difference.

These data suggest that males and females may sometimes use different methods to solve, or attempt to solve, problems of geographical orientation. It follows that, depending on the particular problem, their different methods may produce equivalent or different levels of performance. Presumably the same should be expected for navigational performance in bus and walkabout experiments.

Map-building and navigation   Lord (1941) drove sighted children (173 boys and 144 girls) at 30 km per hour in a bus around a 3-km course in the city of Ann Arbor, stopping now and again to test the subjects' ability to indicate the directions of the previous stopping places. Males performed better than females in all tests.

My own results show the same trend as found by Lord when the data for sighted males and females are compared in walkabout experiments (P (one-tailed) = 0.001; Fig. 5.5) but not in bus experiments (P (one-tailed) = 0.504). Combined probability analysis of my two series of experiments (χ^2 = 15.19; df = 4; P = 0.005) offers support for Lord's suggestion that sighted males are better able to point towards distant and invisible locations than females.

In contrast, for blindfolded subjects, I concluded previously that: 'There is no apparent sexual difference in ability to point in the direction of home while blindfolded' (Baker 1981b, p. 113). This finding has been replicated (but not acknowledged) by Westby & Partridge (1986) in their bus experiments around Sheffield.

5.3.3. *Variation in ability with age*

Judgement of geographical direction   The most intensive analysis of changes in ability with age is that by Murphy (1987) who carried out chair experiments on children (ages 4–18 years) with data presented in 2-year steps. Table 5.17 summarises my own more extensive (ages 6–71 years) but less intensive (5-year steps) data, also from chair experiments. Results are presented separately for males and females. Murphy's data, recalculated in 5-year age classes, is included for comparison. Our experimental methods were essentially the same in all major respects except one: whereas I asked subjects of all ages to use compass terms to describe the geographical direction they were facing, Murphy used four key features in the room which were shown to the subject before being blindfolded. In addition, Murphy calculated mean errors from nine estimates per subject; I calculated mean errors from eight estimates (1980–1982) or nine (1983 onwards).

According to Murphy (1987), males perform best at 13–14 years of age (h = 0.129; N = 129; P = 0.019), whereas females perform best at 15–16 years (h = 0.386; N = 59; $P < 0.001$). In my sample, males performed best at 6–10 years and females at 21–30 years. Whereas Murphy found females to be superior to males from 8 years onwards, in my sample they were not superior until 16 years onwards. Indeed, males performed significantly better than females until at least 10 years old. I found no sexual difference in performance above the age of 41 years, both males and females thereafter performing no better than they could have achieved by guessing.

Figure 5.7 is an age curve for males and females calculated by summating the data from both sources in Table 5.17. The impression given is

Table 5.17. Changes with age in levels of compass orientation by males and females in chair experiments

Age (years)	Males				Females				Mann–Whitney U-test	
		Mean error				Mean error				
	n	$e \pm$ CI	h	P (V-test)	n	$e \pm$ CI	h	P (V-test)	z	P (2-tailed)
From Baker (unpublished)										
6–10	21	$1 \pm 34°$	0.519	<0.001	15	$50°$	0.114	0.265	+2.120	0.034
11–15	32	$40 \pm 49°$	0.248	0.024	21	$106°$	-0.037	0.597	+1.399	0.180
16–20	63	$-174°$	-0.118	0.907	57	$19 \pm 41°$	0.253	0.004	-3.068	0.002
21–30	39	$31°$	0.102	0.184	31	$-6 \pm 58°$	0.284	0.013	-1.070	0.284
31–40	27	$124°$	-0.107	0.785	35	$20 \pm 61°$	0.253	0.017	-2.301	0.021
41–50	24	$33°$	0.034	0.406	17	$-118°$	-0.139	0.794	+0.622	0.533
51–70	15	$67°$	0.060	0.370	11	$-52°$	0.091	0.332	-0.260	0.794
From Murphy (1987)										
6–10	271	$-100°$	-0.011	0.597	232	$-23 \pm 52°$	0.104	0.012	-1.850	0.064
11–15	293	$-10° \pm 51°$	0.094	0.011	282	$-3 \pm 19°$	0.230	<0.001	-2.597	0.009
16–20	114	$-32°$	0.067	0.156	57	$-12 \pm 32°$	0.312	<0.001	-2.445	0.014

Significant values of h and z are underlined.

Negative z-vaules indicate female performance better than male. Positive z-values indicate male performance than female.

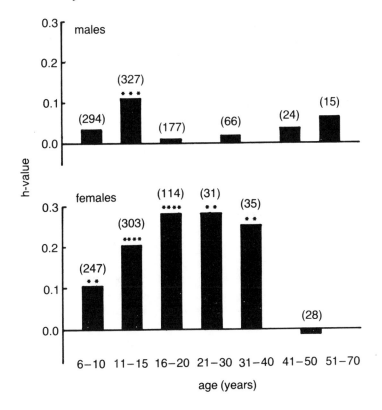

Fig. 5.7. Variation with age in ability of blindfolded males and females to judge geographical direction in chair experiments. Data from Table 5.16. *V*-test: * $P < 0.05$; ** $P < 0.02$; *** $P < 0.01$; **** $P < 0.001$. Numbers in brackets show number of people tested.

that (when blindfolded; in chair experiments with eight or nine bouts of disorientation) males are only able to judge geographical direction early in life (<15 years). Females, on the other hand, slowly gain in ability from 8 to 15 years and retain this ability with little diminution until it disappears, perhaps suddenly, at about 40 years.

Map-building and navigation No comparable data for navigation ability are available, and no mixed-age bus or walkabout experiments have been carried out in any coherent experiments. Although several walk-about experiments have been carried out using 7- to 9- and 16- to 18-year-olds, most cannot easily be compared with experiments on the more usual 19- to 21-year-olds. No experiments have used large numbers of older age groups. Just two walkabouts have been carried out at Woodchester Park on 7- to 9-year-olds under conditions (totally overcast; mid- to late-morning) that allow comparison with two groups of 19-to 21-year-olds matched for location, route and conditions. Results are presented in Table 5.18. The older age group was significantly better at pointing to home but not at judging compass direction and not quite at judging air-line distance to home.

Total data for all 95 of the 7- to 9-year-olds that have been tested in walkabout experiments show an ability to point towards home that is significantly better than could be achieved by guesswork ($h = 0.339$; $P < 0.001$). In contrast, compass orientation is not better than guesswork level ($h = 0.055$; $P = 0.224$) and air-line distances are grossly overestimated (median error = $+3776$ m/km; IQR = $+1388$ to $+6164$). It should be noted, however, that all six walkabout experiments on young children have, by chance, only ever taken place under 'difficult' conditions (e.g. total overcast or at night).

5.3.4. *Influence of cloud cover*
An obvious expectation is that judgement of geographical direction and its use for navigation will be more accurate when the sky is clear and the sun is visible than when the sky is totally overcast.

Judgement of geographical direction   Murphy (personal communication) tested people (19–21 years old) under both clear and totally overcast daytime skies in her series of chair experiments in which an open box on the head allowed subjects to see the sky but not the horizon. Judgement of compass direction under sunny skies ($h = 0.687$; $N = 25$; $P < 0.001$) was significantly better ($z = 2.192$; P (one-tailed) = 0.014) than judgement under overcast skies ($h = 0.079$; $N = 10$; $P = 0.359$). My limited data for sighted subjects on bus experiments also suggest that the judgement of compass orientation when skies are clear and sunny ($h = 0.467$; $N = 25$; $P < 0.001$) is better than when skies are totally overcast ($h = 0.118$; $N = 183$; $P = 0.012$), and the difference is just significant ($z = 1.812$; P (one-tailed) = 0.035). However, by far the most extensive data for the influence of cloud cover on the judgement of compass direction has been obtained in walkabout experiments.

Figure 5.8 divides walkabout data according to cloud cover at the time subjects were making their estimate of compass direction at the test site, irrespective of conditions during the walk itself. Only experiments during daylight hours are included. The most striking feature is that subjects show no evidence of being able to judge compass direction if the sky is totally overcast, or even if there are a few breaks in the cloud. Only if half or more of the sky is clear is compass orientation more accurate than guesswork. Performance under overcast skies is significantly worse than when the sky is clear (i.e. <25% cloud cover) ($z = 3.565$; P (one-tailed) < 0.001). Indeed, if anything, performance by sighted subjects

Table 5.18. Performance by two age groups in walkabout experiments matched for location (Woodchester Park) and conditions (total overcast)

	7–9 years old				19–21 years old				Mann–Whitney U-test	
		Mean error				Mean error				
	n	$e \pm$ CI	h	P (V-test)	n	$e \pm$ CI	h	P (V-test)	z	P (1-tailed)
Compass	29	118 ± 48°	-0.155	0.882	23	-110°	-0.094	0.739	+0.424	0.674
Pointing	29	-29	0.184	0.079	23	31 ± 21°	0.600	<0.001	+2.857	0.004
	error:	median (inter-quartile)				median (inter-quartile)				
Distance	13	1388	(1388–3776)		23	1388	(403–2582)		+1.447	0.148

Significant values of h and z are underlined.
Positive z-values indicate performance by 19- to 21-year-olds is better than 7- to 9-year-olds.

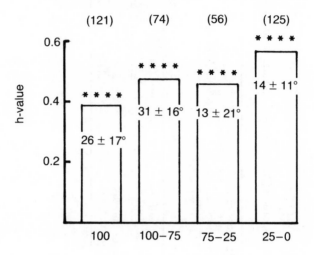

POINTING TO HOME

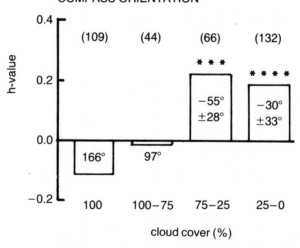

COMPASS ORIENTATION

cloud cover (%)

Fig. 5.8. Influence of cloud cover on ability or sighted subjects to judge compass direction and the direction and distance of home in walkabout experiments. *V*-test: * $P < 0.05$; ** $P < 0.02$; *** $P < 0.01$; **** $P < 0.001$. Numbers in brackets show number of people tested. Angles on histograms show mean errors (±95% confidence limits). Distance estimates shown as median error with inter-quartile range.

AIR-LINE DISTANCE TO HOME

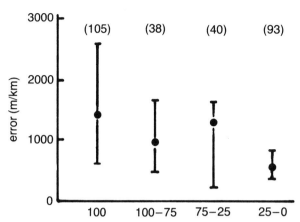

under overcast skies on walkabout experiments ($h = -0.110$) is worse than that achieved ($h = 0.107$; Table 5.3) by blindfolded subjects on a bus.

Map-building and navigation Estimates of the direction and distance of home during walkabout experiments are divided in Fig. 5.8 according to cloud cover. In these cases, however, it is conditions over the course of the walk that are categorised, not those while subjects are at the test site. Again, only daylight walks are included.

The accuracy with which people judge both direction and distance deteriorates as cloud cover increases. Comparison of data for clear (<25% cloud cover) and overcast tests shows the difference to be significant both for judging direction ($z = 2.158$; P (one-tailed) $= 0.016$) and distance ($z = 5.437$; P (one-tailed) < 0.001). Unlike the judgement of compass direction, however, completely overcast skies do not totally destroy the ability to judge the direction of home ($h = 0.391$; $P < 0.001$). In contrast, as noted elsewhere (Baker 1987b), virtually continuous sunshine seems to be necessary for distance to be judged with any accuracy.

5.3.5. *Influence of height of sun above or below the horizon*
Perhaps less obvious than the expected influence of cloud cover is the expectation that the height of the sun may influence the accuracy of orientation and navigation. Yet, clearly, when the sun is directly overhead, at the zenith, it provides no information on geographical direction. The further from the zenith position the sun is located, the easier it becomes for a person to judge direction. Even so, as a walking human

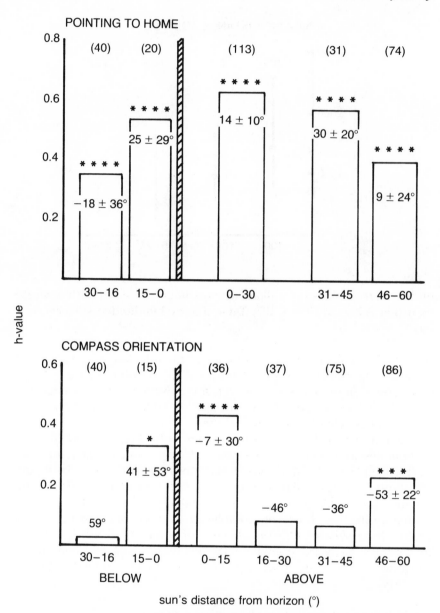

Fig. 5.9. Influence of height of sun above or below the horizon on the ability of sighted subjects to judge compass direction and the direction and distance of home in walkabout experiments. *V*-test: * $P < 0.05$; ** $P < 0.02$; *** $P < 0.01$; **** $P < 0.001$. Numbers in brackets show number of people tested. Angles on histograms show mean errors ($\pm 95\%$ confidence limits). Distance estimates shown as median error with inter-quartile range.

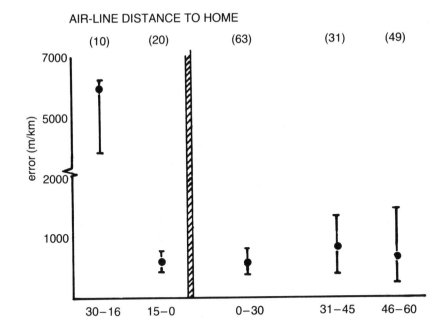

AIR-LINE DISTANCE TO HOME

tends to look forwards or down, it is not until the sun nears the horizon that its disc acts as a visual beacon. Consequently, when the sun is high, the shadow cast by the walking human may often be more useful than the sun's disc itself. Again, the lower the sun, the longer and more obvious the shadow. Even once the sun sets, the twilight glow in the western sky provides useful directional information until the sun is so far beneath the horizon that no glow may be detected.

Judgement of geographical direction   Figure 5.9 shows the extent of variation in performance at judging compass directions on walkabout experiments in relation to the height of the sun. Only tests in which the sun's position could be identified by the experimenter are included. As expected, the most accurate judgements occur when the sun is just above ($h = 0.433$) or just below ($h = 0.332$) the horizon.

Map-building and navigation   Figure 5.9 also shows the influence of the height of the sun during the walk on judgement of the direction and distance of home. As for judging compass direction, distance is judged most accurately when the sun is just above or below the horizon. Direction is judged most accurately with the sun just above the horizon. Even at night, however, with the sun more than 16° below the horizon, and with little twilight glow but with the stars shining, the direction of home is judged significantly better than could be achieved by guesswork ($h = 0.352$; $P < 0.001$).

5.3.6. *Influence of time of day*

People do not function equally well at all times of the day and night. Circadian rhythms and fatigue combine to produce changes in performance in many tasks as the day progresses, and there is no obvious reason to expect ability at orientation and navigation to be an exception. When sighted, physiological changes may be compounded by the celestial changes that also occur as the day progresses.

In order to use the sun for directional information with any precision, it is necessary to allow for the fact that it rises over the eastern horizon in the morning, is due South (if the person is North of the northern tropic line) or North (If South of the southern tropic line) at noon, and sets below the western horizon at night. Failure to make proper allowance for this apparent motion of the sun across the sky would generate patterned errors in orientation.

Judgement of geographical direction   Evidence has already been presented (Baker *et al.* 1982; Baker & Mather 1982; Baker 1984b) that judgement of compass direction by blindfolded people in chair experiments changes with time of day. Peak performance is between 09.00 and 15.00 h after which there is a marked deterioration.

Table 5.19 and Fig. 5.10 summarise the judgement of compass direction by sighted subjects in walkabout experiments in relation to time of day and cloud cover at the time the estimate was made. Data are divided according to whether the sky was totally overcast or cloud was broken enough for the position of the sun (or >50% of stars) to be seen.

Table 5.19. Error at estimating compass direction under clear and overcast skies in morning and afternoon walkabout experiments

	n	$e \pm CI$	r	h	P (V-test)	Watson's $U^2_{n,m}$ test U^2	P
Sun visible							
morning	146	$-45 \pm 22°$	0.279	0.196	<0.001		
afternoon	127	$12 \pm 46°$	0.171	0.167	0.004	0.248	<0.020
Total overcast							
morning	54	$-179 \pm 78°$	0.195	-0.195	0.979		
afternoon	38	$177°$	0.097	-0.097	0.801	0.075	0.500

Significant values of h and U are underlined.

When the sky is clear, morning and afternoon compass estimates are significantly different, morning estimates being anticlockwise in error, afternoon estimate being clockwise in error (Table 5.19). No such difference is found when the skies are overcast. An anticlockwise error (e.g. judging North to be North-West) implies that North is being judged to be East of its true direction. Similarly, clockwise errors imply that North is judged to be West of its true direction. The mean compass bearing of the sun during the 146 morning estimates made was 165° from grid North; during the 127 afternoon estimates the sun's mean compass bearing was 234°. Measured mean errors at judging compass direction were −45° in the morning and +12° in the afternoon (Table 5.19). These errors are consistent with the view that subjects judged the direction of the sun to be ESE (actually 120° from grid North) in the morning and WSW (actually 246°) in the afternoon. In other words, the data are consistent with the view that subjects were using the sun as a cue for compass direction, but were using it crudely and imprecisely.

When skies are clear, strongest compass orientation occurs around noon, with performance deteriorating towards dawn and dusk (Fig. 5.10). When skies are totally overcast, estimates of compass direction in the morning are misoriented by about 180°, North being called South, etc. This morning misorientation changes to simple disorientation through the noon and afternoon periods and tends towards orientation at night. This misorientation under overcast skies seems to be a peculiar feature of walkabout experiments, sighted subjects on chair or bus experiments being either simply disoriented under overcast skies or weakly (but significantly) oriented (Section 5.3.4). No explanation can yet be offered.

Map-building and navigation   The influence of time of day on ability to judge the direction and distance of home on walkabout experiments is summarised in Fig. 5.10. When skies are clear, the strength of homeward orientation declines and errors at judging distance increase as the day progresses. Under overcast skies, however, performance tends to peak at midday.

5.3.7. *Influence of bed alignment*
I have reported (Baker 1984b; 1985a) that the ability of people to judge compass direction in chair experiments was a function of the normal alignment of their bed. In general, the most robust ability was shown by N sleepers; the weakest by W sleepers. People who slept on beds aligned along the N–S axis (±45°) were significantly more robust in their ability to judge compass direction than people whose beds were aligned along the E–W axis, particularly between 09.00 and 15.00 h GMT.

These claims have now been tested, and generally not supported, by Murphy (1987) with a large sample (567) of young females (4–18 years

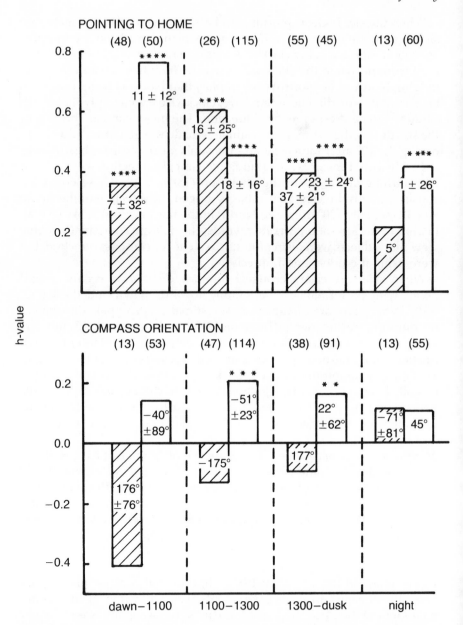

Fig. 5.10. Influence of time of day and cloud cover on the ability of sighted subjects to judge compass direction and the direction and distance of home in walkabout experiments. *V*-test: * $P < 0.05$; ** $P < 0.02$; *** $P < 0.01$; **** $P < 0.001$. Numbers in brackets show number of people tested. Angles on histograms show mean errors (±95% confidence limits). Distance estimates shown as median error with inter-quartile range. Open histograms and dots, skies clear; hatched histograms and solid dots, skies overcast.

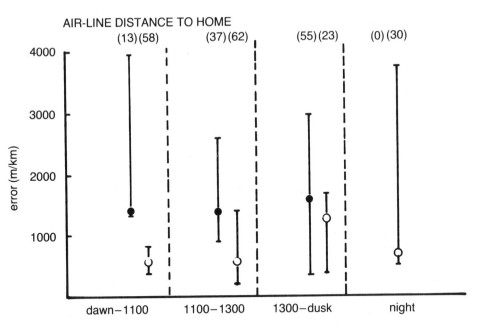

Fig. 5.10

old). Although Murphy also found that W sleepers produced the weakest performance ($h = 0.062$), the strongest performance was not by N sleepers ($h = 0.200$) but by E sleepers ($h = 0.301$). Moreover, for subjects wearing brass bars, Murphy found no significant difference between the performance of N–S sleepers ($h = 0.268$) and E–W sleepers ($h = 0.263$) ($z = 0.299$; P (one-tailed) $= 0.382$). With more data, my own accumulated data-set for control subjects in chair experiments also no longer shows a difference in performance of N–S and E–W sleepers (Chapter 6). On the other hand, accumulated data for bus and walkabout experiments still show that some aspects of orientation and navigation are influenced by bed orientation (Chapter 6).

The question of whether bed orientation influences the normal orientation and navigation of people thus remains unsettled. What is clear, however, from both my own and Murphy's data, is that bed orientation is critical in determining the influence of magnets. This subject is discussed further in Chapter 6.

5.4. *Summary*

This chapter has established that people possess a real ability to discriminate geographical directions and to navigate. When compared with total reliance on familiar landmarks, the level of ability at navigation and map-building, though weak, is nevertheless sufficient, on average, approximately to double the area through which a person can explore and still return home.

Orientation and navigation are most accurate when the sky is clear and the sun is near to the horizon. Any use of a sun compass involves only crude allowance for the sun's apparent motion across the sky during the day. Although less accurate, navigational ability still exists under overcast skies and at night.

Performance varies with age and sex, perhaps because different people use different strategies in solving problems of orientation and navigation. These different strategies may involve the use of different subsets from the available battery of navigational senses.

Experiments with blindfolded people have established that a non-visual sense or senses makes some contribution to navigational ability. Hearing, smell and touch as well as internal gyroscopes, such as the inner ear, could all provide useful (non-visual) navigational information. So, too, could magnetoreception.

The role of magnetoreception in the abilities described in this chapter can be evaluated by changing the ambient magnetic field in such a way that magnetoreception cannot, or does not, occur. Tests carried out under different environmental conditions may then identify when, and under what circumstances, magnetoreception contributes to navigational performance. First, however, it is necessary to know which magnetic treatments disrupt magnetoreception and which do not. This is the aim of the next chapter.

6

The influence of magnets

At first, proof that humans use magnetoreception seems devastatingly simple to obtain. Set a task that needs magnetoreception, change the magnetic field reaching the magnetoreceptor of some people but not of others, and observe how the task is performed. If performance by those experiencing the changed magnetic field is disrupted relative to controls, the use of magnetoreception is proven; if not, there is no evidence that magnetoreception was involved. A moment's thought, however, shows that life for the experimentalist is not that easy.

Consider sight. Suppose we wish to test whether humans use vision. Similar logic would argue: set a task that requires vision, alter the light reaching the eyes of some people but not others, and observe how the task is performed. If performance by those experiencing the changed light rays is disrupted relative to controls, the use of vision is proven; if not, there is no evidence that vision was involved. Yet, suppose, in an ignorance of optics, we chose to alter the light rays with a piece of glass so shaped that it functioned as a magnifying lens. Of course, so long as the lens was not focused, we should indeed find a disruption in performance. However, if we just happened to place the lens so that it focused precisely, we may actually find a marked improvement in performance. If our placement of the lens relative to the eye varied just enough that for some subjects the light was focused but for others not, there may even be no change in average performance. Yet, all subjects were affected. Even if we manage to position the lens precisely the same for all subjects, still they may not all respond in the same way. As anybody with normal sight who has tried the spectacles of a short-sighted friend will know, treatment that improves the performance of one person may actually disrupt the performance of another.

I could expound the analogy even further and describe how dark, coloured or polarised glass may help, hinder or have no effect on visual performance. All depends on ambient light conditions, a person's recent history of exposure to light, and many other factors. However, the point must already have been made: whereas manipulating the light reaching eyes may indeed often interfere with visual acuity, such manipulation may also on occasion have no effect or may even enhance acuity. Moreover, treatment that enhances one person's performance may disrupt that of another.

The visual sense has been studied intensively for decades. The location and anatomy of the eyes is known and, by and large, the physiology of vision is well understood. In contrast, at the time of writing, vertebrate magnetoreception has been studied for only 20 years and human magnetoreception for only seven. Even basic questions such as the location and structure of the sense organ have yet to be answered (Chapters 3 and 8), and our understanding of the physiology of magnetoreception is all but zero. In such a situation, all experiments are effectively 'shots in the dark'.

The urgent need was, and perhaps still is, for a wide range of experiments involving a wide range of magnetic manipulations. We should expect some treatments to disrupt performance, some to enhance, and some to be neutral. Moreover, it should be no surprise if different individuals are influenced in different ways by the same treatment or even if the same individual responds differently to the same treatment on different occasions.

Since 1979, a variety of magnetic manipulations have been carried out during bus, chair and walkabout experiments, not only by myself and my associates at Manchester but also by others at Tulsa, Princeton, Cornell and Keele. My aim in this chapter is to review these manipulations, to present the results, and to draw the most general of conclusions. Having established in this chapter which manipulations are effective (and which are not), I then attempt in Chapter 7 to evaluate the role of magnetoreception in map-building and navigation under different conditions by different people. Finally, in Chapter 8, I use the accumulated data to try to take the first steps along the long road towards an understanding of the physiology of magnetoreception.

6.1. *Large electromagnetic coils*

6.1.1. *Judgement of geographical direction*
The comprehensive series of experiments which demonstrate a role for magnetoreception in the compass orientation of migratory birds have used large electromagnetic coils to reverse the magnetic field through the entire test apparatus (e.g. Merkel & Wiltschko 1965; W. Wiltschko & Wiltschko 1972, 1978; Bingman 1981; Able *et al.* 1982) and thus through the animal's entire body. In such experiments, the test animal moves freely within the changed field. Similar experiments have demonstrated

a role for magnetoreception in the compass orientation of moths (Baker & Mather 1982; Baker 1987a). Three series of chair experiments (in Manchester, Gloucestershire and California, respectively) have used large, stationary electromagnetic coils to study compass orientation by humans.

Only one of these three series rotated the geomagnetic field to produce a static but altered field through the entire body of the subject being tested. The experiments concerned were carried out by R.A. Brian between October 1985 and March 1986 in a room on the fifth floor of the Zoology Department at the University of Manchester. Large coils (radius 1m) mounted on a free-standing aluminium frame with brass fittings were aligned N–S. Separated by their common radius, these coils produced a uniform field through space large enough to accommodate an entire swivel-chair plus seated subject (Fig. 6.1). A variable resistance and transformer allowed control of the amount and direction of a dc current passing through the coils. Five settings were used: two produced a magnetic field with declination unchanged (magnetic N = geomagnetic N); two a field with declination reversed (magnetic N = geomagnetic S); and one a vertical field with no declination. Discussion of the changes in angle of inclination and field strength in this experiment is delayed until Chapter 8.

Six subjects were used (four female; two male), all of them undergraduate students (aged 19–21 years). With one exception because of illness, each subject was tested on 20 different occasions (i.e. four occasions with each of the five settings). Each test occasion involved nine estimates of compass direction. At least 5 days elapsed between successive test occasions with a particular subject. Sequences of field setting over the 20 tests were randomised within and between subjects and on no occasion did either the subject or experimenter know the declination or inclination of the magnetic field in which the test was taking place. Results are shown in Fig. 6.1. Whether analysed by test (as preferred by Kirschvink *et al.* 1985b) or (more properly) by subject, the results show not only a reversal of compass orientation with reversal of magnetic declination but also an absence of compass orientation when the field is vertical.

These experiments by Roz Brian followed protocol that other authors had found to be suitable to demonstrate magnetoreception for compass orientation by birds. In contrast, Kirschvink *et al.* (1985b) opted to use protocol more similar to that (see Wallraff & Gelderloos 1978) that had proved unsuitable for birds. Kirschvink's chair experiments took place in a basement room at the California Institute of Technology. Again the coils were large enough to allow the subject to be rotated within the induced field. Moreover, the coil system was so arranged that magnetic North could be set at geomagnetic N, S, E or W. As in early experiments

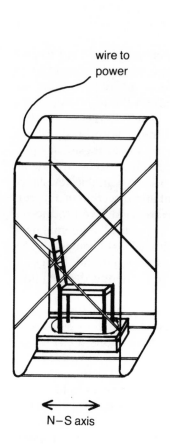

wire to
power

N–S axis

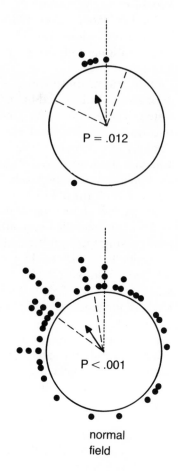

P = .012

P < .001

normal
field

at Manchester, each test involved eight estimates of direction. Unlike all chair experiments at Manchester, however, magnetic declination was not simply changed between each test but was actually changed *between each estimate* within a test. This choice of protocol was surprising in view of the demonstration by Wallraff & Gelderloos (1978) that birds failed to provide evidence of magnetoreception if the ambient field changed during the course of a test.

Kirschvink *et al.* present data for seven subjects (of unspecified gender), each having been tested on a variable number of occasions (with unspecified intervals between tests). Despite the problem of non-independence, the authors prefer to analyse their data by test rather than by subject. Their results are summarised in Table 6.1. There is certainly no indication that subjects could recognise magnetic declination correctly. On the other hand, despite the fact that on 25% of occasions

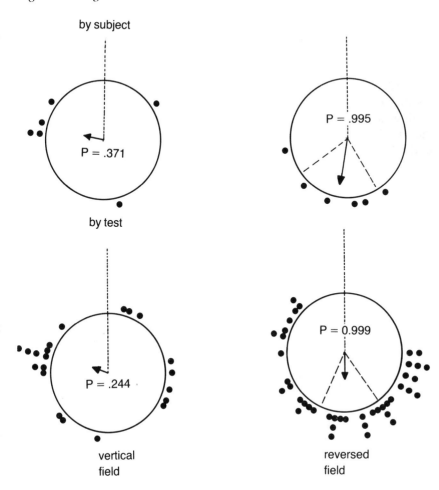

Fig. 6.1. Influence on compass orientation of altering the ambient magnetic field through the whole body of humans. Data are for compass orientation during chair experiments on blindfolded and ear-muffed subjects in a curtained room on the fifth floor of the University of Manchester (October 1985–March 1986). The six subjects were each tested (one test = nine estimates of compass direction): eight times in a normal field (magnetic N = geomagnetic N); eight times in a reversed field (magnetic N = geomagnetic S); and four times in a vertical field (angle of inclination = 90°). Each dot in the lower diagrams is the mean error ($e°$) by one person in one test; in the upper diagrams it is the mean of the eight or four mean errors achieved by each of the six people in each condition. Data points are missing from the lower diagrams because of the illness of one subject. Dotted vertical line: $e = 0°$. Arrow and dashed lines: mean vector and 95% confidence limits. P-value: probability (V-test) that h-value of mean vector is >0.0 by chance. Data from Baker & Brian (unpublished).

magnetic N and 'room N' were the same, comparison of *r*-values (Table 6.1) shows that compass estimates tended to relate more to the changing magnetic field than to the room. Also noticeable is the way the two sets of confidence intervals for verbal estimates include magnetic declination plus 180°. Despite the small sample of people, the results are as expected if subjects were using magnetoreception but, for some reason, were finding accurate orientation difficult. The data are at least interesting and hardly the basis for even a 'tentative' conclusion that 'Caltech students and perhaps humans in general lack any strong or useful ability to sense magnetic direction' (Kirschvink *et al.* 1985b, p. 608).

One other feature of these Caltech chair experiments makes the results difficult to evaluate: there are no control data for subjects tested in a continuously normal field. Quite apart from the continually changing magnetic field, therefore, we do not know that this particular sample of subjects was in any case capable of judging compass direction correctly under the particular test conditions (i.e. given the location, equipment, rate of turning, information provided by the experimenters, etc.). If, for whatever reason, some feature of the protocol caused the subjects to misidentify magnetic direction by 180°, the results obtained would, in fact, represent good evidence for 'a useful ability to sense magnetic direction'. This aspect of the design and interpretation of experiments emerges on several further occasions in this chapter.

Taken together, the experiments by Brian with stationary fields and by Kirschvink *et al.* with changing fields suggest that people use magnetoreception to judge compass direction in chair experiments, but perhaps cannot do so correctly if the field is continually changing. One possible explanation would be that a magnetic declination that changes between each estimate deprives the subject of an opportunity to integrate rotational and directional information. Murphy (1987) has argued that such integration is essential for at least some groups of subjects to perform well in chair experiments.

Both the Manchester and Caltech experiments altered the ambient magnetic field through the whole body of the person being tested. In a chronologically earlier (June/July 1981) series of chair experiments at Woodchester Park, I and a team of students used coils to change the magnetic field through only the head (and, perhaps, upper torso) of the subjects. Tests were made in a non-magnetic wooden hut with brass fittings located 100 m from the only building within a kilometre radius. Electromagnetic coils (radius 40 cm) were suspended from a roof beam and aligned N–S so that the horizontal component of their induced magnetic field was opposed to that of the geomagnetic field. A dc current was provided from a 12-V car battery outside the hut. The coils and swivel-chair were positioned so that the head of a seated subject was approximately mid-way between their centres (see Fig. 6.2). In order to

Table 6.1. Results of Caltech chair experiments in which magnetic declination was changed between each estimate

	Estimates:								
	Relative to room				Relative to magnetic field				
		Mean vector			P		Mean vector			P
n		$e \pm$ CI	r	h	(V-test)	n	$e \pm$ CI	r	h	(V-test)
Analysis by test										
point	64	$-165°$	0.070	-0.068	0.779	64	$-162°$	0.115	-0.109	0.892
verbal	64	$-164°$	0.078	-0.075	0.803	64	$-167 \pm 76°$	0.180	-0.175	0.976
Analysis by subject										
point	7	$-129°$	0.250	-0.157	0.727	7	$-164°$	0.402	-0.387	0.928
verbal	7	$-136°$	0.288	-0.206	0.785	7	$-170 \pm 80°$	0.558	0.550	0.979

Calculated from data in Kirschvink *et al.* (1985b).

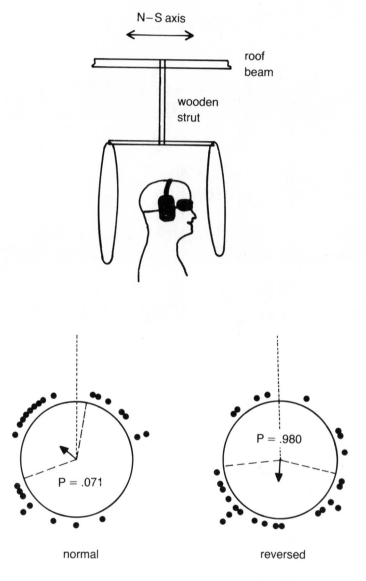

Fig. 6.2. Influence on compass orientation of reversing the ambient magnetic field through the head of humans. Data are for compass orientation during chair experiments on blindfolded and ear-muffed subjects in a dark, wooden hut in rural Gloucestershire in June and July 1981. Subjects were each tested once (one test = eight estimates of compass direction) in the normal geomagnetic field and once in a reversed field (magnetic N = geomagnetic S). ●, Mean error ($e°$). Dotted vertical line: $e = 0°$. Arrow and dashed lines: mean vector and 95% confidence limits. *P*-value: probability (*V*-test) that *h*-value of mean vector is >0.0 by chance. Data from Baker *et al.* (unpublished).

allow the subjects' shoulders to turn as the chair was rotated, it was necessary to separate the two coils, not by their common radius, but by their common diameter (80 cm). This large separation resulted in a complex magnetic field between the two coils. No measurements of field strength or characteristics were made except to confirm that, when the apparatus was activated by throwing a switch, the declination of the magnetic field mid-way between the centres of the two coils changed by 180°.

The 25 test subjects (13 male; 12 female) were all biology undergraduates (aged 19–22 years) from the University of Manchester. For this experiment, each person was tested twice, once in each magnetic field (NB: one test = eight estimates of compass direction). At least one day elapsed between successive tests on a particular subject. Whether a person's first test was in a normal or reversed field was determined randomly by an overseer. Neither subject nor experimenter in any test knew whether or not the coils were activated. Tests were carried out between 08.00 and 16.30 h GMT. The results (Fig. 6.2) are consistent with the expectation that reversal of the magnetic field through the head is associated with a reversal of estimates of compass direction.

6.1.2. *Map-building and navigation*

Whereas large electromagnetic coils that allow the entire body, or part of the body, to move within a changed magnetic field are of obvious use in the laboratory, they are less useful for studies of map-building and navigation during exploration. A few authors have used such coils in navigation experiments on small animals, such as birds and mice, but no one has so far tried such a technique with humans.

The first indication that an altered magnetic field during travel can sometimes influence an animal's eventual ability to orient towards home was obtained by accident. Homing pigeons, transported in a Volkswagen squareback, were noticed sometimes to be more disoriented on release than if transported in some other vehicle (R. Wiltschko & Wiltschko 1978). The effect was particularly noticeable if the crates containing the pigeons were transported on top of the engine in the rear of the car. The Wiltschkos suspected that the effect might be due to the magnetic fields produced by the car's generator.

Since this important initial observation, several authors have tried deliberately to manipulate the magnetic field experienced by pigeons during transport. Papi *et al.* (1978), and later Benvenuti *et al.* (1982), tried to screen the geomagnetic field by displacing birds in containers made of iron. Their birds were disoriented on release when compared with control birds displaced in aluminium containers. In other experiments, Benvenuti and his colleagues found that pigeons were disoriented if exposed during displacement to an oscillating magnetic field induced by three pairs of Helmholtz coils. Such a field should provide little, if any, meaningful information. The Wiltschkos (R. Wiltschko *et al.* 1978; W. Wiltschko & Wiltschko 1981) and Kiepenheuer (1978) used Helmholtz coils to reverse the horizontal component of the geomagnetic field during displacement. The pigeons were often disoriented on release, with a tendency, in Kiepenheuer's experiments, to go either towards home or away from it. In other experiments, Kiepenheuer used Helmholtz coils to reverse the vertical component of the geomagnetic field. Relative to controls, experimental birds exposed to such a reversed field were significantly deflected on release by about 30°.

One of the features of the experiments by the Wiltschkos and Kiepenheuer was that, despite rotation by 180° of the compass information available to the birds during displacement, they were not misoriented by 180° on release. Of course, this could simply mean that each bird's estimate of the direction of displacement was based not only on magnetic information during displacement but also perhaps on landscape information at the release site (Baker 1984b). Even so, this lack of reversal of homeward orientation is a caveat in the evidence that birds may judge their direction of displacement by simple reference to a magnetic compass.

The only experiment to come near to demonstrating that an animal may monitor its direction of travel by reference to a magnetic compass is that on woodmice by Mather & Baker (1981a). In that experiment, reversal of the ambient magnetic field during displacement triggered a rotation in homeward orientation by the mice of 117° (Fig. 6.3).

No attempt has yet been made to test whether displacement in iron boxes (without windows) or within large Helmholtz coils influences the accuracy of map-building and navigation by humans. Nor has any attempt yet been made to determine if these abilities are influenced by variations in the ambient magnetic field during displacement attributable to the make and design of the vehicle used for transport.

6.2. *Electromagnetic coils on helmets*

Three types of electromagnetic helmets have been used in experiments at Manchester (Fig. 6.4); apparently none has been used elsewhere. All types have been used in chair experiments; type 1 has also been used in bus and walkabout experiments.

All helmets were powered by dc batteries: types 1 and 2 by a small, 9-V, pocket-sized battery; type 3 by three large, 12-V car batteries mounted on the base of the swivel-chair. Field strength was adjusted by means of suitable resistors. False connections or switches allowed helmets to be deactivated for control subjects. The major difference between the helmets is that, whereas type 1 produces a horizontal field, types 2 and 3 both produce a vertical field.

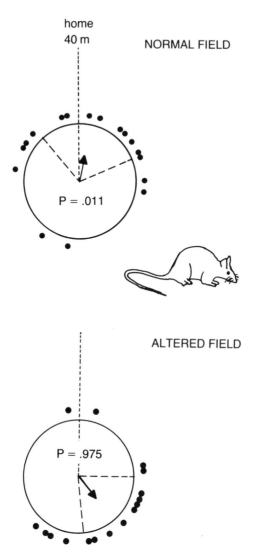

Fig. 6.3. Influence on goal orientation of altering the ambient magnetic field through the whole body of Woodmice (*Apodemus sylvaticus*) during displacement. Each dot is the mean direction of movement of a single mouse as measured in an orientation cage. Dotted, vertical line is the direction of 'home', where 'home' is the place at which the mouse was captured in a Longworth trap. Visual and olfactory information was reduced (by opaque screens and plastic containers or doors, respectively) both during transport and testing. Normal field (magnetic N = geomagnetic N); Altered field (magnetic N = geomagnetic S). Arrow and dashed lines: mean vector and 95% confidence limits. *P*-value: probability (*V*-test) that *h*-value of mean vector is >0.0 by chance. Strength of homeward orientation in normal and reversed geomagnetic fields differs significantly (*P* < 0.01; Wallraff's test). Modified from Mather & Baker (1981a).

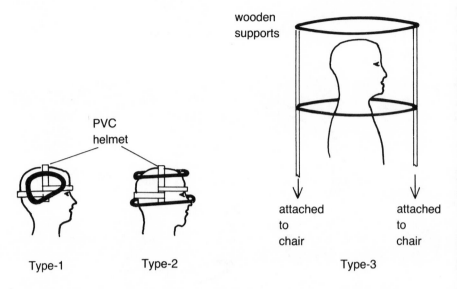

Fig. 6.4. Three types of electromagnetic 'helmets' used in orientation experiments at the University of Manchester. Coils were made from copper wire. Supporting structures were all non-magnetic.

As a subject twists and turns while walking, or is rotated on a chair, the horizontal component due to a type 1 helmet sometimes reinforces and sometimes opposes that due to the geomagnetic field. The horizontal component due to the helmet is three to four times stronger than that of the geomagnetic field so that, when the two components are opposed, the net field is two to three times stronger than that of the geomagnetic field and field declination is reversed (e.g. magnetic N = geomagnetic S). When the horizontal components of the helmet and geomagnetic field are complementary, the net field is four to five times stronger than that of the geomagnetic field but field declination remains unaltered (i.e. magnetic N = geomagnetic N). In experiments, some subjects wore helmets with the North pole of the field to their right (i.e. declination reversed when facing E); others to the left (declination reversed when facing W).

In contrast to the complex interactions between type-1 helmets and the geomagnetic field, the vertical component produced by type-2 and type-3 helmets is always opposed to that of the geomagnetic field. As the component due to the helmets is twice as strong as that due to the geomagnetic field, the result is a net field the strength of which is unaltered from that of the geomagnetic field. Field declination is also unaltered (i.e. magnetic N = geomagnetic N). Angle of inclination of the field, however, is reversed, field lines descending to the South, rather than to the North (all experiments were done in Britain).

Note that type 3 is not a 'helmet' in the conventional sense. It is described here as such because, like helmets but unlike the systems described in Section 6.1, the coils move with the subject. In the case of type-3 coils, which could only be used in chair experiments, they were attached to, and rotated with, the swivel-chair. The result is that the component contributed by the coils to the net magnetic field through the person's head (and upper torso) was static with respect to the person.

It should be stressed that none of these coils were perfect Helmholtz coils (i.e. a pair of identical coils separated by a distance equal to their common radius). As a result the fields generated through subjects' heads were far from uniform (see field diagrams for type-1 helmets in Baker (1981b, p. 60).

6.2.1. *Judgement of geographical direction*

Type-1 helmets were used in the very first series of chair experiments carried out from December 1980 to March 1981 by Mike Meharg and myself. In this pilot series, Meharg tested 44 subjects and I tested 20. Subjects (40 male, 24 female) were all university undergraduates, post-graduates or staff (aged 19–45) and were each tested twice, once with the helmet activated, once deactivated. Each test involved 20 estimates of compass direction. Some subjects were tested first with the helmets activated, others first with the helmets deactivated. The interval between the end of one test and the start of the next was no more than one minute, during which the blindfolds and ear-muffs were not removed. Unlike all other tests to involve magnetic manipulation ever since, this pilot series was not double blind, the experimenter (but not the subject) knowing both whether the helmet was activated and the expected influence on the judgement of compass direction.

When activated, the type-1 helmets used in this first series generated a field with North to the left. Our prediction, therefore, was that, whereas with the helmets deactivated subjects should estimate direction correctly, with the helmets activated subjects should always judge themselves to be facing East. Consequently, when subjects faced East, there should be no difference between activated and deactivated estimates; when facing North, South or West, there should be an appropriate difference. Overall, there should also be a significant reduction in accuracy when the helmets were activated. The results are shown in Tables 6.2 and 6.3. Unlike most tables in this book, the mean estimates given in Table 6.2 are compass bearings, not errors, and the appropriate two-sample test is Watson's $U^2_{n,m}$, not Wallraff's.

Estimates made while the helmets were deactivated were significantly more accurate than guesswork when subjects were facing N or W, but

Table 6.2. Influence of electromagnetic helmet (north to the left) on estimates of compass direction

| | Helmet deactivated | | | | Helmet activated | | | | | |
| | Mean angle | | | | Mean angle | | | | Watson's test | |
	Expected	Observed	h	P (V-test)	Expected	Observed	h	P (V-test)	$U^2_{64,64}$	P
Blindfolded										
Chair experiments										
Facing:										
East	90°	−8°	−0.017	0.576	90°	64 ± 26°	0.372	<0.001	0.347	<0.005
West	270°	306 ± 47°	0.205	0.010	90°	83 ± 50°	0.242	0.003	0.350	<0.002
North	0°	2 ± 47°	0.252	0.002	90°	32 ± 43°	0.140	0.056	0.094	>0.200
South	180°	213°	0.095	0.141	90°	71 ± 35°	0.290	<0.001	0.304	<0.005

Significant values of $U^2_{n,m}$ are underlined.

Data from Meharg & Baker (unpublished); $n = 64$ in all cases.

Table 6.3. Lack of influence of three types of electromagnetic helmets on accuracy of compass orientation

Helmet type (Fig. 6.4)	Helmet deactivated Mean error				Helmet activated Mean error				Wallraff's test	
	n	$e \pm$ CI	h	P (V-test)	n	$e \pm$ CI	h	P (V-test)	z	P (2-tailed)
Blindfolded										
Chair (1980–81)										
Type 1	64	13°	0.153	0.042	64	−50°	0.064	0.235	+0.745	0.456
Type 2	31	−110°	−0.076	0.726	30	167°	−0.051	0.654	−0.297	0.766
Type 3	24	−33°	0.075	0.301	24	149°	−0.142	0.839	+1.228	0.218
Bus (1979–80)										
Type 1	120	26°	0.037	0.284	117	58°	0.040	0.272	−0.157	0.892
Sighted										
Walkabout (1980–81)										
Type 1	84	−49 ± 30°	0.193	0.006	95	−67 ± 43°	0.076	0.146	+1.087	0.276

Combined probability
χ^2_{10}	P
7.953	0.635

Positive z-values: estimates by subjects wearing deactivated helmets are the more accurate of the two sets.

All data from R.R. Baker (unpublished) in collaboration with: S.E.R. Bailey (bus): M. Meharg (chair, type 1): and J.G. Mather (chair, types 2 and 3; bus; walkabout).

not when facing S or E (Table 6.2). As expected, estimates made with the helmets activated were significantly biased towards E, except when subjects were facing N (when estimates were biased towards NE). Also as expected, activated and deactivated estimates differed significantly when the subjects were facing W or S but, and contrary to expectation, not when facing N. Also unexpected was a significant difference in estimates made with activated and deactivated helmets when facing E.

This first chair experiment with type-1 helmets has not yet been repeated. Absence of double-blind protocol combined with some unexpected trends makes interpretation difficult; a difficulty compounded by the fact that overall accuracy at judging direction was not significantly reduced when the helmets were activated (Table 6.3). Bus (1979–1980; Chapter 4) and walkabout (1980–1981; Chapter 4) experiments using type-1 helmets also failed to obtain a significant difference between compass estimates made by subjects wearing activated and deactivated helmets (Table 6.3). Moreover, people wearing 'E-facer' type-1 helmets (i.e. with declination reversed when facing W) did not produce estimates of compass direction that differed from those made by people wearing 'W-facer' helmets ($U^2_{58,59} = 0.070$; $P > 0.500$).

W. Wiltschko & Wiltschko (1972) have shown that reversing the vertical component of the geomagnetic field (albeit with large, static coils) is as effective in reversing compass orientation by migratory birds as is reversing the horizontal component. In contrast, chair experiments with type-2 and type-3 electromagnetic helmets have so far failed to provide evidence that reversing the vertical component through the head and upper torso reverses the compass orientation of humans (Table 6.3). However, though not significant, the data for type-3 (178° change in mean error when coils activated; Table 6.3) suggest that further tests with larger samples ought to be carried out.

Discussion The five series of experiments summarised in Table 6.3 provide no evidence ($P = 0.635$; combined probability) for an influence of electromagnetic helmets on judgement of compass direction.

A clear lack of influence of electromagnetic helmets on magnetoreception could be an important clue to the physiology of the magnetoreceptor (Chapter 8). However, while it is tempting to conclude from Table 6.3 that electromagnetic helmets do not influence human magnetoreception, there are facets to the results that advise some caution. Not least are the significant trends obtained in the single-blind chair experiments by Meharg & Baker (Table 6.2). In addition, whereas overall the five groups of people tested wearing deactivated helmets (Table 6.3) judged compass direction better than expected from guesswork ($\chi^2_{10} = 22.13$; $P = 0.015$; combined probability), those tested wearing activated helmets did not ($\chi^2_{10} = 10.55$; $P = 0.395$).

6.2.2. *Map-building and navigation*

Electromagnetic helmets have been used in navigation experiments on both birds and humans. Unfortunately, only helmets that alter the vertical component of the geomagnetic field have been used on birds; only those that alter the horizontal component on humans.

Pigeons released wearing electromagnetic helmets of 'cap-and-collar' design (similar to type 2, Fig. 6.4) are more scattered in their departure directions on release than suitable control birds (Walcott & Green 1974; Walcott 1977; Visalberghi & Alleva 1979). Under overcast skies, birds with a 'North up' magnetic field through the head even set off with a mean error relative to home of 172°. In contrast, 'South up' birds oriented towards home with a mean error of only 8° (Walcott & Green 1974).

The navigational accuracy of humans wearing electromagnetic helmets has been tested in both bus and walkabout experiments, though only type-1 helmets (Fig. 6.4) have so far been used (Baker 1981b). In both types of experiment, subjects wore the helmets both throughout the journey and while making their estimates at the test site. Although some of the earliest data looked encouraging (Baker 1980c, 1981b), by the end of July 1981 it was clear that the helmets were having no influence on any aspect of map-building and navigation (Table 6.4) and their use was discontinued.

6.3. *Bar magnets on the head*

Whereas large electromagnetic coils appear to offer a reliable means of manipulating compass orientation in the laboratory, they cannot easily be used to study the role of magnetoreception in map-building and navigation by humans during exploration. Electromagnetic helmets could be used but are cumbersome to wear and have so far been ineffective.

A number of studies of bird navigation have attempted to manipulate magnetoreception with bar magnets and to compare the performance of individuals so treated with that of others wearing magnetically inert brass or lead bars (e.g. Keeton 1971; W. Wiltschko & Wiltschko 1981). For studies of humans, bar magnets have the advantage of being relatively portable but have the disadvantage that they generate complex fields with very strong gradients of field intensity. As shown later, they also have the disadvantage that they generate different responses in different people.

6.3.1. *Judgement of geographical direction*

Zusne & Allen (1981) report a chair experiment in which subjects wearing a 'peekless cardboard box blindfold' were led into a window-

Table 6.4. Lack of influence of type-1 electromagnetic helmets (see Fig. 6.4) on navigational performance

Experiments (1979–1981)	Helmet deactivated				Helmet activated				Mann–Whitney U-test	
	n	Mean error			n	Mean error			z	P (2-tailed)
		$e \pm CI$	h	P (V-test)		$e \pm CI$	h	P (V-test)		
Pointing to home										
Bus	120	$-25 \pm 26°$	0.255	<0.001	117	$-17 \pm 29°$	0.245	<0.001	+0.164	0.872
Walkabout	92	$10 \pm 16°$	0.489	<0.001	104	$-5 \pm 15°$	0.511	<0.001	−0.323	0.746
Compass direction of home										
Bus	120	$4 \pm 32°$	0.238	<0.001	117	$-31 \pm 45°$	0.141	0.015	+1.099	0.272
Walkabout	0				0					
Air-line distance to home		Error (m/km)				Error (m/km)				
	n	median	(IQR)		n	median	(IQR)			
Bus	86	547	(333–1000)		89	500	(222–846)		−1.193	0.230
Walkabout	27	1388	(403–1985)		29	1239	(254–2582)		−0.689	0.492
								Combined probability		
								χ^2_{10} 7.822	P 0.648	

Positive z-values: estimates by subjects wearing deactivated helmets are the more accurate of the two sets.
All data from R.R. Baker (unpublished) in collaboration with: S.E.R. Bailey (bus) and J.G. Mather (bus and walkabout).

less, totally dark and unfamiliar room along a path involving three turns. After rotation in a swivel chair, subjects were asked to face North. Twenty-five subjects were tested with no bar; five with a 30-mT bar magnet, the N pole of which was 'over the subject's forehead'. Each subject was given 12 trials. The published account did not present the data obtained, nor did analyses appear to use circular statistics. Instead, according to the authors: 'The mean angle from due North (0°) for the 25 no-magnet subjects was 93°. It was 87° for the magnet group, the expected chance deviation being 90°.' These results are summarised in Table 6.5.

Since 1981, in collaboration with a number of students at the University of Manchester, I have carried out a succession of chair experiments in which subjects wore a bar magnet or brass bar aligned vertically on their right temple (see Fig. 4.16). Murphy (1987), using my magnets and brass bars, has repeated these experiments to test for replicability. However, whereas I and my students tested both males and females over a wide age range (8–42 years), Murphy's sample consisted only of females over a much more limited age range (11–16 years).

In both series of tests, bars were placed in cotton or brown-paper envelopes by a third party, and neither subject nor experimenter knew either the treatment being given or its expected influence on performance. Furthermore, at the time she was carrying out her replicate experiments, Murphy was unaware of the results obtained by myself and my students. The results of both series are summarised in Table 6.5 (and are analysed further in Tables 6.10 and 6.11).

These detailed studies of the influence of magnets on compass orientation in chair experiments are supplemented by two series of bus experiments, one at Manchester, the other at Cornell (Adler & Pelkie 1985). The Manchester series consisted of seven journeys: four in October/November 1981, three in October/November 1982. The Cornell series consisted of one journey in June 1982.

At Manchester, the four journeys at weekly intervals in 1981 were to destinations 15 km S, W, N and E, respectively, of Manchester University and were spaced at weekly intervals. Their design was unusual in that subjects wore nothing on their head (except blindfolds) for the first part of the journey. One test site was used about 3 km out and the data obtained are those used in Table 5.8. When about 7 km from the university, subjects were given type-A (Chapter 4) bars (brass or magnet). All magnets were in Sup alignment. Half the subjects wore the bar behind their right ear; others wore the bar on the right temple (as in Fig. 4.16). The same 25 people (14 males, 11 females) took part on each journey (with some absentees), but each received each of the four bar/position combinations only once. The first test site after bars were in position was about 10 km from the university. Two further test sites were used but,

Table 6.5. Influence of bar magnets (worn on the head) on accuracy of compass orientation

		Brass bars			Bar magnets				Wallraff's test	
		Mean error				Mean error				
	n	$e \pm CI$	h	P (V-test)	n	$e \pm CI$	h	P (V-test)	z	P (2-tailed)
Blindfolded										
Chair (1981–1985)										
Zusne & Allen	25	(93°)	(−0.005)	(0.510)	5	(87°)	(0.005)	(0.490)	(0.000)	(1.000)
Baker *et al.*	164	−17 ± 32°	0.206	<0.001	359	−30 ± 50°	0.075	0.023	+1.917	0.056
Murphy	133	−1 ± 26°	0.265	<0.001	276	−32 ± 88°	0.053	0.105	+2.825	0.004
Bus (1981–1982)										
Adler & Pelkie	18	89 ± 33°	0.005	0.488	18	105 ± 33°		0.808	(+0.700)	(0.484)
Baker *et al.*	77	61 ± 60°	0.093	0.124	98	124 ± 65°		0.891	+1.727	0.084
Sighted										
Walkabout (1982)										
Baker *et al.*	0				60	−102 ± 59°	−0.043	0.683	—	—

Combined probability

χ^2_{10}　　P
23.213　　0.011

Positive z-values: estimates by subjects not wearing magnets are the more accurate of the two sets.

Figures in brackets are conservative estimates based on published data.

Significant values for z and χ^2 are underlined.

Data from: Zusne & Allen (1981); Adler & Pelkie (1985); Murphy (1987); Baker *et al.* (unpublished).

in accordance with the guidelines of Chapter 4, only data from the first (10 km) site are used. Subjects were all undergraduate biology students (aged 19–22 years).

The three journeys at weekly intervals in 1982 were to destinations 15 km S, W and E of Manchester University. There were six test sites on each journey but again, following Adler & Pelkie (1985) and the discussion in Chapter 4, only data from the first test site on each journey can be used. These were each 2–3 km from the university. Bars were in position from the start of each journey and were placed on the right temple. Three treatments were used: brass and Nup and Sup magnets (type-A bars). Subjects were mainly undergraduate and postgraduate students (19–24 years old). None had taken part in the 1981 experiments but the same 27 subjects (14 males, 13 females) took part in each journey (with some absentees). Each received each of the three bar treatments only once.

At Cornell, subjects wore brass bars or Nup magnets on the bridge of the nose. Field strength of the magnets at a distance of 10 cm was 4.4 mT. Thirty-six people took part in the experiment, and, of these, 18 wore brass and 18 wore a magnet. Data for compass orientation are presented under the heading 'hypothesis E' (Adler & Pelkie 1985: Table I, p. 579).

In addition to these various chair and bus experiments on blindfolded people, two walkabout experiments provide data for the influence of magnets on compass orientation when sighted. Both were performed at Woodchester Park in 1982, one in June and one in July. Brass bars were not used on either walk, all subjects wearing magnets (type A), half in Nup alignment and half in Sup.

Ignoring magnet polarity, results for these six series of experiments are summarised in Table 6.5. Compass orientation by subjects wearing brass is variable, h-values ranging from about -0.005 to 0.265. In general, however, the five groups show levels of compass orientation that are better than expected from guesswork alone ($\chi^2_{10} = 34.58$; $P < 0.001$; combined probability). In contrast, orientation by subjects wearing magnets is uniformly weak, even the best h-value being as low as 0.075. Overall, the six groups of magnet wearers show levels of compass orientation that are no better than expected from guesswork alone ($\chi^2_{12} = 14.90$; $P = 0.248$). Magnets on the head have a significant influence on people's ability to judge compass direction ($P = 0.011$; combined probability using two-tailed P-values from Wallraff's test). This influence is generally disruptive ($\chi^2_{10} = 30.14$; $P = 0.001$; combined probability using one-tailed P-values). The impression given is that subjects wearing brass bars are sometimes guessing compass direction and sometimes not; subjects wearing magnets, however, seem always to be guessing.

The information in Table 6.5 focuses attention for the second time in this chapter on the importance of designing experiments around tasks that can be mastered by subjects wearing brass bars. Tasks so difficult, locations so unsuitable, or perhaps even experimenters so intimidating, that subjects have to resort to guesswork or some other inappropriate strategy (Chapter 4), cannot yield useful information in the study of magnetoreception.

6.3.2. *Map-building and navigation*

Bar magnets have been used to study the role of magnetoreception in the navigation of birds, horses and humans. In most cases the magnets have been placed somewhere on the head, but in the study of birds the magnets are usually positioned on the back, between the wings or 'shoulders'.

The first demonstration that bar magnets influenced the navigational accuracy of birds was provided by Keeton (1971) for homing pigeons. Since then, the conclusion has been reinforced by results obtained by a number of other authors (e.g. Walcott 1977; Visalberghi & Alleva 1979; Wiltschko *et al.* 1981). In all cases, groups of pigeons wearing magnets were less well oriented than control birds wearing brass bars.

Experiments on the role of magnetoreception in horse navigation were pioneered by Sarah Panagakis, an undergraduate working under my supervision between September 1983 and March 1984. Panagakis showed that horses displaced in a horse-box and 'released' 8–80 km North or South of their home stable (in Cheshire or North Wales, UK) were homeward oriented 15 minutes after the rider had dropped the reins (Fig. 6.5). Six horses were used on 29 occasions. When the same six horses were displaced on a further 18 occasions wearing six Nup magnets (three on each side of the head, positioned on the bridle, and spaced 1 cm apart), the accuracy of homeward orientation was significantly reduced (P (two-tailed) $= 0.004$; Fig. 6.5). Throughout this first series of pilot tests, the rider knew both the correct direction of home and the treatment that the horse had received.

In a second, double-blind, series the rider did not know the treatment the horse had received during the outward journey. Seven further horses were tested, each on two occasions. Each horse on one occasion wore six brass bars during displacement; on another it wore six Nup magnets. Three of the horses wore brass on their first test and magnets on their second; four the converse. Release sites were 15–25 km from the home stable. Again, 15 minutes after the reins were dropped, horses that had worn brass during the outward journey were oriented towards home much better than could be expected by chance (Fig. 6.5). In comparison, horses that had worn Nup magnets during the outward journey were significantly less oriented towards home (P (two-tailed) $= 0.012$) and in fact were not more homeward oriented than could have been expected by chance.

Since Panagakis' pioneer experiments, a succession of students (Fiona Nelson, 1985–86; Suzanne Cox, 1986–87; Vicky Jones, 1987–88), working under my supervision, have each confirmed that when a horse is displaced by horse-box, it has a significant ability to head towards its home stable (using horse's location 15 min after its rider has dropped the reins measured as a compass bearing from the point of release). No attempt has yet been made, however, to replicate the influence of bar magnets reported by Panagakis.

In all of these experiments, as in the tests of compass orientation summarised in Table 6.5, magnets on or near the head disrupted the navigational accuracy of the animals concerned. The same tendency was observed at Barnard Castle in the first experiment to test for an influence of magnets on the navigational accuracy of humans (Baker 1980d, 1981b). In that experiment, Nup magnets were placed on the back of the head and subjects were asked only to judge the compass direction of home. Although estimates were made at two stops, only data from the first stop can now be used (see Chapter 4 and Adler & Pelkie 1985). As can be confirmed by the reader from the raw data illustrated in Baker (1980d, 1981b), Dayton's analysis (Dayton 1985, p. 567) of estimates made at the first stop is incorrect. Using his tie-breaking teachnique (i.e. assigning the average rank to ties), which is also the technique used throughout this book (but not by Baker 1985a), Wallraff's test gives $U = 74$, not $U = 93$ as calculated by Dayton. P (two-tailed) is thus about 0.07 (Table 6.6).

In contrast to the disruptive influence of magnets on navigation by birds and horses and to the trend observed at Barnard Castle, experiments in the USA have shown a significant *improvement* in navigational ability when subjects wear magnets. Three of the American experiments have used magnets on the head during displacement (Gould 1980; Gould & Able 1981; Adler & Pelkie 1985; see Dayton 1985 for a proper analysis of Gould's data). Twice, magnets have been placed on the front of the head (at Princeton 1980 and Cornell 1982); once on the back (at Princeton 1981). Only estimates of the compass direction of home are available for all three experiments, and the combined data are illustrated in Baker (1985b). The observed improvement in homeward orientation when subjects wear magnets is significant (Table 6.6).

Protocol in bus experiments at Manchester in 1981 and 1982 in which subjects wore bars on their head during the journey has been described above. There were several stops on each journey once bars were on the head (three stops in 1981; six in 1982) and second-order analysis (averaging errors by each person over all stops) showed that subjects wearing magnets were significantly better oriented than subjects wearing brass (Baker 1985c). However, if, as throughout this book, we use data from only the first stop on each journey, the situation is less clear.

The influence of magnets on navigational performance is summarised in Tables 6.6–6.8. These show estimates of the compass direction of home (Table 6.6), attempts to point towards home (Table 6.7), and estimates of the air-line distance to home (Table 6.8). The tables also show the results of combined probability analyses for all of the series for which data are available.

Combined probability analyses show that magnets, worn on the head during displacement, do have a significant influence on ability to indicate the direction of home, both as a compass bearing ($P = 0.019$; Table 6.6) and by pointing ($P = 0.020$; Table 6.7). There is no evidence that such magnets also influence ability to indicate the air-line distance to home ($P = 0.655$; Table 6.8).

More detailed examination of Tables 6.6 and 6.7 shows that, unlike the consistently disruptive influence of magnets on compass orientation, there is no consistent direction to the influence of magnets on accuracy of judging the direction of home; in some series of experiments magnets improve performance, in others they disrupt. It may be important to note, however, that the performance of subjects wearing magnets is much more consistent than that by controls. In judging the compass bearing of home, h-values vary from 0.130 to 0.299 if wearing magnets but from -0.027 to 0.568 if wearing brass or lead. Comparable ranges for pointing to home are 0.119 to 0.367 with magnets as against -0.017 to 0.579 with brass. Perhaps magnets impose a certain level of performance, the outcome of the experiment then being determined by how well the control subjects are able to perform on the journeys concerned.

Fig. 6.5. Influence of magnets on homeward orientation of horses. Each dot is the compass bearing of the direction a horse travels from its point of release, measured 15 minutes after release. 'Home' direction is shown by the vertical, dotted line (where 'home' is the horse's normal stable from which the journey began. Horses were released with a rider but with the reins dropped. Controls exposed to normal geomagnetic field during displacement by horse box; experimentals with six bar magnets (Nup alignment; pole strength 16 mT) fixed to the bridle during displacement, three either side of the head and spaced between eye and nose. Arrow and dashed lines: mean vector and 95% confidence limits. P-value: probability (V-test) that h-value of mean vector is >0.0 by chance. *Series I:* navigational response of six horses, each displaced several times. Controls wore no bars during displacement and the rider knew whether the horse was a control or experimental. *Series II:* navigational response of seven horses, each displaced once as a control and once as an experimental. Controls wore six brass bars during displacement. All bars were positioned by a third party and enclosed in an opaque brown-paper envelope. Thus, the rider did not know whether the horse was a control or experimental. In both series, controls and experimentals differ significantly in their strength of homeward orientation (Series I: $z = 2.867$; P (2-tailed) = 0.04; Wallraff's test. Series II: $U = 5$; P (2-tailed) = 0.012). Data from Panagakis & Baker (unpublished).

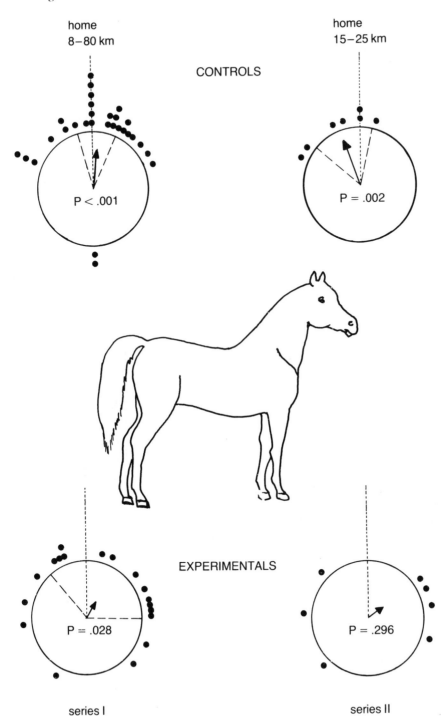

home
8–80 km

home
15–25 km

CONTROLS

P < .001

P = .002

EXPERIMENTALS

P = .028

P = .296

series I

series II

Table 6.6. Influence of bar magnets (worn on the head) on accuracy of judging the compass direction of home

| | Brass/lead | | | | Bar magnets | | | | Wallraff's test | |
| | Mean error | | | | Mean error | | | | | |
	n	$e \pm$ CI	h	P (V-test)	n	$e \pm$ CI	h	P (V-test)	z	P (2-tailed)
Blindfolded										
Bus (1979–1982)										
Barnard Castle	16	−28 ± 29°	0.568	<0.001	15	−74 ± 37°	0.155	0.196	+1.861	0.070
USA 1980–82	48	−88 ± 50°	0.008	0.467	53	−38 ± 29°	0.299	0.001	−2.276	0.023
Manchester 1981	50	107°	−0.027	0.605	45	42°	0.130	0.108	−1.138	0.358
Manchester 1982	27	25 ± 34°	0.422	<0.001	53	−1 ± 60°	0.208	0.016	+1.360	0.174

Combined probability

χ^2_8	P
18.41	0.019

Positive z-values: estimates by subjects not wearing magnets are the more accurate of the two sets.

Significant values for z and χ^2 are underlined.

Data from: Baker (1980a, 1981b, 1985b, unpublished). USA figures from Baker (1985b) from data in Gould (1980); Gould & Able (1981); Adler & Pelkie (1985).

Table 6.7. Influence of bar magnets (worn on the head) on accuracy of pointing to home

| | Brass/lead | | | | Bar magnets | | | | Wallraff's test | |
| | | Mean error | | | | Mean error | | | | |
	n	$e \pm$ CI	h	P (V-test)	n	$e \pm$ CI	h	P (V-test)	z	P (2-tailed)
Blindfolded										
Bus										
Manchester 1981	50	−99°	−0.017	0.567	45	−52°	0.119	0.130	−1.066	0.288
Cornell 1982	18	−15 ± 31°	0.560	<0.001	18	39 ± 42°	0.367	0.015	+1.426	0.154
Manchester 1982	27	−24 ± 24°	0.579	<0.001	53	−60 ± 28°	0.184	0.029	+2.514	0.012
Sighted										
Walkabout (1982)										
Woodchester Park	0				60	18 ± 34°	0.517	<0.001	—	—

	Combined probability	
	χ^2_6	P
	15.08	0.020

Positive z-values: estimates by subjects not wearing magnets are the more accurate of the two sets.

Significant values for z and χ^2 are underlined.

Data from: Adler & Pelkie (1985); R.R. Baker (unpublished).

Table 6.8. Lack of influence of bar magnets (worn on the head) on estimation of the air-line distance to home

| | Absolute error (m/km) | | | | | | Mann–Whitney U-test | |
| | Brass/lead | | | Bar magnets | | | | |
	n	median	(IQR)	n	median	(IQR)	z	P (2-tailed)
Blindfolded								
Bus (1981–1982)								
Princeton	11	920	(40–2200)	15	360	(40–1240)	−0.811	0.417
Manchester	27	467	(200–600)	53	467	(200–733)	+0.384	0.700
Sighted								
Walkabout (1982)								
Woodchester Park	0			60	746	(209–1388)	—	—

Combined probability

χ_4^2 = 2.46 P = 0.655

Positive z-values: estimates by subjects not wearing magnets are the more accurate of the two sets.

Data from J.L. Gould (unpublished); R.R. Baker (unpublished).

6.3.3. *Polarity of magnets and normal bed orientation of subjects*

Table 6.9 summarises experiments carried out in Britain and the United States to test for an influence of magnets on the accuracy of compass orientation in chair, bus and walkabout experiments. It differs from Table 6.5 in that results are separated for magnets that were in Nup and Sup alignment. Not one of the six groups of people wearing Nup magnets was able to judge compass direction significantly better than expected by guesswork. In contrast, some of the groups wearing brass bars or Sup magnets were significantly oriented. The results suggest that the polarity of magnets may be important in determining the nature, or even existence, of influence. This possibility has been the subject of intensive study.

In a pilot study (Baker 1984a, b; 1985a), ten people from an initial sample living in a Manchester suburb were selected for testing on 15 occasions (one week between each test) with either a bar magnet or a brass bar aligned vertically on the right temple. Tests continued over 4 months from December 1981 to March 1982 until each subject had been tested five times wearing a brass bar and ten times wearing a bar magnet (five times with the N pole uppermost, five with S pole uppermost). Conditions were randomly allocated by computer and implemented by a third party.

Table 6.9. Summary of all experiments to test for an influence of bar magnets (worn vertically on the head) on the accuracy of compass orientation

	Strength of compass orientation		
	Brass bar	Bar magnets	
		Sup	Nup
	h	h	h
Blindfolded			
Chair			
Zusne & Allen	−0.005	—	0.005
Murphy	**0.265**	**0.116**	−0.006
Baker *et al.*	**0.206**	**0.198**	0.010
Bus			
Adler & Pelkie	0.005	—	−0.144
Baker *et al.*	0.092	−0.084	−0.099
Sighted			
Walkabout			
Baker *et al.*	—	−0.052	−0.036

Significant *h*-values shown in **bold**.
Data from Zusne & Allen (1981); Adler & Pelkie (1985); Murphy (1987); Baker *et al.* (unpublished).

Subjects were all N–S sleepers (i.e. their normal bed orientation was along the N–S axis ±45°) and were always tested between 10.00 and 15.00 h GMT. They, and the experimenter, wore only clothes made of 100% cotton and subjects had not worn stereo headphones, travelled by train, or used nose drops or nasal spray during the preceding 48 hours.

Results have been published elsewhere, in varying detail (Baker 1984a, b; 1985a). Good orientation was achieved by the ten subjects while wearing a brass bar ($h = 0.648$; $P = 0.003$) or a Sup magnet ($h = 0.790$; $P < 0.001$) but not while wearing a Nup magnet ($h = -0.734$; $P = 0.99$). Indeed, the results were consistent with the view that orientation while wearing a Nup magnet was reversed compared with orientation under the other two conditions. A similar, unpublished, series of experiments on a sample of ten E–W sleepers, however, failed to find any influence of either Nup or Sup magnets.

Since 1982, this study of the apparent interaction between polarity of magnet and normal bed orientation has been extended to much larger samples. Murphy (1987) also subdivided her data for 11- to 16-year-old females according to magnet polarity and bed orientation. The results of both studies are shown in Tables 6.10 and 6.11.

Neither Murphy nor I found any significant diference between N–S and E–W sleepers wearing brass bars or Sup magnets, but both obtained a significant difference for subjects wearing Nup magnets (Table 6.10). In both studies, Nup magnets disrupted judgement of direction by N–S sleepers yet left that by E–W sleepers unimpaired (P (two-tailed) > 0.05 in both studies). These two studies by Murphy (1987) and myself do not differ significantly in any way ($P > 0.1$ for all comparisons of z-values in Table 6.10) and data from the two studies are combined in Fig. 6.6.

Murphy (1987) and I have thus shown independently that a general tendency for vertical magnets on the right temple to disrupt compass orientation in chair experiments (Table 6.5) is in fact significant for only part of the population. People who sleep on beds aligned within 45° of the E–W axis appear unaffected while wearing such magnets. Of the 397 E–W sleepers tested, those wearing magnets still produced an h-value of 0.174, a non-significant reduction relative to the 0.203 achieved if wearing brass. Moreover, polarity of the magnets seemed unimportant (Fig. 6.6 and Table 6.11). In contrast, of the 535 N–S sleepers tested, those wearing magnets managed an h-value of only -0.012, a significant ($z = 3.985$; $P < 0.001$) reduction relative to the 0.257 achieved if wearing brass. Even this high level of disruption is in fact due primarily to magnets of one polarity. Nup and Sup magnets have significantly different effects and only Nup magnets cause significant disruption (Table 6.10). With the S pole uppermost any tendency for the magnets to disrupt is not significant and judgement of compass direction remains better than could be achieved by guesswork (Fig. 6.6). Even with the N

Table 6.10. Influence of bar magnets (worn on the head) on accuracy of compass orientation: interaction of polarity of magnet and normal bed orientation of subject

| | N–S sleepers | | | | E–W sleepers | | | | Wallraff's test | |
| | | Mean error | | | | Mean error | | | | |
	n	$e \pm$ CI	h	P (V-test)	n	$e \pm$ CI	h	P (V-test)	z	P (2-tailed)
Blindfolded chair										
Brass bars										
Baker et al.	98	$-15 \pm 30°$	0.249	<0.001	66	$-23 \pm 40°$	0.143	0.050	+1.024	0.307
Murphy	66	$11 \pm 40°$	0.268	0.001	67	$-14 \pm 40°$	0.263	0.001	+0.299	0.764
Nup magnets										
Baker et al.	150	$-165°$	−0.072	0.893	86	$-13 \pm 70°$	0.153	0.023	−2.376	0.017
Murphy	70	$-159 \pm 40°$	−0.230	0.997	72	$28 \pm 40°$	0.212	0.006	−3.479	<0.001
Sup magnets										
Baker et al.	78	$-4 \pm 32°$	0.227	0.002	45	$-51 \pm 57°$	0.149	0.079	+0.626	0.535
Murphy	73	$-65 \pm 90°$	0.067	0.210	61	$-3 \pm 81°$	0.176	0.026	−0.925	0.356

Combined probability

χ^2_{12}	P
28.181	0.006

Positive z-values: estimates by N–S sleepers are the more accurate of the two sets.

Significant values for h, a and χ^2 are underlined.

Data from Murphy (1987); R.R. Baker et al. (unpublished).

Table 6.11. Influence of bar magnets (worn on the head) on accuracy of compass orientation: interaction of polarity of magnets and normal bed orientation of subjects

	N–S sleepers				E–W sleepers				Sample sizes			
	Magnets		Wallraff's test		Magnets		Wallraff's test		N–S		E–W	
	$\frac{Nup}{h}$	$\frac{Sup}{h}$	z_1	P (2-tailed)	$\frac{Nup}{h}$	$\frac{Sup}{h}$	z_2	P (2-tailed)	Nup	Sup	Nup	Sup
Blindfolded												
Chair												
Baker *et al.*	−0.072	**0.227**	−3.219	0.001	**0.153**	0.149	+0.041	0.968	150	78	86	45
Murphy	−0.230	0.067	−2.476	0.013	**0.212**	**0.176**	0.000	1.000	70	73	72	61
Bus												
Baker *et al.*	−0.305	−0.169	−0.546	0.586	0.039	0.031	+0.059	0.952	10	42	15	31
			Combined probability				Combined probability					
			χ^2_6	P			χ^2_6	P				
			22.90	0.001			0.16	>0.999				

Significant *h*-values shown in **bold**.

Significant *z*- and χ^2-values underlined.

Positive *z*-values indicate subjects wearing Nup magnets are the more accurate of the two sets.

Data from Murphy (1987); R.R. Baker *et al.* (unpublished).

pole uppermost, however, estimates still cannot be attributed to guesswork. Orientation remains non-uniform but is reversed, errors being clustered around 180° (Fig. 6.6).

Also included in Table 6.11 are results for the interaction of magnet polarity and normal bed orientation in influencing the accuracy of compass orientation in bus experiments at Manchester (1981 and 1982). Combined probability analysis of the three (two chair, one bus) series of experiments to test for such an effect confirms that only N–S sleepers are influenced by the polarity of magnets ($P < 0.001$). There is no indication of any difference in response to polarity by E–W sleepers ($P > 0.999$).

Although it is clear from Table 6.11 that N–S sleepers are influenced by magnet polarity in their judgement of compass direction whereas E–W sleepers are not, it does not necessarily follow that the observed difference in response is greater than could occur by chance. Table 6.12 tests this possibility by comparing the z-values given in Table 6.11. Two null hypotheses are tested: (1) N–S and E–W sleepers do not respond differently to magnet polarity; and (2) N–S sleepers are not more sensitive to magnet polarity than E–W sleepers. As far as judgement of compass direction is concerned, both null hypotheses are rejected. The rather meagre data for navigational ability, however, which are also included in Table 6.12, are insufficient to reject either null hypothesis.

6.3.4. *Conclusions*

The combined results from chair, bus and walkabout experiments carried out in Britain and the United States show that magnets, worn on the head, have a significant influence on the accuracy of compass orientation (Table 6.5). In experiments on map-building and navigation, such magnets also influence ability to judge the direction of home, both in terms of its compass bearing (Table 6.6) and by pointing (Table 6.7). As yet, however, there is no evidence for an influence on estimates of the air-line distance to home (Table 6.8).

Overall, the accuracy of *compass orientation* is reduced when magnets are worn on the head (Table 6.5), vertical magnets with the N pole uppermost being particularly disruptive (Table 6.9). This disruption, however, is confined to only a section of the population; individuals responding to magnets on the head in a way that is a function of their normal bed orientation. People who normally sleep on beds aligned along the N–S axis (± 45°) respond to magnet polarity in a way that is significantly different (Table 6.12) from people who normally sleep on beds aligned along the E–W axis. N–S sleepers are significantly more sensitive to polarity than E–W sleepers (Table 6.12), compass orientation by the latter apparently being unaffected (Table 6.11; but see Section 6.4). This increased sensitivity of N–S sleepers derives primarily from

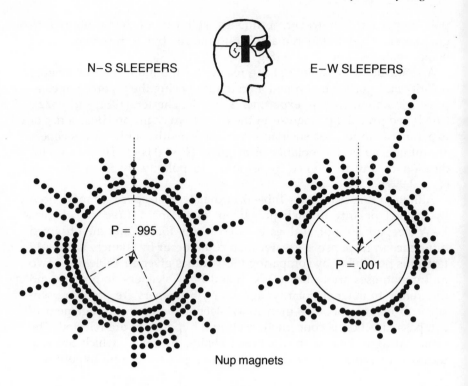

N–S SLEEPERS   E–W SLEEPERS

P = .995

P = .001

Nup magnets

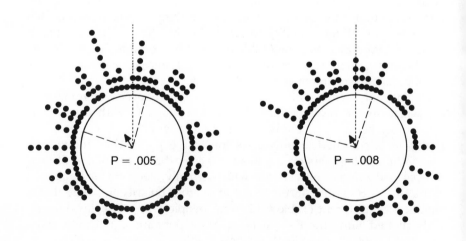

P = .005

P = .008

Sup magnets

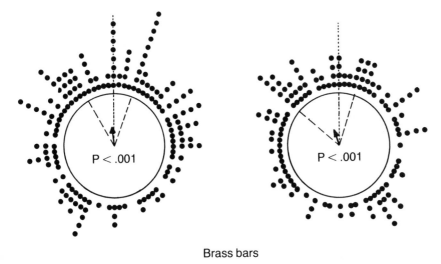

Brass bars

Fig. 6.6. Interaction of polarity of magnet and normal bed orientation of subjects in influencing accuracy of compass orientation in chair experiments. Each dot is the mean error ($e°$) in judging compass direction by one blindfolded and ear-muffed person in a single test (one test = eight or nine estimates of compass direction). A few people were tested under more than one condition (minimum interval between tests = 1 week). Bars (either brass or magnets) are worn on the right temple as illustrated (for clarity, ear-muffs are not shown). Dotted vertical line: $e = 0°$. Arrow and dashed lines: mean vector and 95% confidence limits. *P*-value: probability (*V*-test) that *h*-value of mean vector is > 0.0 by chance. N–S or E–W sleepers: subjects with normal bed orientation along N–S or E–W axis ($\pm 45°$), respectively. A person's 'normal' bed is identified as the last in which they spent 14 consecutive nights. Data combined from Murphy (1987); Baker *et al.* (unpublished).

a reversal in orientation when wearing Nup magnets (Fig. 6.6). Sup magnets on the head of N–S sleepers have no disruptive influence.

Although the interaction of magnet polarity and normal bed orientation is of primary importance in determining the accuracy with which people judge compass direction, there is as yet no evidence that the same is true for the accuracy of *map-building and navigation*. The relationship between polarity and bed orientation becomes important, however, once the magnet is removed.

6.4. *Magnetic pretreatment: manipulating the magnetoreceptor*

Walcott (1982) reports provisional results from an experiment by himself and J. L. Gould in which they attempted to influence the homing per-

Table 6.12. Test of two hypotheses for the influence of magnets (worn on the head) on accuracy of orientation and navigation: (1) Nup and Sup magnets have different effects on N–S and E–W sleepers; and (2) N–S sleepers are the more sensitive to magnet polarity

| | Compass orientation | | | | Pointing to home | | | | Air-line distance to home | | | |
| | Hypothesis 1 | | Hypothesis 2 | | Hypothesis 1 | | Hypothesis 2 | | Hypothesis 1 | | Hypothesis 2 | |
	z_a	P 2-tailed	z_b	P 1-tailed	z_a	P 2-tailed	z_b	P 1-tailed	z_a	P 2-tailed	z_b	P 1-tailed
Blindfolded												
Bus												
Baker	0.428	0.667	+0.344	0.367	0.863	0.390	+0.614	0.270	0.241	0.810	+0.241	0.405
Chair												
Baker	2.305	0.021	+2.247	0.012								
Murphy	1.751	0.080	+1.751	0.040								
Combined probability	χ^2_6	P	χ^2_6	P	χ^2_2	P	χ^2_2	P	χ^2_2	P	χ^2_2	P
	13.59	0.035	17.29	0.009	1.88	0.390	2.62	0.270	0.42	0.810	1.81	0.405

z_a and z_b calculated from z_1 and z_2 in Table 6.11.

$z_a = $ abs $(z_1 - z_2)/$sqr2; $z_b = $ (abs $z_1 - $ abs $z_2)/$sqr2.

Positive values of z_b indicate N–S sleepers show the greater sensitivity.

Significant values of z and χ^2 are underlined.

Data from Murphy (1987); Baker et al. (unpublished).

formance of pigeons by manipulating the magnetoreceptor rather than by changing the magnetic field. The experiment involved exposing pigeons to strong magnetic fields before testing them in homing experiments. This 'pretreatment' seemed to influence homing performance and, depending on treatment, may have improved or disrupted the birds' ability to detect magnetic fields. 'Aftereffects' of exposure to magnetic fields in the performance of homing pigeons have since also been reported by Papi *et al.* (1983) and Kiepenheuer *et al.* (1986).

Independently from Walcott, and concurrently, it was discovered (in the 1981–82 chair experiments on ten N–S sleepers described in Section 6.3.3) that bar magnets on the head of humans influenced compass orientation for longer than simply the time that the magnets were in position. When tested in the normal geomagnetic field immediately after the magnet had been removed, an influence of the treatment each of the ten subjects had received was still apparent (Baker 1984a, b, 1985a). This study of the immediate aftereffect of wearing a vertically aligned, 10- to 20-mT bar magnet on the right temple for 10–15 minutes has continued (R.R. Baker, K. Tricker, A. Ganss, P. Walker, S. Bird, M. Cropper, V. Mellor, K. Perchard & S. Khan, unpublished). So far (to August 1986), 235 N–S sleepers and 205 E–W sleepers have been tested.

The difference in response of N–S sleepers to Nup and Sup magnets while wearing the magnet (Fig. 6.6) is still apparent when tested in the normal geomagnetic field immediately (i.e. 2–10 minutes) after the magnet is removed (Table 6.13). Subjects exposed to Sup magnets are still able to judge compass direction; those exposed to Nup magnets now perform as if guessing (rather than misjudging direction by 180° as they do when wearing the magnet; Fig. 6.6). Magnet polarity still has no significant influence on E–W sleepers (Table 6.13), though those subjects exposed to Nup magnets no longer perform better than expected from guesswork.

Confirmation of this aftereffect of wearing magnets has several important ramifications. First, it has far-reaching implications concerning the nature and physiology of the magnetoreceptor. Secondly, it has to be taken into account in deciding the interval between successive tests when experimental design requires a subject to be tested under several different conditions. Thirdly, it provides a way of studying the role of magnetoreception in map-building and navigation without the need for subjects to be encumbered by helmets or magnets during actual displacement or exploration.

Discussion of the implications of this aftereffect for the structure and physiology of the magnetic sense organ of humans is deferred until Chapter 8. Ramifications concerning experimental design are considered here.

Table 6.13. Accuracy of compass orientation in normal geomagnetic field immediately after wearing a Nup or Sup magnet on the right temple for 10–15 minutes

| | N–S sleepers | | | | E–W sleepers | | | | Wallraff's test | |
| | Mean error | | | | Mean error | | | | | |
	n	e ± CI	h	P (V-test)	n	e ± CI	h	P (V-test)	z	P (2-tailed)
Blindfolded chair										
Nup magnets	162	99°	−0.007	0.553	133	−5°	0.047	0.222	−0.676	0.499
Sup magnets	73	30 ± 41°	0.229	0.003	72	22 ± 70°	0.164	0.025	+0.292	0.772
Wallraff's test		z		P (2-tailed)		z		P (2-tailed)		
		−2.432		0.015		−0.877		0.382		

Positive z-values: estimates by N–S sleepers, or subjects after Nup magnets, are the more accurate of the two sets.
Significant h-and z-values are underlined.
Data from Baker *et al.* (unpublished).

6.4.1. *Judgement of compass direction: pilot study*

In order to allow proper time intervals between treatments and to make maximum use of pretreatment in experimental design, it is necessary to know how quickly subjects recover from exposure to a magnet and what pattern of performance is followed during the recovery period. Since 1982, the same team of investigators that studied the immediate after-effect has also attempted to trace the pattern of recovery. In all, 1270 tests have been performed (one test = nine estimates of direction) on 348 different subjects. It should be stressed, however, that, exhausting though this study has been, its primary aim was always ultilitarian: to assist in the design of other experiments. Thus, tests and treatments were all opportunistic. Although (and, in part, because) all tests were double blind, no attempt was made to ensure that each experimenter randomised treatments (i.e. combinations of magnet polarity and time intervals after exposure). Some subjects were tested only once after exposure; others at a succession of time intervals. Some were exposed to only one polarity; others were exposed a week or more later to the other polarity. Everything was determined by the joint time schedules and cooperation of experimenters and subjects. Most importantly, to reduce our demands on the limited pool (and sympathy) of available subjects, we economised by not carrying out a complete series of control tests. Thus, although each subject was also tested while wearing a brass bar, they were not tested at different time intervals thereafter. This lack of formal controls limits the conclusions to be drawn from this pilot series but speeded the design of other, more formal, experiments. The observed pattern of recovery is illustrated in Figs 6.7 and 6.8 and analysed in Table 6.14.

Ignoring for a moment any interaction between magnet polarity and normal bed orientation, the disruption of compass orientation observed when people wear vertical magnets on the right temple persists, not only when the magnet is first removed but for some time afterwards (Fig. 6.7). In fact, there is no real sign of recovery until 2–6 hours after the magnet is removed, and performance may not have returned entirely to normal until even 2 days later.

If we now take into account magnet polarity, but continue to ignore bed orientation (Table 6.14, first column), it emerges that Nup and Sup magnets have significantly different effects while the magnet is worn and immediately it is removed, but not thereafter. However, neither of these analyses can be fully justified; further analysis shows there are no ground for combining data for N–S and E–W sleepers (Fig. 6.8; Table 6.14)

N–S sleepers exposed to *Nup magnets* are 180° in error while wearing the magnet (Fig. 6.6) and disoriented immediately the magnet is removed (Table 6.13). Thereafter, they show a gradual improvement in performance (Fig. 6.8) until 1–2 hours after the magnet was removed, by which

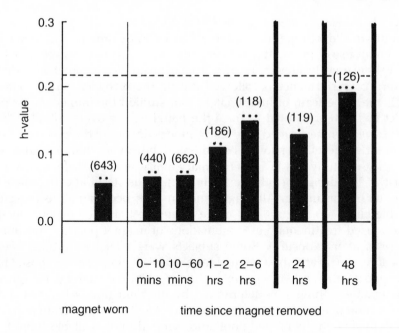

Fig. 6.7. Recovery of ability to judge compass direction in chair experiments after wearing a magnet on the right temple for 10–15 minutes. Horizontal dashed line: level of performance by subjects tested wearing brass bars. Histogram shows *h*-value of mean vector for groups of subjects tested by chair experiments while, and at various time intervals after, wearing a bar magnet (10–20 mT; Sup or Nup) on the right temple (as in Fig. 6.6). Solid, thick vertical line indicates a night's sleep. Number of subjects tested shown in brackets. Asterisks show whether *h*-values are more positive than expected by chance (*V*-test): *, $P < 0.05$; **, $P < 0.02$; ***, $P < 0.01$. Recovery appears to be gradual over 48 hours. Data from Baker *et al.* (unpublished). 'Magnet-worn' category includes data from Murphy (1987).

the recovery seems to be complete. However, there then begins an apparent deterioration, performance being no better than guesswork even 48 hours after exposure.

N–S sleepers exposed to *Sup magnets* are able to orient while wearing the magnet (Fig. 6.6) and immediately afterwards (Table 6.13), but this good performance appears short-lived (Fig. 6.8). Ten minutes or so after the magnet has been removed, there is a sudden deterioration in orientation followed by a slow recovery, normal performance returning only 2–6 hours later or perhaps not until the next day (Fig. 6.8).

E–W sleepers exposed to *Nup magnets* are able to orient while wearing the magnet (Fig. 6.6) but are disoriented immediately the magnet is removed (Table 6.13). Disorientation persists for the remainder of the day

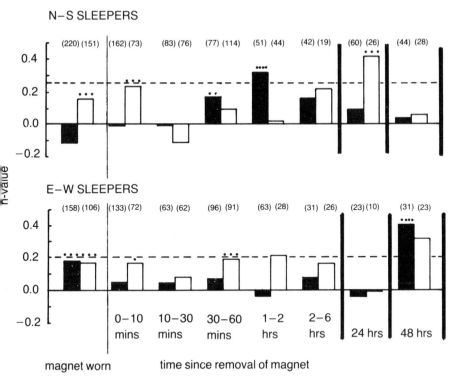

Fig. 6.8. Interaction of polarity of magnet and normal bed orientation of subject in influencing recovery of ability to judge compass direction in chair experiments. N–S or E–W sleepers: subjects with normal bed orientation along N–S or E–W axis (±45°), respectively. A person's 'normal' bed is identified as the last in which they spent 14 consecutive nights. Solid histograms: subjects exposed to Nup magnets (10–15 minutes on right temple, as in Fig. 6.6). Open histograms: subjects exposed to Sup magnets. Horizontal dashed lines: levels of performance by subjects tested wearing brass bars. Histograms show h-value of mean vector for groups of subjects tested while, and at various time-intervals after, wearing a bar magnet (10–20 mT). Solid, thick vertical line indicates a night's sleep. Number of subjects tested shown in brackets. Asterisks show whether h-values are more positive than expected by chance (V-test): *, $P < 0.05$; **, $P < 0.02$; ***, $P < 0.01$. Data from Baker *et al.* (unpublished). 'Magnet-worn' category includes data from Murphy (1987).

and, though sample size is small, even on the next day there is no sign of recovery (Fig. 6.8). Not until 48 hours after the magnet is removed does recovery seem to be complete.

E–W sleepers exposed to *Sup magnets* are able to orient, not only while wearing the magnet (Fig. 6.6) but also immediately afterwards (Table

Table 6.14. Relative influence of Nup and Sup magnets (while worn on the head and after) on accuracy of compass orientation: interaction with normal bed orientation

| | All subjects | z-values from Wallraff's test (Nup vs Sup magnets) | | Test of N–S/E–W difference | |
| | | N–S sleepers | E–W sleepers | | |
	z	z_1	z_2	z_a	P (2-tailed)
Blindfolded					
Chair					
while wearing magnet	−2.860	−3.682	+0.007	2.609	0.009
after magnet removed					
0–10 min	−2.331	−2.432	−0.877	1.100	0.271
10–30 min	−0.344	+0.417	−0.131	0.387	0.698
30–60 min	−0.792	+1.030	−1.279	1.633	0.103
1–2 min	−0.010	+1.810	−1.673	2.463	0.014
2–6 h	−0.044	+0.117	−0.272	0.276	0.787
24 h	−1.378	−1.599	−0.137	1.034	0.303
48 h	+0.281	−0.104	+0.788	0.631	0.528

Combined probability

χ^2_{16}	P
29.98	0.019

$z_a = \mathrm{abs}(z_1 - z_2)/\mathrm{sqr}2$.
Positive values of z_1 and z_2 indicate compass orientation is more accurate on exposure to Nup magnets.
Significant values of z and χ^2 are underlined.
Calculated from data shown in Fig. 6.8.

6.13). More data are needed, but there is no real indication of any after-effect at any time interval after removal. The apparent disorientation 24 hours after exposure is based on only ten subjects and, until confirmed by more data, should perhaps be disregarded.

The influence of Nup and Sup magnets on compass orientation by all subjects (and by N–S and E–W sleepers, separately) is analysed statistically in Table 6.14. Combined probability analysis confirms that, in general, N–S and E–W sleepers respond differently to magnet polarity. This difference in response, however, is localised to two phases: (1) while the magnet is on the head; and (2) between one and two hours after the magnet has been removed. Whereas, while the magnet is being worn, the difference is due to a greater sensitivity of N–S sleepers (Table 6.12), one to two hours after the magnet is removed it is due to their equal but opposite responses: N–S sleepers tend to perform better after pretreatment with Nup magnets, E–W sleepers after Sup magnets (Fig. 6.8 and Table 6.14). This phase of maximum separation of response is particularly useful in the design of bus and walkabout experiments.

This extensive pilot study has allowed two important decisions to be made. First, in showing that magnets may influence a person's ability to judge compass direction for up to 48 hours after exposure, it dictates the minimum time interval between successive tests on the same person. At Manchester, we now err on the safe side and leave at least 5 days and preferably a week between any consecutive treatments. Secondly, in producing Fig. 6.8 and Table 6.14, it has allowed treatments to be selected in advance in accordance with other demands of the experiment. It warns, also, that rarely is it justified to combine data obtained from mixtures of N–S and E–W sleepers or to combine results obtained with Nup and Sup magnets. To combine such data is to risk the error of concluding that subjects were not using magnetoreception when in fact this was not the case.

6.4.2. *Judgement of compass direction: formal experiments*
Pretreatment with bar magnets has been used as a tool in the study of the role of magnetoreception in judgement of compass direction in several discrete series of experiments. I have carried out one series of chair and two series of bus experiments. Dr Mary Campion at Keele University has carried out an independent series of chair experiments and also a series of bus experiments at which I was an observer and adviser. In addition to these series by myself and Campion using blindfolded subjects, I have carried out a further four series of experiments (one chair, one bus and two walkabout) using subjects who could see. Results from all of these summarised in Table 6.15.

Since 1983, two types of magnets (and two sets of appropriately matching brass bars) have been used for pretreatment. These two types (A and

Table 6.15. Influence of bar magnets (15-minute pretreatment) on accuracy of compass orientation: interaction of polarity of magnets and normal bed orientation of subjects

Magnet type (A or B)	N–S sleepers				E–W sleepers				Sample sizes			
	Magnets		Wallraff's test		Magnets		Wallraff's test		N–S		E–W	
	Nup h	Sup h	z_1	P (2-tailed)	Nup h	Sup h	z_2	P (2-tailed)	Nup	Sup	Nup	Sup
Blindfolded												
Chair												
(B) Keele	**0.340**	0.178	+0.805	0.420	0.018	0.205	−1.074	0.284	29	27	14	15
(B) Bahamas	0.000	0.129	−0.557	0.580	−0.338	**0.348**	−2.286	0.022	14	16	8	15
Bus												
(A) Manchester	−0.067	−0.018	−0.367	0.720	−0.152	**0.712**	−3.260	0.001	24	19	19	10
(A) Keele	−0.110	−0.022	−0.347	0.734	0.102	−0.304	+1.946	0.052	24	22	21	29
(B) Manchester	0.018	−0.263	+0.793	0.430	−0.064	0.083	−0.888	0.374	35	35	26	34
Sighted												
Chair												
(B) Bahamas	**0.446**	**0.372**	+0.900	0.368	0.000	**0.730**	−1.703	0.089	14	16	8	15
Bus												
(B) Manchester	−0.151	0.091	−1.553	0.120	0.116	0.121	−0.252	0.802	33	37	37	28
Walkabout												
(A) WP, DF, BW	**0.248**	0.018	+1.160	0.246	−0.025	**0.272**	−1.869	0.061	33	34	35	30
(B) WP, DF, BW, LY	**0.213**	0.028	+1.152	0.250	**0.199**	**0.457**	−1.369	0.170	41	46	36	36

Combined probability (N–S): χ^2_{18} = 17.61, P = 0.517

Combined probability (E–W): χ^2_{18} = 45.74, P < 0.001

Significant h-values shown in **bold**; significant z- and χ^2-values underlined.

Positive z-values indicate subjects wearing Nup magnets are the more accurate of the two sets.

Keele data from Campion (unpublished); other data from Baker *et al.* (Unpublished).

B) have been described in Chapter 4. All of the data presented in Section 6.3 and so far in this section are for experiments carried out using type-A magnets; Murphy also used magnets provided from among my batch of type-A magnets. In my bus and walkabout experiments, type A were used until November 1984 and type B ever since, though a single walk-about experiment in June 1986 used both types in order specifically to test for a difference in influence. Campion used type-A magnets in her bus experiments but type-B in her chair experiments. The type of mag-net used is identified in Table 6.15 and data are presented separately for series that used different magnet batches. However, as far as their influence on compass orientation is concerned, there is no indication that the two batches of magnets differ in any way. The same is not true in relation to map-building and navigation (Section 6.4.3).

Combined probability analyses of the pretreatment data in Table 6.15 show that the accuracy of compass orientation is influenced by the polarity of magnets only for E–W sleepers, not N–S sleepers. Table 6.16 tests these data further against two null hypotheses: (1) that there is no difference in the response of N–S and E–W sleepers to pretreatment with magnets of different polarity; and (2) that E–W sleepers are not the more sensitive. Combined probability analysis shows that the data reject the first null hypothesis ($P = 0.003$), but not quite the second ($P = 0.095$). Thus, N–S and E–W sleepers do respond differently to magnet polarity but one group may not be more sensitive than the other.

The directions of response to pretreatment observed in these experi-ments are the same as those observed in the pilot chair experiments and summarised in Fig. 6.8. N–S sleepers tend to perform better after pretreatment with Nup than with Sup magnets, though combining the probabilities shows the tendency is not significant when subjects are either blindfolded ($\chi^2_{10} = 8.69$; $P = 0.563$) or sighted ($\chi^2_8 = 11.86$; $P = 0.159$). In contrast, E–W sleepers not only tend conversely to perform better after pretreatment with Sup magnets, but the tendency is signifi-cant both when blindfolded ($\chi^2_{10} = 31.01$; $P < 0.001$) and when sighted ($\chi^2_8 = 19.96$; $P = 0.011$). As indicators of magnetoreception, therefore, E–W sleepers are the more sensitive if an experimental is designed around pretreatment.

6.4.3. *Map-building and navigation*
Magnets, aligned vertically and placed on a person's right temple, influence the ability to judge compass direction for at least two hours after the magnet is removed (Fig. 6.7). This influence is complex and dynamic and has important repercussions when an attempt is made to use pretreatment to study the role of magnetoreception in map-building and navigation.

Judgement of compass direction, as measured in the experiments

Table 6.16. Test of two hypotheses for the influence of magnets (15-minute pretreatment) on the accuracy of compass orientation: (1) Nup and Sup magnets have different effects on N–S and E–W sleepers; and (2) E–W sleepers are the more sensitive to magnet polarity

	hypothesis (1)		hypothesis (2)	
	z_a	P (2-tailed)	z_b	P (1-tailed)
Blindfolded				
Chair				
(B) Keele	1.329	0.184	+0.190	0.425
(B) Bahamas	1.223	0.222	+1.223	0.111
Bus				
(A) Manchester	2.046	0.041	+2.046	0.021
(A) Keele	1.621	0.105	+1.131	0.129
(B) Manchester	1.189	0.234	+0.067	0.476
Sighted				
Chair				
(B) Bahamas	1.841	0.066	+0.568	0.285
Bus				
(B) Manchester	0.920	0.358	−0.920	0.830
Walkabout				
(A) WP, DF, BW	2.142	0.032	+0.501	0.308
(B) WP, DF, BW, LY	1.783	0.075	+0.153	0.440
	Combined probability		Combined probability	
	χ^2_{18}	P	χ^2_{18}	P
	39.75	0.003	26.29	0.095

z_a and z_b calculated from z_1 and z_2 in Table 6.15.
$z_a = \mathrm{abs}\,(z_1 - z_2)/\mathrm{sqr}2$; $z_b = (\mathrm{abs}\,z_1 - \mathrm{abs}\,z_2)/\mathrm{sqr}2$.
Positive values of z_b indicate E–W sleepers show the greater sensitivity.
Significant values of z and χ^2 are underlined.

reported in this chapter, is an instantaneous phenomenon. The subject makes an on-the-spot assessment of the direction he or she is facing. In contrast, route-based navigation (Chapter 3) has an extended time base: the subject needs to refer to environmental information at intervals from the moment of setting out on the journey to the moment of judging home direction and distance. This important difference in the nature of the two tasks means it cannot be assumed that an influence of magnets on compass orientation will also be found on navigation. This is particularly so when pretreatment is used. A subject who estimates compass direction two hours after removal of the magnet may only be influenced by the current aftereffect of the magnet. The same subject who estimates home direction, however, is influenced by the pattern of effect over the whole of the previous two hours. This interaction of the two estimates and what they can tell us about the nature of the magnetoreceptor is discussed in Chapter 8. In this chapter, the task is simply to identify what influence on the different facets of navigation can be expected from pretreatment with different types and polarities of magnets.

Tables 6.17 to 6.20 repeat for estimates of the direction and distance of home the analyses that were carried out for estimates of compass direction.

Attempts to *point towards home* after displacement show many of the same characteristics of response to pretreatment as shown by compass orientation. Every one of the six series of experiments has produced a significant influence of magnet polarity on the performance of E–W sleepers (Table 6.17); not one of the six has produced a significant influence on N–S sleepers. The response of E–W sleepers is significantly different from that of N–S sleepers ($P = 0.006$; Table 6.19) due, in part, to a significantly greater sensitivity of E–W sleepers ($P = 0.009$; Table 6.19).

In contrast, attempts to estimate the *air-line distance to home* show no evidence of an influence due to interaction between polarity of magnets and normal bed orientation (Tables 6.18 and 6.19). In analysing estimates of air-line distance, therefore, it is justifiable to combine data for N–S and E–W sleepers, and this is done in Table 6.20. Comparison of performance after pretreatment with Nup and Sup magnets shows a significant influence of magnet polarity when people can see ($P = 0.028$), but not when they are blindfolded ($P = 0.586$).

Although the data for pointing to home in Tables 6.17 and 6.19 offer no justification for combining data from N–S and E–W sleepers after pretreatment with Nup and Sup magnets, this is done for completeness in Table 6.20. Despite the lack of response of N–S sleepers to magnet polarity (Table 6.17), a simple comparison of performance by subjects pretreated with Nup and Sup magnets still shows a significant influence of magnet polarity when people can see ($P = 0.007$) but not when they are blindfolded ($P = 0.235$).

One feature of Table 6.20, also evident in Table 6.17 and 6.18, is the apparently different influence of type-A and type-B magnets on navigational accuracy in walkabout experiments ($z = (1.533 + 2.042)/\text{sqr2} = 2.528$, $P = 0.011$, for pointing to home; $z = (1.548 + 1.807)/\text{sqr2} = 2.372$, $P = 0.018$, for judging air-line distance). This apparent influence of magnet type is not evident in the data either for compass orientation in walkabout experiments (Table 6.15) or for navigational accuracy in bus experiments (Tables 6.17 and 6.18). The possibility that the two types of magnets may have different influences on navigational accuracy was tested directly in a single walkabout experiment carried out with 40 subjects at Delamere Forest in June 1986. All subjects wore magnets, half

Table 6.17. Influence of bar magnets (15-minute pretreatment) on ability to point towards home: interaction of polarity of magnets and normal bed orientation of subjects

Magnet type (A or B)	N–S sleepers				E–W sleepers				Sample sizes			
	Magnets		Wallraff's test		Magnets		Wallraff's test		N–S		E–W	
	Nup h	Sup h	z_1	P (2-tailed)	Nup h	Sup h	z_2	P (2-tailed)	Nup	Sup	Nup	Sup
Blindfolded Bus												
(A) Manchester	**0.255**	0.176	+0.428	0.668	**0.396**	**0.682**	−1.974	0.048	24	19	19	10
(B) Keele	0.159	0.071	+0.353	0.726	**0.442**	0.030	+2.104	0.035	24	21	21	29
(B) Manchester	−0.038	−0.081	+0.866	0.388	−0.116	**0.318**	−2.005	0.044	32	35	30	34
Sighted Bus												
(B) Manchester	**0.333**	0.168	+0.683	0.496	**0.441**	0.028	+2.478	0.013	33	37	37	28
Walkabout												
(A) WP, DF, BW	**0.251**	**0.313**	−0.460	0.646	**0.561**	**0.203**	+2.863	0.004	60	58	57	53
(B) WP, DF, BW, LY	**0.461**	**0.504**	−0.580	0.562	**0.292**	**0.479**	−2.282	0.022	94	99	85	87

Combined probability (N–S): χ^2_{12} 6.77, P 0.872

Combined probability (E–W): χ^2_{12} 46.39, P <0.001

Significant h-values shown in **bold**; significant z- and χ^2-values underlined.

Positive z-values indicate subjects wearing Nup magnets are the more accurate of the two sets.

Keele data from Campion (unpublished); other data from Baker *et al.* (Unpublished).

Table 6.18. Influence of bar magnets (15-min pretreatment) on ability to judge air-line distance to home: lack of interaction of polarity of magnets and normal bed orientation of subjects

Magnet type (A or B)	N–S sleepers median error (m/km) Magnets Nup	Sup	Wallraff's test z_1	P (2-tailed)	E–W sleepers median error (m/km) Magnets Nup	Sup	Wallraff's test z_2	P (2-tailed)	Sample sizes N–S Nup	Sup	E–W Nup	Sup
Blindfolded Bus												
(A) Manchester	373	250	−0.025	0.984	429	374	−0.988	0.323	23	19	19	10
(B) Keele	547	529	+0.399	0.689	633	482	−1.118	0.263	24	21	18	29
(B) Manchester	620	913	−0.006	0.999	558	858	+1.052	0.290	32	35	30	34
Sighted Bus												
(B) Manchester	647	375	−1.595	0.110	538	419	−0.709	0.480	33	37	37	28
Walkabout												
(A) WP, DF, BW	403	653	+0.988	0.323	625	1388	+1.485	0.138	31	32	34	32
(B) WP, DF, BW, LY	639	485	−1.813	0.071	639	637	−0.689	0.491	83	82	69	74

Combined probability (N–S sleepers): χ^2_{12} 12.74, P 0.389

Combined probability (E–W sleepers): χ^2_{12} 14.26, P 0.286

Significant z- and χ^2-values would have been underlined!

Positive z-values indicate subjects wearing Nup magnets are the more accurate of the two sets.

Keele data from Campion (unpublished); other data from Baker *et al.* (unpublished).

Table 6.19. Test of two hypotheses for the influence of magnets (15-minute pretreatment) on the accuracy of navigation: (1) Nup and Sup magnets have different effects on N–S and E–W sleepers; and (2) E–W sleepers are the more sensitive to magnet polarity

	Pointing to home				Air-line distance to home			
	Hypothesis 1		Hypothesis 2		Hypothesis 1		Hypothesis 2	
Magnet type (A or B)	z_a	P 2-tailed	z_b	P 1-tailed	z_a	P 2-tailed	z_b	P 1-tailed
Blindfolded								
Bus								
(A) Manchester	1.698	0.090	+1.093	0.138	0.681	0.496	+0.681	0.248
(A) Keele	1.238	0.216	+1.238	0.108	1.073	0.284	+0.508	0.306
(B) Manchester	2.030	0.042	+0.805	0.210	0.748	0.452	+0.739	0.230
Sighted								
Bus								
(B) Manchester	1.269	0.204	+1.269	0.102	0.626	0.530	−0.626	0.735
Walkabout								
(A) WP, DF, BW	2.350	0.018	+1.699	0.045	0.351	0.726	+0.351	0.363
(B) LY, WP, BW, DF	1.230	0.230	+1.203	0.115	0.795	0.424	−0.795	0.788
Combined probability	χ^2_{12}	P	χ^2_{12}	P	χ^2_{12}	P	χ^2_{12}	P
	28.37	0.006	26.63	0.009	9.13	0.692	11.22	0.512

z_a and z_b calculated from values for z_1 and z_2 in Tables 6.17 and 6.18.

z_a = abs ($z_1 - z_2$)/sqr2; z_b = (abs z_1 − abs z_2)/sqr2.

Positive values of z_b indicate E–W sleepers show the greater sensitivity.

Significant values of z and χ^2 are underlined.

Table 6.20. Influence of 15-minute pretreatment with Nup and Sup magnets on navigational accuracy

Magnet type (A or B)	Pointing to home				Air-line distance to home				Sample sizes			
	Polarity		Wallraff's test		Polarity		Mann–Whitney–U-test		Pointing		Distance	
	Nup h	Sup h	z_1	P (2-tailed)	Nup error (m/km)	Sup error (m/km)	z_2	P (2-tailed)	Nup	Sup	Nup	Sup
Blindfolded												
Bus												
(A) Manchester	**0.317**	**0.350**	−0.517	0.608	385	373	−0.720	0.472	43	29	42	29
(B) Keele	**0.291**	0.009	+1.762	0.078	615	482	−0.758	0.448	45	51	42	51
(B) Manchester	−0.036	0.116	−0.881	0.378	615	870	+0.749	0.453	62	69	62	69
Sighted												
Bus												
(B) Manchester	**0.390**	0.108	+2.231	0.026	583	375	−1.661	0.097	70	65	70	65
Walkabout												
(A) WP, DF, BW	**0.402**	**0.261**	+1.533	0.126	563	749	+1.548	0.121	117	111	65	64
(B) WP, DF, BW, LY	**0.381**	**0.492**	−2.042	0.041	639	616	−1.807	0.071	152	156	152	156
Combined probability			χ^2_6	P			χ^2_6	P				
Blindfolded			8.04	0.235			4.69	0.586				
Sighted			17.83	0.007			14.18	0.028				

Significant h-values shown in **bold**; significant z- and χ^2-values underlined.

Positive z-values indicate subjects wearing Nup magnets are the more accurate of the two sets.

Keele data from Campion (unpublished); other data from Baker *et al.* (Unpublished).

being of type A, half of type B. Half of each type were Nup, half Sup (Chapter 4).

If magnet type (A or B) were the cause of the apparent differences (Table 6.20) in influence of magnet polarity (Nup or Sup) on navigational accuracy in walkabout experiments, the same differences should emerge during the single walkabout through Delamere Forest. Using the convention that superiority of people pretreated with Nup magnets yields a positive z-value from the Mann–Whitney U-test, the expectation would be a positive z-value for type-A magnets and a negative z-value for type-B magnets. These signs should be found for comparisons of air-line distance by all subjects, but for pointing to home by only E–W sleepers. The probability that these z-values differ only by chance in the manner predicted may be calculated. Combined probability analysis of the two probability values obtained (one for distance; one for pointing) will then determine whether the evidence from this controlled experiment supports the view that the differences obtained for other walkabout experiments (Table 6.20) were due to magnet type. Details of the Delamere Forest results are given in Table 6.21.

Despite the anomalous direction of response shown by subjects pointing to home after treatment type-A magnets (P = approximately 0.773), the other three comparisons are sufficiently as expected (P = approximately 0.008; 0.200; 0.124) for combined probability analysis (Table 6.21) to confirm that responses were in the directions expected (P = 0.025). The z-values obtained for estimates of distance differed significantly (z = (2.405 + 0.844)/sqr2 = 2.297; P = 0.011) whereas those for pointing to home did not (z = ($-$0.745 + 1.155)/sqr2 = 0.290; P = 0.386). However, combined probability analysis gives (χ_4^2 = 10.924; P = 0.028). The overall conclusion, therefore, is that type-A and type-B magnets do have different and consistent polarity effects on navigational accuracy, at least in walkabout experiments.

6.4.4. *Magnet strength*

There are two obvious facets of type A and type B magnets that could conceivably promote different influences in experiments involving pretreatment: size and strength. Type A magnets are larger (Chapter 4) and, in most tests in which they were involved, weaker (Fig. 4.18). If size were the critical factor, the relative influence of the two magnet types would stay constant with time; if strength were the critical factor, influence would change with age of the magnets (Fig. 4.18).

In August 1987, a retrospective analysis was carried out of all experiments (bus and walkabout) since 1983 that involved a 15-minute pretreatments of *sighted* subjects by magnets aligned vertically on the right temple. The test parameter was the absolute z-value (Wallraff's test) for differences in the strength of homeward orientation (pointing)

Table 6.21. Influence of magnets (15-minute pretreatment) on navigational performance: interaction of magnet type (A or B) and polarity (Nup or Sup)

	Polarity of magnets						Mann-Whitney U-test	
	Nup			Sup				
		Error (m/km)			Error (m/km)			
	n	Median	(IQR)	n	Median	(IQR)	z	P (1-tailed)
Sighted								
Walkabout (DF: 6 June 1986)								
Estimating distance (all subjects)								
Type-A magnets	10	437	(126–563)	10	710	(421–781)	+2.405	0.008
Type-B magnets	10	508	(235–639)	10	219	(126–749)	−0.844	0.200
Pointing to home (E–W sleepers only)	n	h		n	h			
Type-A magnets	5	0.351		3	0.379		−0.745	0.773
Type-B magnets	4	−0.364		4	−0.136		−1.155	0.124

Combined probability

χ^2_8	P
17.57	0.025

Significant values of z and χ^2 are underlined.

Positive z-values indicate subjects wearing Nup magnets are the more accurate of the two sets.

Data from Baker (unpublished).

by subjects pretreated with Nup and Sup magnets. Thus, larger z-values indicate a greater influence of magnet polarity on navigational performance. There were significant negative correlations with magnet age and, with magnet age partialled out, with the number of times the magnets had been used. Primarily, however, there was a significant positive correlation (Spearman's rank-order correlation coefficient (r_s = 0.323; n = 48; P (one-tailed) = 0.012) between level of influence of magnet (z-value) and median magnet strength (from Fig. 4.18) at the time of any given experiment (over 48 experiments).

Table 6.22 combines data for experiments involving pretreatment according to three different strengths of magnet: 10–12 mT, 12–14 mT, and 14–16 mT (no *pretreatment* experiment has used magnets stronger than 16 mT). Subdividing magnet strengths still further, Fig. 6.9 compares the response of N–S and E–W sleepers. It would seem that strength of magnet is critical in determining not only the extent, but also the direction, of influence of magnet polarity. Moreover, the increased sensitivity of E–W sleepers to magnetic pretreatment (when pointing to home) is only found at magnet strength <15 mT (given 15-minute pretreatments). At 15 mT or stronger, both N–S and E–W sleepers respond similarly to magnet polarity.

The analyses presented in Table 6.22 and Fig. 6.9 are retrospective, carried out after the experiments had been performed. Although the analyses suggest that relative performance forms a pattern that correlates with magnet strength, they do not constitute proof that magnet strength is the critical factor. The analyses do, however, establish a set of empirical hypotheses by which predictions of the expected influence of magnets of different strength may be made. Since August 1987, three walkabout experiments have been performed (two at Burnt Wood, one at Woodchester Park) in which magnets were tested for strength both just before and just after each experiment and only those of between 14.4 and 16.0 mT (median 15.0 mT) were used. The prediction, therefore, was that, even with data for N–S and E–W sleepers lumped together, subjects pretreated with Sup magnets should be less able to judge the direction and distance of home than subjects pretreated with Nup magnets or brass bars. The results were consistent with this prediction in all three experiments (Table 6.23) and, when combined, are fully consistent with the pilot experiments that gave rise to the prediction (Fig. 6.10).

This section warns that it is not possible to be casual about the selection of magnets for experiments on human navigation. The extent and even the direction of influence may well depend critically on the strength and thus on the age of the magnet, how often it has been used and under what conditions it has been stored. On the more positive side, the possibility at last emerges that careful control of the strength of magnet

Table 6.22. Influence of magnet strength (15-minute pretreatment) on navigational ability of sighted subjects: all bus and walkabout experiments (1983–1987)

Magnet strength (mT)	Navigational performance			Sample size			Mann–Whitney U-test						
							Nup vs brass		Sup vs brass		Nup vs Sup	
	Brass	Nup	Sup	Brass	Nup	Sup	z	P	z	P	z	P
Pointing to home												
Homeward component (h)												
10–12	**0.332**	**0.316**	**0.293**	288	196	165	−0.424	0.670	−0.481	0.631	0.096	0.928
12–14	**0.550**	**0.361**	**0.533**	167	158	163	−3.308	0.001	−0.748	0.454	2.768	0.006
14–16	**0.328**	**0.363**	0.096	129	104	96	1.012	0.312	−2.694	0.007	2.783	0.006
Judgement of air-line distance												
Median error (m/km)												
10–12	600	420	670	253	171	141	2.034	0.041	−1.377	0.171	2.982	0.002
12–14	770	695	550	167	158	163	0.223	0.821	2.883	0.004	−2.309	0.021
14–16	630	590	500	116	89	84	0.809	0.418	1.298	0.194	−0.498	0.617

Significant *h*-values ($P < 0.05$; *V*-test) shown in **bold**; significant *z*-values (*P* (two-tailed) < 0.05) underlined.

Sign of *z* indicates direction of difference (i.e. positive signs indicate: Nup more accurate than brass; Sup than brass; and Nup than Sup).

Table 6.23. Experiments to test replicability of influence of magnets of pole strength 15 mT (15-minute pretreatment): pointing to home by sighted subjects in bus and walkabout experiments

Date	Type	Place	Homeward component (h)			Sample size			Wallraff's test (Nup vs Sup)	
			Brass	Nup	Sup	Brass	Nup	Sup	z	P (2-tailed)
Pilot experiments										
1983										
21 June	Walk	WP	**0.471**	**0.805**	0.212	10	11	11	+2.695	0.007
8 July	Walk	WP	−0.039	0.345	0.282	7	9	8	+0.192	0.849
4 September	Walk	WP	0.213	−0.094	−0.157	13	14	12	+0.026	0.980
1984										
22 November	Walk	BW	**0.412**	0.343	−0.252	16	3	3	+0.664	0.507
20 December	Walk	LY	0.403	0.816	0.726	6	3	4	+0.535	0.591
1985										
28 March	Bus	Mc	**0.493**	**0.471**	0.090	37	33	29	+1.778	0.075
29 March	Bus	Mc	**0.217**	**0.259**	0.028	40	31	29	+1.268	0.204
Total			**0.328**	**0.363**	0.096	129	104	96	+2.783	0.005
Test experiments										(1-tailed)
1987										
18 November	Walk	BW	0.217	**0.530**	−0.209	10	12	12	+2.309	0.010
19 November	Walk	BW	**0.713**	**0.728**	0.178	12	10	10	+1.589	0.056
1988										
1 May	Walk	WP	0.340	**0.425**	−0.277	8	8	7	+1.853	0.032
Total			**0.448**	**0.568**	−0.092	30	30	29	+3.268	<0.001

WP = Woodchester Park; BW = Burnt Wood; LY = Lucaya; DF = Delamere Forest; Mc = Manchester.

Significant h-values (P < 0.05; V-test) shown in bold; significant z-values underlined.

Positive signs for z indicate that in every experiment subjects pretreated with Nup magnets are more accurate at pointing to home than those pretreated with Sup magnets.

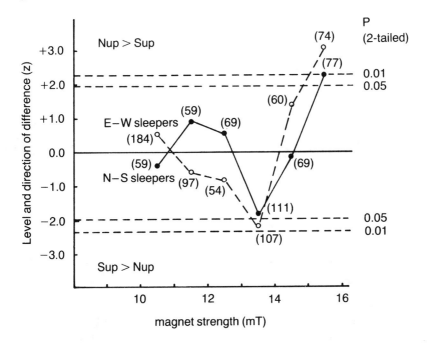

Fig. 6.9. Influence of pretreatment with magnets of different strength on ability of sighted subjects to point towards the start of the journey in bus and walk-about experiments (combined data). Dots show level and direction of difference (z-value from Wallraff's test) in performance by subjects pretreated by Nup and Sup magnets of particular pole-strengths. Positive z-values indicate subjects pretreated with Nup magnets are more accurate at pointing towards home than those pretreated with Sup; negative z-values the converse. Probability levels (P = 0.05 and 0.01; 2-tailed) of the observed values for z being obtained by chance are shown by horizontal dashed lines. ○, Data for E–W sleepers; ●, N–S sleepers. Sample sizes (total subjects pretreated by magnets, split more or less evenly between Nup and Sup magnets) are shown in brackets. Pretreatment with magnets stronger than 13 mT has similar effects on E–W and N–S sleepers, with the fomer being the more sensitive. When magnets are 15–16 mT, both groups are significantly more accurate when pretreated with Nup magnets than Sup. When magnets are 13–14 mT, the converse is true, with the effect of 14–15 mT magnets being intermediate. With magnets weaker than 13 mT the influence is not significant and there is a tendency for N–S and E–W sleepers to respond differently. Data from Baker (unpublished).

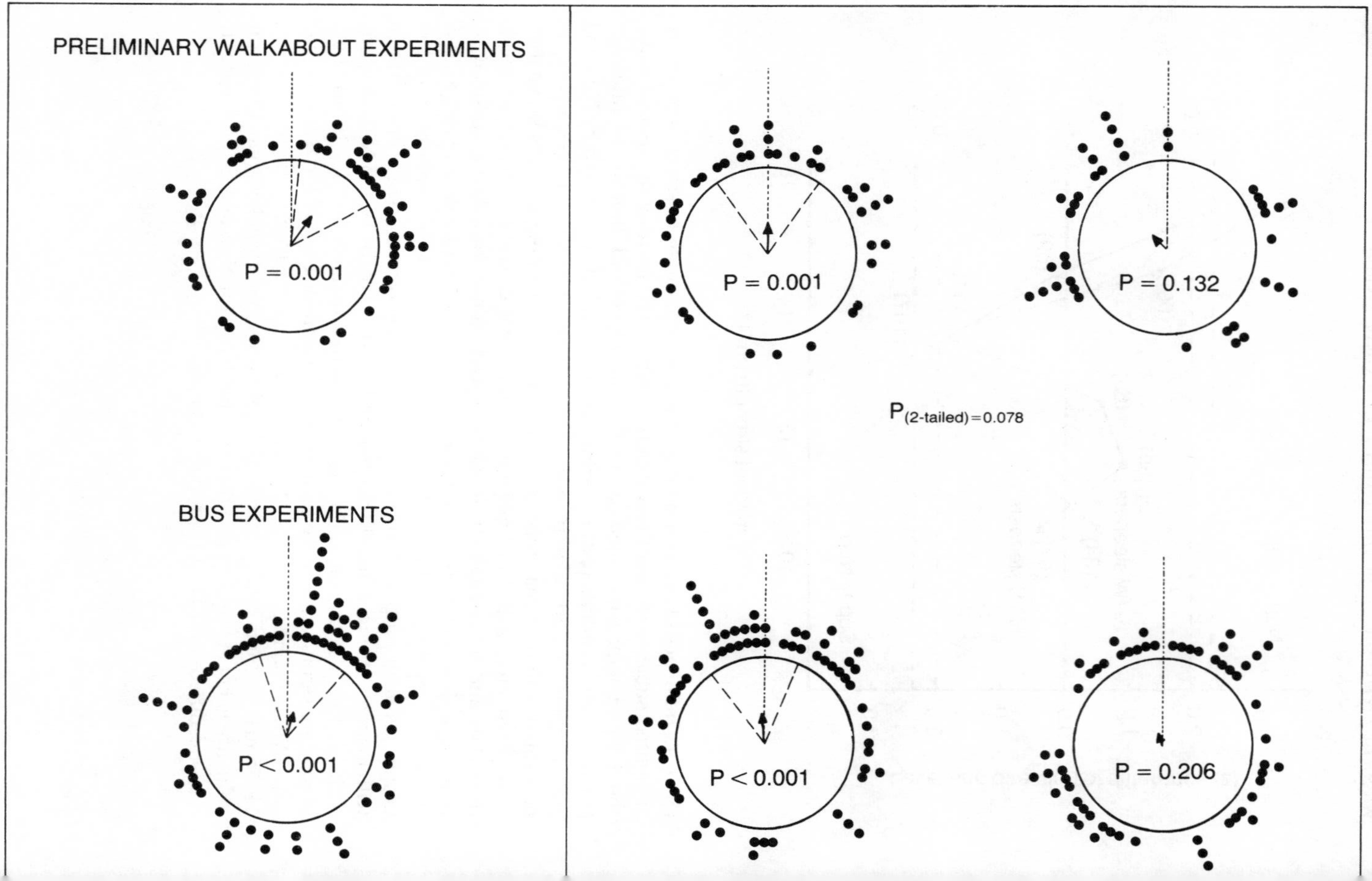

PRELIMINARY WALKABOUT EXPERIMENTS

P = 0.001

P = 0.001

P = 0.132

P$_{(2\text{-tailed})}$ = 0.078

BUS EXPERIMENTS

P < 0.001

P < 0.001

P = 0.206

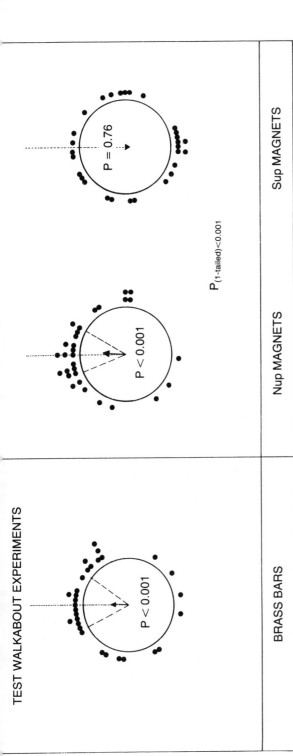

Fig. 6.10. Influence of 15 minute pretreatment with 15-mT bar magnets on ability of sighted subjects to point towards home in bus and walkabout experiments. Each dot shows error at pointing to the start of the journey (vertical dotted line) by one sighted subject in a bus or walkabout experiment. Arrows and dashed lines show mean vector and 95% confidence limits. Subjects pretreated with brass bars or magnets as shown *P*-values inside circle show probability of the pattern of estimates occurring by chance or from pure guesswork (*V*-test). *P*-values between estimates by subjects pretreated with Nup and Sup magnets show the probability that the difference in strength of homeward orientation by the subjects pretreated with Nup and Sup magnets could have arisen by chance. The top two rows show data for the period June 1983 to June 1987, separated retrospectively for magnet strength (all magnets 14.1–16.0 mT). The bottom row shows the results of three experiments (November 1987–May 1988) designed specifically to test the empirical hypothesis generated by the top two rows (magnets 14.4–16.0 mT). Pretreatment of 15 minutes with a Nup magnet on the right temple (Chapter 4) has no influence on ability of sighted subjects to point towards home; the same pretreatment with a Sup magnet significantly reduces performance to the level of guesswork. Walkabout data from Baker (unpublished); bus data from Baker and Murphy (unpublished).

used and the length of pretreatment allows precise predictions to be made and perhaps consistent results to be obtained.

6.5. *Summary*

This chapter has shown that the judgements of direction and distance made by people taking part in chair, bus and walkabout experiments are influenced by manipulation of the ambient magnetic field. However, some manipulations are more effective than others. Thus, large and stationary electromagnetic coils on the one hand, and bar magnets on the head on the other, are both effective. As yet, however, there is no clear evidence that the same is true for electromagnetic helmets.

I presume, as do Walcott & Gould (In Walcott 1982), that pretreatment is effective through some long-term influence (for humans up to 2–48 hours) on the physiology of the magnetoreceptor. In contrast, I presume that large electromagnetic coils (used to rotate the geomagnetic field to produce a net field of about the same strength as the geomagnetic field) leave the magnetoreceptor intact and unaltered and change only the field being sensed. Perhaps bar magnets left in position on the head throughout an experiment have both effects: change the field being sensed and the structure or physiology of the magnetoreceptor.

6.5.1. *Judgement of compass direction*

The role of magnetoreception in the judgement of compass direction can be studied by the use of both bar magnets and large, stationary, electromagnetic coils.

Rotation of the ambient magnetic field by large electromagnetic coils produces a corresponding rotation in estimates of compass direction. Such rotation of estimate occurs whether the changed field encompasses the whole body (Fig. 6.1) or just the head (Fig. 6.2).

Compass orientation is generally disrupted by a vertically aligned bar magnet placed on the head forward of the ear (Table 6.5). Disruption persists even after the magnet is removed (Fig. 6.7). Recovery from a 10- to 15-minute exposure to such a magnet begins about one hour after the magnet is removed but may not be complete until 48 hours afterwards (Fig. 6.7). Magnets with the N pole uppermost are particularly disruptive both while on the head (Table 6.9) and for up to 10 minutes after removal (Tables 6.13 and 6.14).

N–S and E–W sleepers respond differently to magnet polarity (Tables 6.14 and 6.16), particularly while the magnets are on the head (Table 6.12) and again between one and two hours after the magnets are removed (Tables 6.14 and 6.16). While magnets are on the head, N–S sleepers are the more responsive (Table 6.12); after the magnets are removed, E–W sleepers are the more responsive (Table 6.15). Moreover, once the magnets have been removed for 30 minutes or more (up to two hours), the direction of response to the previous exposure also depends on bed orientation. Sup magnets are the more disruptive to N–S sleepers; Nup magnets to E–W sleepers (Table 6.15).

6.5.2. *Map-building and navigation*
In navigation experiments, a vertically aligned bar magnet, worn on the head forward of the ear, influences ability both to point towards home (Table 6.7) and to judge its compass bearing (Table 6.6) but has no influence on ability to judge the air-line distance to home (Table 6.8). The direction of influence is variable. Magnets seem to impart a relatively consistent level of performance on people wearing them, the outcome of an experiment then depending on the more variable level of performance of the controls.

As for compass orientation, the influence of a bar magnet on navigational performance persists for up to 2 hours after the magnet is removed. The nature of the influence depends on the polarity of the magnet to which the person was exposed. Moreover, not only the ability to point to home (Table 6.20) but also the ability to judge the air-line distance to home (Table 6.20) is influenced by magnet polarity. In general, there is no clear pattern as to when performance is better after exposure to Nup magnets and when better after exposure to Sup. At least in walkabout experiments, part of the cause of variability is due to differences between batches of magnets (Tables 6.20 and 6.21). The critical factor appears to be pole strength, and the possibility has emerged that careful attention to magnet strength and length of exposure may allow precise predictions and consistent results (Fig. 6.10).

In judging the air-line distance to home, N–S and E–W sleepers are not influenced differently by the polarity of the magnet to which they were previously exposed (Table 6.19). However, they are influenced differently when pointing to home (Table 6.19). Then, E–W sleepers are much the more responsive (Tables 6.17 and 6.19) unless magnet strength is 15–16 mT.

This chapter has achieved two ends. First, it has demonstrated that magnetoreception is involved in the judgement of direction and distance in chair, bus and walkabout experiments. Secondly, it has identified the most sensitive ways of evaluating whether magnetoreception has a role in any particular performance. These discoveries may now be used as tools to ask such questions as:

> During exploration, is there any integration of magnetic and celestial information, or is one used at the expense of the other?
> Do people use magnetoreception more when blindfolded or when sighted?
> Do males and females make different use of magnetoreception?
> Does the use of magnetoreception vary with age?

These and other questions are the subject of the next chapter.

7

The role of magnetoreception

Magnetoreception is part of the sensory armoury used by humans to solve problems of orientation and navigation. No other conclusion is possible from the range and variety of results presented in Chapter 6. Moreover, combined probability analyses (Baker 1987c) show that the evidence has been replicated by other authors.

It is not the aim of this chapter to provide yet more evidence for magnetoreception. Instead, the aim is to determine when magneto-reception is used and when it is not. The technique adopted (in contrast to Baker 1987b) is to study, under different conditions, the performance of only the subgroup of subjects known (from Chapter 6) to be the most sensitive to the magnetic treatment being used. If this subgroup shows a significant response to magnetic manipulation, it is concluded that magnetoreception has a role in solving the task being studied under the particular test conditions (e.g. sunny; overcast). On the other hand, if this subgroup shows no response, it is concluded that magnetoreception *may* be redundant for that task under those conditions. However, it is an unfortunate feature of all such experiments (not only on humans; Baker 1984b) that we can never prove that magnetoreception *is* redundant under such conditions. At least two other explanations are always possible: (1) the particular test conditions may in some way prevent the magnetoreceptor from being affected by the experimental treatment; and (2) although magnetoreception would normally have been used, when people are denied this sense by the treatment given, they simply switch to some other source of information.

The subgroup of subjects to be used as indicators that magnetorecep-tion is or may not be in operation is determined by the analyses detailed in Chapter 6. These subgroups are summarised in Table 7.1 and depend on the task being studied (e.g. compass orientation; pointing to home; judging the distance to home), the treatment given, and the time inter-val between treatment and testing. Results are given in Tables 7.2 to 7.11

Table 7.1. The most sensitive groups of subjects and treatments in experiments to test for the use of magnetoreception in specific tasks

Treatment	Most sensitive group (sleepers)			Most sensitive comparison		
	Compass	Pointing	Distance	Compass	Pointing	Distance
Bars worn	N–S	?	?	Bb vs Nup	?	?
Pretreatment tested after:						
0–10 min	N–S	?	?	Bb vs Nup	?	?
10–30 min	All	E–W	All	Bb vs Mgs	Nup vs Sup	Nup vs Sup
30–120 min	E–W	E–W	All	Nup vs Sup	Nup vs Sup	Nup vs Sup
>120 min	None	None	None	None	None	None

Bb, exposed to brass bars; Mgs, exposed to magnets (Nup + Sup).
Based on analyses in Chapter 6.

and Figs 7.1 to 7.7; a summary of the conditions under which magneto-reception has or may not play some role is given in Table 7.12.

In an attempt to ease presentation and interpretation, sample sizes are not given in individual tables but are collected together in a single table (Table 7.13) at the end of the chapter. In two-sample tests, when both sample sizes are less than 20 and use is made of the z-value from a Mann–Whitney U-test (or Wallraff's modification), the procedure used is that described in Chapter 4.

7.1. *Interactive roles of magnetoreception and vision*

7.1.1. *The role of magnetoreception when blindfolded and sighted*

The earliest experiments on human magnetoreception all used blind-folded subjects (Baker 1980c, d, 1981b; Gould 1980; Gould & Able 1981). In part, this was because the bus experiments being performed took people through areas with signposts and other obvious clues to location and direction. In part, also, it was because of the assumption that people would only use magnetoreception if visual information were not available.

In contrast, magnetoreception experiments on homing pigeons and other birds have most often used individuals that could see. Indeed, in recent years, interest has turned to the possibility that magnetoreception can only occur if a minimum amount of light is reaching the retina (Leask 1977; Wiltschko & Wiltschko 1981; Semm *et al.* 1984; Semm 1988. See also comments in Schmidt-Koenig 1979; Baker 1984b, 1988a). In such a case, far from being most in evidence in complete darkness, magneto-reception may in fact be more obvious in orientation and navigation when people and other animals can see.

In Chapter 6, data were presented for a variety of experiments in which the influence of magnets was tested on sighted and blindfolded subjects. Combined probability analysis of data for the most sensitive subgroups and treatments in Tables 6.15, 6.17 and 6.18 shows that magnets influence orientation and navigation both when people can see and when they are blindfolded (Table 7.2).

In addition to these general measures of the influence of magnets on blindfolded and sighted people, two series of bus experiments were designed specifically to test the effect of blindfolding on the role of magnetoreception, with other variables controlled. These were the series carried out at Manchester in 1985 and 1987 in which sighted and blind-folded subjects sat side by side (see Chapter 4). The results are shown in Table 7.3 and identify the influence of magnets (type B: median pole strength = 15.0 mT (1985); 10.7 mT (1987)) on blindfolded and sighted subjects in three tasks: judging compass direction, pointing towards home, and judging air-line distance. The three comparisons together

Table 7.2. Influence of magnets on compass orientation, map-building and navigation on blindfolded and sighted subjects: combined probabilities for data from Tables 6.15, 6.17 and 6.18

	Compass orientation			Pointing to home			Air-line distance to home		
	df	χ^2	P	df	χ^2	P	df	χ^2	P
Blindfolded	10	31.85	<0.001	6	19.03	0.005	6	4.69	0.586
Sighted	8	14.42	0.072	6	27.36	<0.001	6	14.18	0.028

Significant values for χ^2 are underlined.

establish that the influence of magnets does depend on whether people can see ($\chi_6^2 = 18.06$; $P = 0.007$; combined probability). Individually, however, the comparisons suggest that the interaction of magnets and blindfolds depends on the particular task. Thus, the influence of magnets on blindfolded and sighted subjects was significantly different ($P = 0.002$) for the ability to point towards home, nearly so ($P = 0.089$) for judgement of the air-line distance to home, but clearly not ($P = 0.674$) for the judgement of compass direction.

On the whole, sighted subjects appear to be the more sensitive to magnets (greater absolute z-values in all three tasks; Table 7.3) but in no case is the difference significant. Rather, particularly when judging the direction of home, the influence of blindfolds is to change the *direction* of response to magnets. When blindfold, subjects pretreated with Sup magnets showed stronger homeward orientation than those pretreated with Nup magnets; when sighted, the converse was the case. However, subjects pretreated with Nup magnets were not disoriented when blindfolded; rather they were misoriented by 100° or so in a clockwise direction (Fig. 7.1).

In these 1985/87 bus experiments, subjects were tested about 15–20 minutes after the magnets were removed, the journeys being relatively short (approximately 5 km). We know from Fig. 6.8 that, during the first 30 minutes or so after a magnet is removed, the way in which people read the ambient field shows rapid changes. Subjects exposed to Nup magnets change either from misorientation by 180° back to good orientation (N–S sleepers) or from good orientation to disorientation (E–W sleepers). Major changes either may not occur (E–W sleepers) or are slower (N–S sleepers) after exposure to Sup magnets, the main effect of which is to reduce acuity.

One interpretation of Fig. 7.1, therefore, would be that, when blindfolded, subjects pretreated with Nup magnets have a frame of reference for their exploration (see Fig. 2.5A) that, in effect, rotates through 100° or so during the course of their journey, causing the subject to point to home with an error of an equivalent amount. When sighted, however, the subject continuously calibrates the changing magnetic frame of reference against successive visual frames of reference, thus (presumably subconsciously) effectively correcting for the changes that are taking place in the way the magnetoreceptor is interpreting the geomagnetic field. The effective rotation of the ambient magnetic field thus passes uncorrected by blindfolded subjects but is corrected by sighted subjects. Sup magnets, which simply impart reduced acuity of magnetoreception, do not produce patterned changes in magnetic reference large enough to require correction and thus impart similar performance to both sighted and blindfolded subjects.

In the 1985/87 bus experiments, and overall in other bus, chair and

Table 7.3. Comparison of the influence of type-B magnets (15-minute pretreatment) on sighted and blindfolded subjects in controlled bus experiments

	Compass orientation				Pointing to home				Air-line distance to home			
	Brass magnets		Wallraff's test		Magnets		Wallraff's test		Magnets		Mann–Whitney U-test	
	h	h	z	P (1-tailed)	Nup h	Sup h	z	P (2-tailed)	Nup median error (m/km)	Sup median error (m/km)	z	P (2-tailed)
Bus												
blindfolded	0.05	−0.06	+0.87	0.19	−0.12	**0.32**	−2.01	0.04	615	870	+0.75	0.45
sighted	**0.18**	0.04	+1.47	0.07	**0.44**	0.03	+2.48	0.01	600	375	−1.66	0.09
Comparison of z-values:	z_{diff}	P (2-tailed)			z_{diff}	P (2-tailed)			z_{diff}	P (2-tailed)		
	0.42	0.674			3.17	0.002			1.70	0.089		

Significant h-values shown in **bold**; significant z-values underlined.

$z_{\text{diff}} = \text{abs}\,(z_b - z_s)/\text{sqr2}$; where z_b is the value of z for blindfolded subjects and z_s is the value of z for sighted subjects.

Positive values for z show that subjects pretreated with brass (for compass orientation) or Nup magnets (for pointing and distance) are the more accurate.

For sample sizes, see Table 7.13.

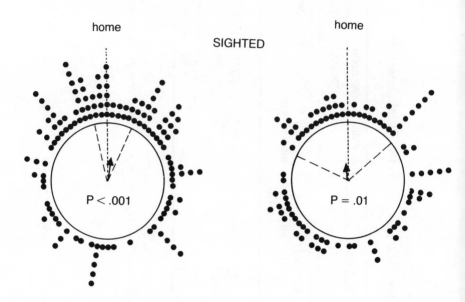

SIGHTED

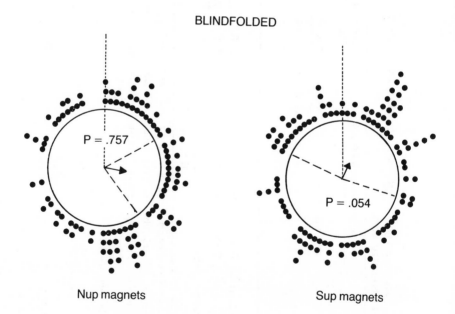

BLINDFOLDED

walkabout experiments, there were, in effect, four different categories of subject: (1) with both vision and magnetoreception impaired (by blind-folds and magnets, respectively); (2) with only vision impaired; (3) with only magnetoreception impaired; and (4) with neither sense impaired. The relative performance of the four categories is illustrated in Fig 7.2. Best performance was by subjects with both senses intact; worst by subjects with neither sense intact. Subjects with only one of the two senses intact showed intermediate levels of ability, with magnetorecep-tion appearing the more useful of the two. The implication is that, to judge compass direction and the direction of home, people normally use magnetoreception and vision together though, if necessary and with some loss of acuity, each sense can function alone. Without either sense, judgement of direction is reduced to the level of guesswork.

7.1.2. The role of magnetoreception at night

Relatively few (six) walkabout experiments have been carried out at night. On only one of these was the sky overcast and on none was the moon shining. On three of the five occasions with a clear, starlit sky a planet (Venus twice; Jupiter once) was particularly conspicuous in the SW or SE sky; on the remaining two occasions the star pattern was that normal for early evening in autumn in the Northern Hemisphere.

In these night-time experiments, subjects are still able to judge the direction of home better than expected from guesswork but have been unable to judge compass direction and have been wildly inaccurate at judging distance, usually overestimating by several orders of magnitude (Chapter 5).

Fig. 7.1. Bus experiments: ability of sighted and blindfolded subjects to draw an arrow towards home after pretreatment with Nup and Sup magnets. Data for 1985/87 experiments in which sighted and blindfolded subjects sat side by side, thus controlling for factors other than sight and magnetic treatment. All subjects exposed to magnets. Sight leads to a significant general improvement in ability to point towards home ($X_4^2 = 24.16$; $P < 0.001$; combined probability), but only for people pretreated with Nup magnets ($z = 4.005$; P (1-tailed) $= 0.00003$; Wallraff's test) not for people pretreated with Sup magnets ($z = 0.883$; P (1-tailed) $= 0.189$; Wallraff's test). The influence of sight is significantly different for subjects pretreated with magnets of different polarity ($z = 2.207$; P (2-tailed) $= 0.028$. Difference in zs). Magnet polarity during pretreatment has a significant influence on ability to point towards home ($X_4^2 = 9.76$; $P = 0.045$; combined probability), but only for sighted people ($z = 1.965$; P (2-tailed) $= 0.049$; Wal-lraff's) not for blindfolded ($z = -1.422$; P (2-tailed) $= 0.155$; Wallraff's). The influence of polarity is significantly different for sighted and blindfolded people ($z = 2.352$; P (2-tailed) $= 0.018$. Difference in zs). The results suggest some specific interaction between sight and magnetoreception.

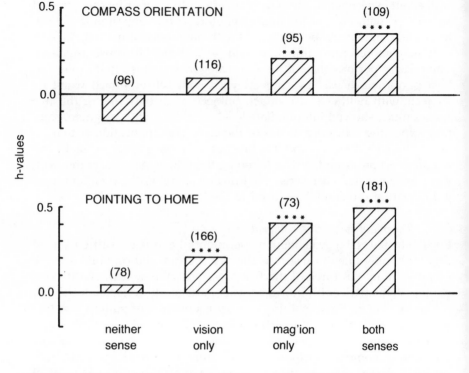

Fig. 7.2. Ability to judge compass direction or the direction of home: subjects with different access to vision and magnetoreception. Histograms show homeward components for subjects with access to vision only (treated with disruptive magnets); magnetoreception only (neutral magnets and blindfolded); both senses (neutral magnets, not blindfolded); or neither sense (disruptive magnet and blindfolded). Total data for E–W sleepers from bus and walkabout experiments.

As subjects are apparently using simple guesswork to judge compass direction and distance on night-time walkabouts, it is not surprising that there is no evidence of a role for magnetoreception in these tasks (Table 7.4). In contrast, the significant ability to point towards home does involve magnetoreception overall ($\chi^2_6 = 17.25$; $P = 0.009$; combined probability for the three different data sets in Table 7.4). More detailed analysis suggests that the role of magnetoreception may be most important when the sky is over cast ($P = 0.01$; Table 7.4) and less so when stars (+ planets) are visible ($P = 0.084$). However, sample sizes are still small (Table 7.13) and more data are needed. Walkabout experiments on moonlit nights would be particularly interesting, particularly in view of the recent demonstration of integration of moon and magnetic compasses in moths (Baker 1987a).

Table 7.4. The role of magnetoreception in night-time tests when the sky is: (a) starlit (no moon); and (b) overcast

| | Compass orientation | | | | Pointing to home | | | | Air-line distance to home | | | |
| | Magnets | | Wallraff's test | | Magnets | | Wallraff's test | | Magnets | | Mann–Whitney U-test | |
	Nup h	Sup h	z	P (1-tailed)	Nup h	Sup h	z	P (1-tailed)	Nup median error (m/km)	Sup median error (m/km)	z	P (1-tailed)
Sighted												
Walkabout												
Starlit sky												
A-magnets	0.13	−0.26	−1.60	0.95	**0.71**	0.11	+1.60	0.06	1388			
B-magnets	−0.06	−0.14	−0.37	0.65	**0.23**	**0.27**	+0.53	0.30		2582	−0.41	0.66
Overcast sky												
A-magnets	0.17	−0.06	−0.83	0.80	**0.44**	−0.12	$\underline{+2.31}$	$\underline{0.01}$				
Combined probability			χ^2	P			χ^2	P			χ^2	P
Starlit sky			0.99	0.910			8.22	0.084			0.83	0.660
Overcast sky			0.45	0.797			$\underline{9.21}$	$\underline{0.010}$				

Significant h-values shown in **bold**; significant z- and χ^2-values underlined.

Positive values for z show that relative performance after treatment with Nup and Sup magnets is as expected if magnetoreception has a role under the conditions tested.

For sample sizes, see Table 7.13.

7.1.3. The role of magnetoreception by day: overcast and sunny skies

When young inexperienced homing pigeons are transported in a distorted magnetic field, they are unable to orient towards home. In contrast, exposure to the same distorted field only on arrival at the release site is not disruptive (R. Wiltschko & Wiltschko 1978). When transported in an unaltered magnetic field but released with a magnet glued to their back, such young and inexperienced pigeons are disoriented (Keeton 1971). Evidently, such novice navigators rely on their magnetic compass both to record the net direction of the outward journey (integrating detours if necessary) and to localise the reverse of this direction when released (W. Wiltschko & Wiltschko 1988).

This reliance of young pigeons on a magnetic compass persists for only their very first few flights. With flying experience, they learn to use other cues. At about 3 months of age, depending on flight experience, they begin to use the sun compass spontaneously. A few early training flights accelerate the development of the sun compass considerably (R. Wiltschko 1983).

The early view (Keeton 1971) that, if the sun is shining, experienced pigeons abandon magnetoreception when judging the direction of home has since been revised (Walcott 1977; Visalberghi & Alleva 1979). Although it is accepted that, with the ambient magnetic field disrupted, experienced pigeons remain able to orient towards home if the sun is shining, they are nevertheless less accurate than controls that, presumably, gain additional information from magnetoreception. As a result, the current view is that magnetoreception has a role in pigeon navigation that is particularly important to young birds under all conditions and to experienced birds under overcast skies. Under sunny skies, however, even experienced birds do not totally ignore the geomagnetic field.

It thus seems that, in solving navigational problems, homing pigeons integrate information from the sun and geomagnetic field in a way that changes with age and experience. Details of the mechanisms involved are still being identified. A number of studies by the Wiltschkos (see summary given by R. Wiltschko & Wiltschko 1984; W. Wiltschko & Wiltschko 1988) suggest that a pigeon's ability to use a sun compass depends on the bird's observing and learning the way that the sun moves across geomagnetic compass directions during the course of the day. Moreover, the amount of extrapolation involved is limited and, in effect, pigeons must observe more or less every portion of the sun's arc across the sky before they associate the sun's position with time and geographic direction. Finally, there is some evidence (Alexander & Keeton 1974; W. Wiltschko *et al.* 1976; Edrich & Keeton 1977; see summary in Baker 1984b) that, even once pigeons have a functional sun compass, they continue at intervals to check the sun's position against other factors (such as, perhaps, the geomagnetic field) and to recalibrate their sun compass as necessary. Such occasional recalibration would allow the birds to compensate for seasonal changes in the sun's arc.

Walkabout experiments provide data ideally suited to analysis of the possibility that humans may also use the sun and geomagnetic field in an interactive way (Baker 1987b). Table 7.5 shows the influence of magnets on human navigation and compass orientation during walkabout experiments under total overcast and *continuous* sunshine. Combined probabilities show that the ability to judge the direction and distance of home involves magnetoreception under total overcast, but apparently not under continuous sunshine. In contrast, judgement of compass direction involves magnetoreception when the sun is shining, but not when it is overcast.

At first sight, the conclusion that magnetoreception is involved in the judgement of compass direction when the sun is shining seems particularly surprising. In Chapter 5 (Table 5.19), data were presented to suggest that walkabout subjects use a sun compass, albeit inefficiently and with systematic errors at different times of day (i.e. anticlockwise in the morning; clockwise in the afternoon). The conclusion reached was that in the morning people assume the sun lies to the ESE; in the afternoon to the WSW. Such consistent errors hint at some form of psychological misconception, perhaps over where the sun should be at different times of day. If this interpretation were correct, there would be no obvious role for magnetoreception in compass orientation when the sun was visible, and magnets should have no effect. Yet magnets do have an effect (Table 7.5). It seems that magnetoreception does play some part in people's use of the sun as a compass. This apparent contradiction can be examined further by more detailed analysis of the influence of magnets.

The tendency to swing from anticlockwise errors in the morning to clockwise errors in the afternoon may be analysed by 2×2 contingency tables (Table 7.6). The swing is significant for control subjects and subjects pretreated with Nup magnets if the sun is shining, but not if the sky is overcast, and is not significant under either condition for subjects pretreated with Sup magnets. It is this lack of swing from extreme anticlockwise to clockwise errors by such (Sup-treated) subjects that is the basis for their overall superior performance when the sun is shining (compass orientation; Table 7.5).

The directions in which different groups of subjects seem to interpret the sun to lie may be calculated using the same logic as described in Chapter 5. The results (Fig. 7.3) are consistent with the view that subjects (E–W sleepers) pretreated with Nup magnets consider the sun to lie due E in the morning and due W in the afternoon. These directions compare with directions of ESE and WSW, respectively, for people pretreated with brass bars, and SE and SW for people pretreated with Sup magnets. Such changes in assumed compass bearing of the sun in

Table 7.5. The role of magnetoreception in daytime tests under: (a) total overcast; and (b) continuous sunshine

	Compass orientation				Pointing to home				Air-line distance to home			
	Magnets		Wallraff's test		Magnets		Wallraff's test		Magnets		Mann–Whitney U-test	
	Nup h	Sup h	z	P (1-tailed)	Nup h	Sup h	z	P (1-tailed)	Nup median error (m/km)	Sup median error (m/km)	z	P (1-tailed)
Sighted												
Walkabout												
Total overcast												
A-magnets	−0.39	−0.30	+0.59	0.28	**0.51**	0.06	+1.42	0.08	623	1667	+1.97	0.02
B-magnets	−0.18	−0.41	−1.29	0.90	**0.23**	**0.67**	+3.07	<0.01	791	791	+0.86	0.20
Continuous sun												
A-magnets	−0.02	**0.27**	−1.56	0.06	**0.63**	**0.58**	+0.82	0.21	625	625	+0.02	0.50
B-magnets	−0.01	**0.46**	+1.98	0.02	**0.29**	**0.56**	+1.08	0.14	543	314	+1.04	0.15
Combined probability			χ^2_4	P			χ^2_4	P			χ^2_4	P
Total overcast			2.75	0.604			18.92	0.001			10.73	0.030
Continuous sun			13.12	0.011			7.10	0.130			5.21	0.266

Significant h-values shown in **bold**; significant z- and χ^2-values underlined.

Positive values for z show that relative performance after treatment with Nup and Sup magnets is as expected if magnetoreception has a role under the conditions tested.

For sample sizes, see Table 7.13.

Table 7.6. Possible interaction of magnetic and sun compasses: analysis of directions of errors at judging compass bearings in walkabout experiments (2 × 2 contingency tables)

	Sunny				Overcast			
	No. of errors				No. of errors			
	CCW	CW	χ^2	P	CCW	CW	χ^2	P
Brass bars								
morning	28	19			6	11		
afternoon	15	32	7.24	0.007	16	19	0.51	0.517
Nup magnets								
morning	30	14			10	11		
afternoon	12	19	6.41	0.011	6	10	0.38	0.546
Sup magnets								
morning	24	11			6	16		
afternoon	18	12	0.52	0.522	11	14	1.42	0.232

Table shows the number of estimates of compass direction that were in error in either a counter-clockwise (CCW) or clockwise (CW) direction in morning and afternoon tests under sunny and overcast conditions for subjects pretreated with brass bars or magnets.

Data for E–W sleepers only.

Significant χ^2-values are underlined.

response to exposure to magnets are inconsistent with the hypothesis that the assumptions have a purely psychological basis; sensory errors seem the more likely.

The following hypothesis of what happens when a subject is tested under sunny skies on walkabout experiments would be consistent with the above results: (1) the subject draws an arrow towards home; (2) the experimenter asks for an estimate of the compass direction in which the subject's arrow is pointing; (3) consciously or subconsciously, the subject assesses the compass bearing of the sun by magnetoreception; (4) the subject judges the compass bearing of his/her arrow relative to the assessed direction of the sun. On this model, pretreatment affects the accuracy of magnetoreception and thus the accuracy of assessment of the compass bearing of the sun. This is turn affects assessment of the compass bearing of the arrow. The model does not preclude the possibility that judgement of the time of day is also involved, as it is known to be in birds (Hoffmann 1954; see reviews by Schmidt-Koenig 1979; Baker 1984b). In that event, the final error will be the combined result of errors in magnetoreception, errors in judging time, and inaccuracies in the learned position of the sun at different times of day in different seasons.

This apparent role of magnetoreception in judging the compass bear-

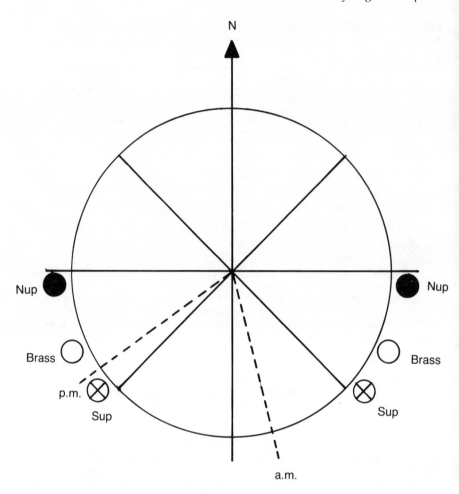

Fig. 7.3. Possible interaction of sun and magnetic compasses in the judgement of compass direction during walkabout experiments. When judging compass direction under sunny skies, subjects on walkabout experiments tend to make anticlockwise errors in morning tests and clockwise errors in afternoon tests. Such errors are not found under overcast skies. Perhaps people use a sun compass but do so inaccurately. The diagram shows a compass rose. Marked on (dashed lines) are the mean compass bearings of the sun's azimuth during morning and afternoon tests. Circles show mean errors at judging compass direction by subjects pretreated with brass bars (Table 5.19) and Nup or Sup magnets (Table 7.5). Data are consistent with the view that subjects pretreated with brass bars judge the sun to be ESE in the morning and WSW in the afternoon. Comparable figures are SE and SW for subjects pretreated with Sup magnets and E and W for subjects pretreated with Nup magnets. Perhaps people judge the compass direction of the sun in part by reference to their magnetic compass. Data from Tables 5.19 and 7.5.

ing of the sun seems to be most important ($P = 0.005$; Table 7.7) when the sun is high (>30°) in the sky. When the sun is nearer the horizon (between 15° below to 30° above), magnetoreception is less, or no longer, important ($P = 0.139$; Table 7.7). Similarly, when the same data are plotted against time of day (Fig. 7.4), magnetoreception seems to be most important around noon (11.00–13.00 h). Circular plots of the estimates made by people (E–W sleepers; see Chapter 6) within an hour either side of noon after pretreatment with Sup and Nup magnets show (Fig. 7.5) that, whereas people treated with Sup magnets correctly judge the sun to be due S, those treated with Nup magnets misjudge the sun to be due E.

The evidence for *compass orientation* is that both the sun and the geomagnetic field are needed if subjects on walkabout experiments are to judge compass direction better than expected from guesswork (Fig. 7.6). The ability to *point towards home*, however, deteriorates only if neither the sun nor the geomagnetic field is available (Fig. 7.5). Although one series of experiments produced an apparently significant ($P = 0.03$; Table 7.7) influence of (type-B) magnets on the ability to point towards home when the sun was low in the sky, combined probability analysis suggests this may have been a chance result ($P = 0.092$; Table 7.7). So far, there is no clear evidence that magnetoreception plays a part in judging the direction of home when the sun is shining, whether its disc is high in the sky or near the horizon (Table 7.7). Thus, although accuracy may suffer more if the geomagnetic field rather than the sun is obscured (Fig. 7.5), it seems that the sun can be used as an adequate substitute for geomagnetism. Finally, the ability to judge the *air-line distance to home* suffers most if the sun is obscured (Fig. 7.7), even though significantly useful information can be obtained from the geomagnetic field (Table 7.5).

In summary: information from both the sun and geomagnetic field seem to be useful when people attempt to judge both direction and distance during walkabout experiments. Compass orientation requires both cues; navigation is possible with only one. When navigating, the geomagnetic field is the more important in judging the direction of home; the sun the more important in judging distance. If neither cue is available, neither compass orientation nor navigation is any better than expected from guesswork.

7.1.4. *The conscious and subconscious roles of magnetoreception*
I have argued (Baker 1981a, 1985c; see also Chapter 2) that the primary value of magnetoreception during exploration is as a subconscious sense that frees vision, hearing and olfaction for other crucial roles such as the detection of resources and danger. A number of experiments have now been carried out that allow this hypothesis to be evaluated.

Table 7.7. The role of magnetoreception in daytime tests when the sun is: (a) near the horizon; and (b) high in the sky.

	Compass orientation				Pointing to home				Air-line distance to home			
	Magnets		Wallraff's test		Magnets		Wallraff's test		Magnets		Mann–Whitney U-test	
	N_{up} h	S_{up} h	z	P (1-tailed)	N_{up} h	S_{up} h	z	P (1-tailed)	N_{up} median error (m/km)	S_{up} median error (m/km)	z	P (1-tailed)
Sighted, walkabout												
Sun near horizon												
A-magnets	0.12	−0.01	−0.38	0.65	**0.69**	**0.77**	−0.29	0.61	458	458	−0.27	0.61
B-magnets	0.20	**0.65**	+1.66	0.05	**0.34**	**0.71**	+1.84	0.03	543	334	+1.33	0.09
Sun high in sky												
A-magnets	−0.11	**0.46**	+2.65	<0.01	**0.56**	0.27	+1.62	0.05	563	749	+1.03	0.15
B-magnets	0.19	**0.41**	+1.06	0.15	0.23	0.25	+0.21	0.42	543	371	+1.37	0.09
Combined probability		χ_4^2	P			χ_4^2	P			χ_4^2	P	
Sun near horizon		6.93	0.139			7.99	0.092			5.88	0.208	
Sun high in sky		14.91	0.005			7.65	0.105			8.67	0.069	

Significant *h*-values shown in **bold**; significant z- and χ^2-values underlined.

Positive values for z show that relative performance after treatment with Nup and Sup magnets is as expected if magnetoreception has a role under the conditions tested.

For sample sizes, see Table 7.13.

Near horizon = between 15° below horizon to 30° above.

High in sky = 31° to 61° above horizon.

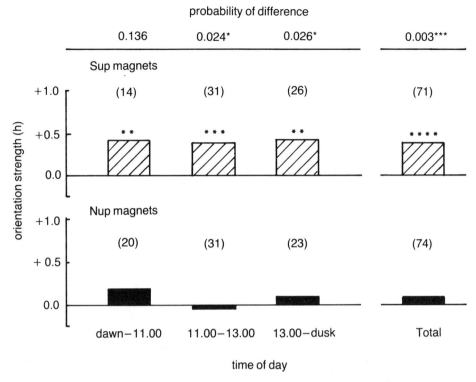

Fig. 7.4. Strength of compass orientation under sunny skies on walkabout experiments for subjects tested at different times of day. *P*-values at top show probability of difference (Wallraff's test) in strength of orientation of subjects pretreated with Sup and Nup magnets. Greatest involvement of magneto-reception in compass orientation when the sun is shining occurs around noon. Although dis- or mis-oriented throughout the day, subjects treated with Nup magnets show least ability to judge compass direction around noon.

Experiments on *blindfolded* subjects at Manchester have usually tested people making a conscious effort to orient or navigate. Chair experiments, by virtue of the fact that people make nine successive estimates of compass direction, inevitably trigger conscious mechanisms. Most series of bus experiments have also used people aware of the questions they are to be asked on arrival at the test site. Exceptions were the 1985/1987 series in which sighted and blindfolded subjects sat side by side. So far (see data in Chapter 6), blindfolded subjects have been influenced by magnets when judging direction consciously, but not when judging direction subconsciously. However, no controlled experiments on blindfolded subjects have yet been attempted in which informed people, navigating consciously, and uninformed people, nav-

COMPASS ORIENTATION: 11.00–13.00 hrs; sunny

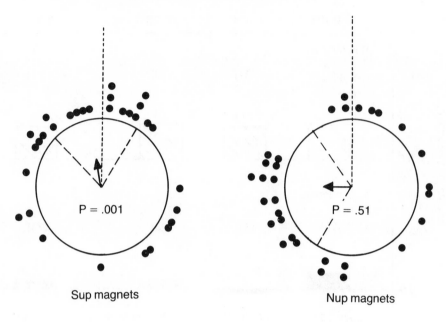

Fig. 7.5. Compass orientation around noon by subjects on walkabout experiments. With the sun shining at noon, subjects pretreated with Nup magnets are not disoriented but misoriented by about 90°. Each dot shows one person's estimate relative to true compass direction (dotted line).

igating subconsciously, sit side by side in the same test. As yet, therefore, it is perhaps premature to draw any firm conclusions on the conscious and subconscious role of magnetoreception when people cannot see.

In contrast to most tests on blindfolded subjects, the majority of (walkabout) experiments on *sighted* subjects have tested for subconscious navigation (Baker 1987b). Subjects have not known the aims of the experiment and often engage in other tasks (Chapter 4). It is a safe assumption that any navigation in these tests is subconscious. However, in one experiment (Woodchester Park, June 1986), all subjects were told the aims of the experiment and were asked to concentrate on judging direction and distance during the walk. Comparison of performance in this experiment with 'informed' subjects with performance in those with 'uninformed' subjects could give an indication of the role of magnetoreception in conscious and subconscious orientation and navigation. Such comparison, however, is open to the danger than factors other than degree of concentration may have been different in the two sets of experiments. For example, the sun was visible during the experiment on

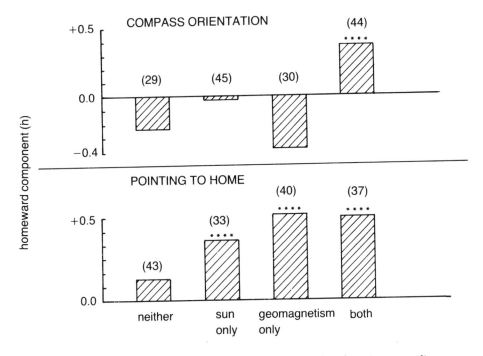

Fig. 7.6. Walkabout experiments: ability of subjects to judge direction according to availability of sun and magnetic information. Bars are homeward components (*h*) for subjects who have access: only to the sun (sunny walks, pretreated with disruptive magnets); only to geomagnetism (overcast, pretreated with neutral magnets); both clues (sunny, pretreated with neutral magnets); or neither (overcast, pretreated with disruptive magnets).

informed people, but not in all of the experiments on uninformed people. Controlled experiments, in which some subjects are informed and others are uninformed, are also necessary; so far six have been performed (Chapter 5). All used pretreatment with type-B magnets to study the role of magnetoreception.

In these six walkabout experiments, subjects were divided into two groups. Half were told the nature of the task and were asked to concentrate on solving the questions to be posed at the test site. The other half remained naive and uninformed (Chapter 4). Four of the six experiments took place under overcast daytime skies.

Results from these 'general' and 'controlled' experiments show that magnetoreception has a significant role in subconscious ($P = 0.002$), but not in conscious ($P = 0.988$), compass orientation (Table 7.8). Similarly, in navigation, magnetoreception again appears to have a role only in subconscious judgement ($\chi^2_8 = 21.85$; $P = 0.006$; combined probability),

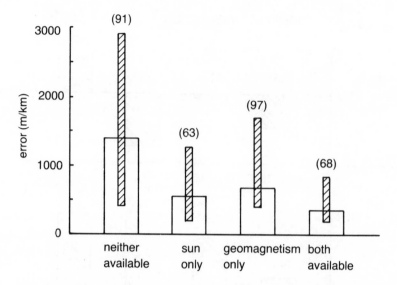

Fig. 7.7. Walkabout experiments: ability of subjects to judge air-line distance to home according to availability of sun and magnetic information. Bars show median errors (and inter-quartile ranges) at judging air-line distance for subjects who have access: only to the sun (sunny walks, pretreated with disruptive magnets); only to geomagnetism (overcast, pretreated with neutral magnets); both clues (sunny, pretreated with neutral magnets); or neither (overcast, pretreated with disruptive magnets).

not in conscious ($\chi^2_8 = 9.30$; $P = 0.318$), though the difference is clearer in relation to direction than to distance (Table 7.8).

On the whole, the hypothesis that sighted subjects use magnetoreception primarily for subconscious navigation and orientation is supported. There is a tendency for conscious orientation and navigation to be better than subconscious only in subjects treated with disruptive magnets, implying that it is possible, when sighted, to compensate for an absence of geomagnetic information by concentrating on other clues. This in turn implies that the major selective advantage of magnetoreception is as a background, subconscious mechanism that frees other senses, such as vision, for roles in exploration other than that of navigation.

7.2. *The use of magnetoreception by males and females*

7.2.1. *Chair experiments*

In her extensive study of the performance of schoolchildren in chair experiments, Murphy (1987) reached the following conclusions (Chapter 5). When the chair is first turned, both males and females attempt to

Table 7.8. Tests of the role of magnetoreception in conscious and subconscious orientation and navigation

	Compass orientation				Pointing to home				Air-line distance to home			
	Magnets		Wallraff's test		Magnets		Wallraff's test		Magnets		Mann–Whitney U-test	
	Nup h	Sup h	z	P (1-tailed)	Nup h	Sup h	z	P (1-tailed)	Nup median error (m/km)	Sup median error (m/km)	z	P (1-tailed)
Sighted, walkabout												
Informed subjects ('conscious')												
general	**0.66**	**0.09**	−2.44	0.99	**0.56**	**0.63**	+0.10	0.46	403	597	−0.57	0.72
controlled	0.13	−0.11	−1.18	0.88	0.22	**0.39**	+0.93	0.18	791	633	+1.00	0.16
Uninformed subjects ('subconscious')												
general	0.10	**0.37**	+2.46	0.01	0.32	**0.57**	+2.09	0.02	684	543	+1.73	0.04
controlled	−0.10	**0.27**	+2.04	0.02	0.08	**0.48**	+1.95	0.03	592	633	−0.68	0.75
Combined probability			χ^2_4	P			χ^2_4	P			χ^2_4	P
Informed subjects			0.28	0.988			4.98	0.289			4.32	0.365
Uninformed subjects			17.03	0.002			13.45	0.010			7.01	0.139

Significant h-values shown in **bold**; significant z- and χ^2-values underlined.

Positive values for z show that relative performance after treatment with (type-B) Nup and Sup magnets is as expected if magnetoreception has a role under the conditions tested.

For sample sizes, see Table 7.13.

judge direction by noting their starting direction and then following the turns using internally generated information (based, for example, on inertia). This technique rapidly becomes inaccurate and both sexes become disoriented. Males remain disoriented for the remainder of the test whereas, mid-way through the test, females regain accurate orientation by switching to an external reference system.

Murphy (1987) studied the role of magnetoreception for orientation during chair experiments by fixing bar magnets to the right temple of her subjects' heads. Figure 7.8 illustrates her results for what should be (Table 7.1) the most sensitive indicator of magnetoreception: comparison of the performance of N–S sleepers wearing brass bars with those wearing Nup magnets. Second-order analysis (Table 6.10 and Fig. 6.6) has shown that N–S sleepers judge compass direction with an error of 180° when wearing Nup magnets in chair experiments. Figure 7.8 suggests that the influence of Nup magnets is immediate but does not prevent the period of disorientation that occurs after the first estimate. When controls begin to recover (around the fourth estimate), the influence of Nup magnets returns.

These results imply that these subjects (11- to 16-year-old females) used magnetoreception to judge their starting position. Inertial mechanisms, presumably based on 'internal' reference systems, were then used to judge turns from this starting position. Cumulative errors rapidly lead to disorientation. The external reference system proposed by Murphy to be the cue by which females, but not males, regain their orientation mid-way through the test also appears to be detected by magnetoreception and is thus, presumably, the ambient geomagnetic field. This elegant study by Murphy has given a great deal of insight into precisely how chair experiments test the way females use the ambient magnetic field to judge direction. Unfortunately, comparable data are not yet available for males from this age group; and older males do not seem to use an external reference system in chair experiments.

7.2.2. *Integration of visual and magnetic information*
Although the data were equivocal, it was suggested in Chapter 5 that the relative ability of males and females to judge compass direction might be influenced by blindfolding, females tending to be more accurate than males when blindfolded and improving little when allowed to see, at least under overcast skies. Males, on the other hand, may improve considerably when allowed to see, and then become more accurate than females.

The role of magnetoreception in these apparently different abilities or strategies for compass orientation by males and females was investigated by means of the 1985/1987 series of bus experiments in which sighted and blindfolded males and females sat side by side (Chapter 4).

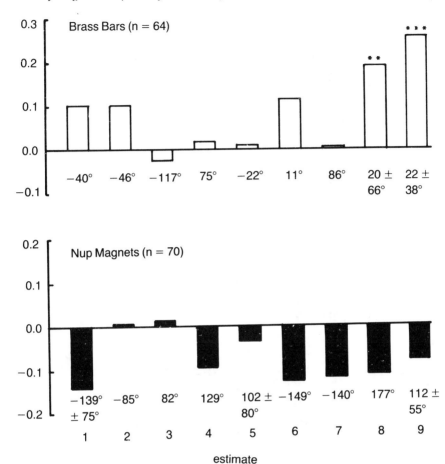

Fig. 7.8. Varying role of magnetoreception in judging compass direction during the course of a chair experiment involving nine estimates. Histograms show *h*-values for the first to ninth estimates of direction in a series of chair experiments on 11- to 16-year-old girls. Data are for N–S sleepers wearing either a brass bar or a Nup magnet on the head. The chair is rotated between each estimate. *V*-test: * $P < 0.05$; ** $P < 0.02$; *** $P < 0.01$; **** $P < 0.001$. Data from Murphy (1987).

Males are influenced by magnetic treatment when they see but not when they are blindfolded (Table 7.9); the converse is true for females. This tendency for magnetoreception and vision to interact differently for males and females is on the verge of being significantly greater than expected from chance ($z = 1.64$; P (one-tailed) $= 0.05$; test to compare zs).

The results obtained in these experiments allow formulation of the following hypothesis for judgement of compass direction under overcast

Table 7.9. Interaction of magnetoreception and sight in the ability of males and females to judge compass direction and navigate during controlled bus experiments

	Compass orientation				Pointing to home				Air-line distance to home			
	Brass magnets		Wallraff's test		Magnets		Wallraff's test		Magnets		Mann–Whitney U-test	
	h	h	z	P (1-tailed)	Nup h	Sup h	z	P (2-tailed)	Nup median error (m/km)	Sup median error (m/km)	z	P (2-tailed)
Males												
Blindfolded	−0.03	0.03	−0.54	0.71	−0.26	0.25	−1.76	0.08	615	957	+1.49	0.14
Sighted	**0.34**	0.10	+1.77	0.04	**0.57**	0.12	+1.77	0.08	552	386	−0.61	0.54
Females												
Blindfolded	0.10	−0.14	+1.68	0.05	0.01	**0.37**	−0.98	0.33	600	731	−0.17	0.87
Sighted	0.09	−0.01	+0.72	0.24	**0.36**	−0.05	+1.87	0.06	647	375	−1.72	0.08

Significant h-values shown in **bold**; significant z- and χ^2-values underlined.

Positive values for z show that subjects pretreated with brass (for compass orientation) or Nup magnets (for pointing and distance) are the more accurate of the two groups.

For sample sizes, see Table 7.13.

skies in bus experiments. When blindfolded, females use magnetoreception and alter their strategy for orientation relatively little when allowed to see. Blindfolded males, on the other hand, do not use magnetoreception and are disoriented. However, when males are allowed to see, magnetoreception becomes effective. In order to judge compass direction any better than they could achieve by guesswork, males need to be able to use *both* vision and magnetoreception.

The other task in which males and females have shown different levels of ability is when attempting to point towards home in walkabout experiments: males are clearly and significantly more accurate (Table 5.15). There is no unambiguous indication, however, that this difference is in any way due to different use of the ambient magnetic field (Table 7.10). The six analyses for each sex in Table 7.10 show that, over a range of conditions, both males ($\chi^2_{12} = 26.51$; $P = 0.010$; combined probability) and females ($\chi^2_{10} = 26.64$; $P = 0.009$) are using magnetoreception to judge the direction of home. There is a hint, no more, that males may be more inclined than females to use the geomagnetic field at night and less inclined when the sun is visible. Under overcast skies by day, both seem equally inclined to use geomagnetic information.

7.3. *The use of magnetoreception at different ages*

Ability to judge geographical direction in chair experiments varies with age (Chapter 5). Males reach peak performance between the age of 11 and 15 and thereafter judge direction no better than by guesswork. Females, on the other hand, gradually improve during adolescence before plateauing between the ages of 20 and 40. Thereafter, performance deteriorates to the guesswork level shown by males. There is also some evidence from walkabout experiments of an improvement in navigational performance with age from about 10 to 20 years old.

Murphy (1987) showed convincingly that 11- to 16-year-old females use magnetoreception to judge direction during chair experiments but obtained no data for males. I have insufficient data involving magnetic manipulation of these adolescent age groups to comment on their use of magnetoreception during chair experiments. The only data currently available that allow any analysis of the use of magnetoreception by different age groups are those obtained for the ability to point towards home during walkabout and bus experiments (Table 7.11). All three age groups tested (6–10 years; 16–18 years; 19–21 years) are capable of magnetoreception. It is not possible, however, to draw any further conclusions about changes in magnetoreceptive acuity with age. The variation in performance reported in Chapter 5 may or may not, therefore, be due to variation in magnetoreception acuity. The primary need is for a series of experiments on mixed-age groups.

Table 7.10. The role of magnetoreception in the ability of males and females to point towards home when 'exploring' under different conditions

	At night				By day: overcast				By day: sun visible			
	Magnets		Wallraff's test		Magnets		Wallraff's test		Magnets		Wallraff's test	
	Nup h	Sup h	z	P (1-tailed)	Nup h	Sup h	z	P (1-tailed)	Nup h	Sup h	z	P (1-tailed)
Sighted, Walkabout												
Males												
A-magnets	**0.66**	0.11	+2.08	0.02	**0.57**	−0.19	+1.54	0.06	**0.53**	**0.68**	−0.37	0.65
B-magnets	0.35	**0.43**	+0.77	0.22	**0.46**	**0.83**	+1.59	0.06	**0.34**	**0.57**	+0.95	0.17
Females												
A-magnets	0.40	−0.21	+1.89	0.03	**0.48**	0.33	+0.32	0.38	**0.70**	**0.37**	+1.31	0.10
B-magnets	0.14	−0.02	−0.25	0.60	0.15	**0.54**	+2.20	0.01	0.17	**0.42**	+0.72	0.24
Combined probability			χ^2_4	P			χ^2_4	P			χ^2_4	P
Males			10.95	0.027			11.33	0.023			4.37	0.358
Females			8.05	0.090			10.49	0.033			7.60	0.107

Significant h-values shown in **bold**; significant z- and χ^2-values underlined.

Positive values for z show that relative performance after treatment with Nup and Sup magnets is as expected if magnetoreception has a role under the conditions tested.

For sample sizes, see Table 7.13.

Table 7.11. The role of magnetoreception in the ability of people of different ages to point towards home

| | Aged 6–10 years | | | | Aged 16–18 years | | | | Aged 19–21 years | | | |
| | Magnets | | Wallraff's test | | Magnets | | Wallraff's test | | Magnets | | Wallraff's test | |
	Nup l_1	Sup l_1	z	P (2-tailed)	Nup l_1	Sup l_1	z	P (2-tailed)	Nup l_1	Sup l_1	z	P (2-tailed)
Blindfolded												
A-magnets									0.40	**0.68**	−1.97	0.05
A-magnets*									0.44	−0.03	+2.10	0.04
B-magnets					−0.09	**0.31**	−0.56	0.12				
Sighted												
Overcast/dark												
A-magnets	**0.49**	0.14	+2.00	0.05					0.67	−0.15	+1.69	0.09
B-magnets	0.13	**0.40**	−1.46	0.14	0.40	−0.03	+2.39	0.02	0.30	**0.65**	−2.63	0.01
Sunny												
A-magnets									0.62	**0.50**	+0.95	0.34
B-magnets					0.28	**0.48**	−1.42	0.16	0.23	**0.64**	−1.15	0.25
Combined probability	χ^2_4 10.08		P 0.039		χ^2_6 16.11		P 0.014		χ^2_{12} 32.15		P 0.002	

Significant l-values shown in **bold**; significant z- and χ^2-values underlined.

Positive values for z show that subjects pretreated with Nup magnets are the more accurate.

*Data for Keele (Campion, personal communication); remainder from Baker (unpublished).

For sample sizes, see Table 7.13.

7.4. *General discussion*

The analyses presented in the previous sections allow, for the first time, the formulation of hypotheses concerning the way that humans integrate their use of magnetoreception and vision (see also Baker 1987b). The major features of the data presented in Chapters 5–7 are summarised simply in Table 7.12.

7.4.1. *Judgement of compass direction*

In all of my experiments, magnetoreception seems to be essential to compass orientation. Under no conditions could subjects with impaired magnetoreception judge compass direction better than expected from guesswork. This was true even for sighted subjects with opportunity to refer to the sun or stars.

Failure to judge compass direction with the sun or stars visible but without magnetoreception should probably not be taken to reflect the technique and ability of experienced human navigators. People experienced in the interpretation of sun and star compasses may have little use for magnetoreception (Lewis 1972), though real data are not available. Instead, this measured failure probably reflects the naivety of my subjects. The average schoolchild or student in modern Britain has little reason to train themselves in the use of sun, and particularly star, compasses. For example, it was sobering to discover that, of 200 university biology students (aged 18–22) only 18 knew (i.e. could state), when questioned, that the sun in Britain was always due South at local noon.

Not that my subjects ignored the sun when estimating compass direction: performance was significantly better when the sun was shining (Fig. 5.8) and low in the sky (Fig. 5.9). Moreover, there were systematic errors with time of day under sunny, but not overcast, skies (Table 7.6) that also hinted strongly at a badly used sun compass. However, rather than the sun being used instead of magnetoreception, it now seems (Figs 7.3–7.5; Tables 7.5–7.7) that sun and magnetic compasses are used interactively, the basic compass being that due to the geomagnetic field.

One peculiarity in the data for compass orientation is the inability of sighted subjects to judge compass direction on walkabout experiments if the skies are overcast. The simple explanation, that people cannot use magnetoreception to judge compass direction when denied sight of the sun, is difficult to sustain. Sighted males, at least, use magnetoreception to judge compass direction under overcast skies in bus experiments (Table 7.9). So, too, do both sexes (particularly females) when blindfolded. There seems, then, to be some particular problem with overcast conditions on walkabouts. This problem is confined to compass orientation; on the same experiments, magnetoreception is involved in judging the distance and direction of home (Table 7.5). Two possible explanations

Table 7.12. Summary of the role of magnetoreception in orientation and navigation, and levels of performance with magnetoreception functional and disrupted

	Compass orientation			Pointing to home			Distance to home
	Is role signif.? (Y/n)	Is ability significant when magnetoreception		Is role signif.? (Y/n)	Is ability significant when magnetoreception		Is role signif.? (Y/n)
		functional? (Y/n)	disrupted? (Y/n)		functional? (Y/n)	disrupted? (Y/n)	
'Subconscious'							
Blindfolded	n	n	n	n	n	n	n
Sighted: by night							
overcast	n	n	n	Y	Y	n	?
starlit	n	n	n	Y (♂)	Y (♂)	n	n
moonlit	?	?	?	?	?	?	?
Sighted: by day							
overcast	Y (♂)	Y (♂)	n	Y	Y	n	Y
sun high	Y	Y	n	?	Y	Y	?
sun low	?	Y	n	?	Y	Y	n
'Conscious'							
Blindfolded	Y (♀)	Y (♀)	n	Y	Y	n	n
Sighted: by day							
overcast	Y	Y	n	?	Y	n	n
sunny	Y	Y	n	n	Y	Y	n

Compiled from data in Chapters 5–7.

Table 7.13. Sample sizes for categories of subjects used in analyses presented in Chapter 7

	Number of subjects					
	Compass direction		Pointing Home		Distance home	
	Bar		Magnet		Magnet	
Table and category	brass	magnet	Nup	Sup	Nup	Sup
Table 7.3						
blindfolded	92	130	30	34	62	69
sighted	83	136	37	28	71	65
	Magnet					
Table 7.4						
Starlit night	Nup	Sup				
type-A magnets	4	4	4	4	0	0
type-B magnets	16	13	18	14	29	31
Overcast night						
type-A magnets	7	7	7	7	0	0
type-B magnets	0	0	0	0	0	0
Table 7.5						
Overcast						
type-A magnets	7	10	12	17	16	17
type-B magnets	22	20	26	28	74	81
Continuous sun						
type-A magnets	26	21	20	17	28	26
type-B magnets	19	23	16	17	37	40
Table 7.7						
Sun low in sky ($-15°$ to $+30°$)						
type-A magnets	13	12	15	11	16	14
type-B magnets	16	14	25	21	44	46
Sun high in sky ($+31°$ to $+61°$)						
type-A magnets	22	18	16	13	29	29
type-B magnets	24	27	17	17	46	49
Table 7.8						
Informed						
general	7	10	7	10	10	10
controlled	23	17	23	17	33	26
Uninformed						
general	72	66	48	52	104	111
controlled	17	20	17	20	29	34

Table 7.13. (Continued)

Table and category	Number of subjects					
	Compass direction		Pointing Home		Distance home	
	Bar		Magnet		Magnet	
	brass	magnet	Nup	Sup	Nup	Sup
Table 7.9						
Males	Brass	magnet				
Blindfolded	37	44	7	15	21	28
sighted	29	58	12	13	23	30
Females						
blindfolded	55	86	19	19	41	43
sighted	54	78	26	15	46	35
Table 7.10	Pointing night		Pointing overcast		Pointing sunny	
Males	Nup	Sup				
type-A magnets	6	6	4	9	13	10
type-B magnets	8	9	8	13	17	15
Females						
type-A magnets	5	5	7	7	18	14
type-B magnets	10	5	19	16	15	14
Table 7.11	Aged 6–10 years		Aged 16–18 years		Aged 19–21 years	
Blindfolded						
type-A magnets	0	0	0	0	19	10
type-A magnets*	0	0	0	0	21	29
type-B magnets	0	0	23	31	0	0
Sighted						
Overcast/dark						
type-A magnets	17	15	0	0	5	12
type-B magnets	19	20	35	24	27	23
Sunny						
type-A magnets	0	0	0	0	31	24
type-B magnets	0	0	20	20	22	19

* See Fig. 7.11.

would fit the data for the poor judgement of compass direction during overcast walkabouts: (1) magnetoreception is not used and subjects simply guess; (2) magnetic orientation is overridden by judgement of compass direction based on other, inappropriate cues. As yet, there is no indication from the data as to which of these reasons for disorientation is the more likely. On the one hand, there seems no obvious reason for subjects under overcast skies to be more likely to guess on walkabout experiments than on bus. On the other, the ability to orient under overcast skies on bus experiments suggests that any confusion either does not arise from the sky or is filtered out by the glass in bus windows. As the bus experiments in question all ended in urban surroundings, it is possible that any confusing factor on walkabout experiments emanates from vegetation: some subjects, for example, claimed to have attempted to judge direction by looking at the pattern of moss growing on trees, an inappropriate strategy in the areas in which experiments were carried out. For the moment, however, ability of sighted people to judge compass direction under totally overcast skies on bus experiments, but not on walkabouts, remains enigmatic and unexplained.

7.4.2. *Map-building and navigation*

Magnetoreception appears to be essential for subconscious navigation at night and under overcast skies by day. In contrast, when the subject concentrates on solving navigational problems during exploration, magnetoreception is essential only when blindfolded and perhaps under overcast skies. When the sun is visible, magnetoreception may be more or less redundant, particularly for conscious navigation but perhaps also for subconscious navigation.

Magnetoreception appears to play a relatively minor role in the judgement of the air-line distance to home while travelling, being important only under overcast skies by day. At night, judgement of distance is very poor (Chapter 5); yet it is relatively good when blindfolded and displaced by bus. In neither case, however, does there seem to be a role for magnetoreception. When sighted, the most useful aid to the judgement of distance is the sun (Baker 1987b). No explanation is yet available, though the most intriguing possibility is that the sun in some way aids the judgement of time, necessary to convert walking speeds into distances.

7.5. *Summary*

Magnetoreception is involved in all aspects of orientation and navigation as measured in chair, bus and walkabout experiments.

Normally, to judge compass direction or the direction of home during exploration, magnetoreception and vision work together (Fig. 7.2). However, if necessary, though with some loss of acuity, each sense can function alone. Without either sense, judgement of direction appears to be reduced to the level of guesswork.

At night, sighted subjects on walkabout experiments seem only to guess at both compass direction and distance; magnetoreception is not involved. However, magnetoreception is used to judge the direction of home, particularly when the sky is overcast; less so when stars (+ planets) are visible. No data are yet available for the interaction of moon and magnetic orientation.

By day, explorers use both the sun and geomagnetic field to judge direction and distance. Compass orientation requires both cues (at least with the navigationally naive subjects tested so far); navigation is possible with only one. When navigating, the geomagnetic field is the more important in judging the direction of home; the sun the more important in judging distance. The relative importance of magnetoreception, however, declines the nearer the sun to the horizon. Without access either to sight of the sun or perception of the geomagnetic field, neither compass orientation nor navigation is any better than expected from guesswork.

On the whole, the hypothesis that sighted subjects use magnetoreception primarily as a subconscious aid to orientation and navigation is supported. Conscious orientation tends only to be better than subconscious when subjects are treated with disruptive magnets. This implies it is possible, when sighted, to compensate for an absence of geomagnetic information by concentrating on other cues.

Females seem more inclined, or able, to use magnetoreception when blindfolded; males when sighted. All ages from 6 to 21 use magnetoreception, but there are as yet no data on changes in magnetoreceptive acuity with age.

We now know that magnetoreception is part of the sensory armoury used by humans to solve problems of orientation and navigation. We now also know the situations in which it is most useful and those in which it is most redundant. In demonstrating these facts, Chapter 5–7 have unearthed some clear and intriguing characteristics of the way the human magnetic sense responds to exposure to artificial magnetic fields. These characteristics must be clues to the remaining major questions surrounding this unexplored vertebrate sense: where is the magnetoreceptor and how does it work? These are the central questions in the next chapter.

8

The physiology of magnetoreception

In Chapter 3, a variety of hypotheses for the way humans and other animals may be able to detect the magnetic field and the way the magnetoreceptor might work were reviewed. In subsequent chapters, the results of a wide variety of experiments have been presented. In some of these, alteration of the geomagnetic field (e.g. by electromagnetic helmets) appears to have no effect on the way in which subjects 'read' the geomagnetic field. In others, alteration of the ambient field has a clear influence. Different magnets with different polarities have different effects. Different people respond differently to the same magnetic treatment. The ability to judge compass direction is not always affected in the same way as the ability to point towards home or to judge distance. The influence of magnets persists beyond the time that the magnet is in position; the 'aftereffect' persisting for up to two to perhaps even 48 hours.

The range and variety of these results should form a massive set of clues as to the nature, physiology and behaviour of the magnetoreceptor itself, clues that are not available to any comparable extent for any other animal. The aim of this chapter is to take the first step towards trying to piece together these clues and to begin to form a picture of the nature of the magnetoreceptor and of the way it works.

8.1. *Location of the magnetoreceptor*

8.1.1. *The Cheshire nudist experiment*
Among the currently less fashionable hypotheses concerning the location, form and function of vertebrate magnetoreceptors are a whole series based on the assumption that more or less the whole body is involved in sensitivity. Most of these, as reviewed in Chapter 3, involve in some way the generation of electric charges or currents. These stimulate nerves to generate a patterned response that can be converted into

directional information within the central nervous system. All hypotheses thus require the detection of minute electric variations against considerable background 'noise' due to such features as charged cloud particles, the Earth's electrostatic field, and currents generated within the body itself by normal electric activity.

The generation of electric charges on the surface of feathers or hairs as an animal changes orientation within the geomagnetic field has an endearing simplicity. Such a sensory mechanism, however, though perhaps appropriate to our African forebears, encounters a problem unique to recent generations of humans living in temperate and cold regions: the wearing of clothes. Throughout almost the entire period of human evolution, people were naked, or nearly so. Any whole-body sensory system could have functioned unimpeded. As various groups of ancestral humans colonised temperate and subpolar regions, however, such a sensory system would increasingly have had to function within the constraints of physical pressure from clothes and spurious electric charges generated by friction between the body and garments. In recent years, since the advent of artificial fibres (e.g. nylon in 1937; polyesters in 1946; acrylics in 1950 (Hollen & Saddler 1968)), many modern humans have lived most of their lives within an electrostatic cocoon generated by their clothes and furniture.

It seemed possible, therefore, that one way of testing whether the whole body might be involved in magnetoreception was to compare people's ability to judge direction, both when naked and clothed and also when wearing cotton (which does not generate electrostatic fields and which has been used for clothing for at least 3500 years; Hollen & Saddler 1968) and polyester (which does and has been used for only 40 years). With the cooperation of a nudist group with land in Cheshire, this experiment was carried out in the spring and summer of 1982. Only chair experiments were performed; walkabout and bus experiments being impracticable.

Two full-length robes were made to the same design, one constructed of pure cotton, one of 100% polyester. Thirty-nine subjects (21 males, 18 females) took part in the experiment. Ages ranged from 9 to 71 years. Over a period of 4 months, each person took part in four tests (eight estimates of direction in each test). In two tests, the subject was naked (apart from double blindfolds and ear muffs). In the other two tests, the subject wore only a robe (plus blindfolds and ear muffs); once the cotton robe, once the polyester. The sequence of clothing states was randomised between subjects. The experimenter was naked throughout all tests. Subjects assumed the aim of the experiment was to test for an influence of clothes and, being nudists, were naturally prejudiced towards superior performance when naked. They were unaware that the experiment was also designed to test for a difference in performance when wearing

cotton and polyester robes. The time interval between cotton and polyester test on each subject was usually a month or more, and few subjects
commented that they had worn two different robes. In order to add
some control for subject bias, a brass bar (in an opaque cotton envelope)
was placed on the right temple during testing, and subjects were told
that this bar might be a magnet and might prevent them from being able
to judge direction. The only difference from a normal chair experiment
as described in Chapter 4 was that, before sitting down, subjects walked
vigorously around the chair, once clockwise and once anticlockwise.
This procedure was introduced to generate static electricity when wearing the polyester robe (though, to avoid artefact, the procedure was
adopted on all tests, whether the polyester robe was worn or not).
Results have been presented elsewhere (Baker 1984b, 1985a) and are
summarised in Fig. 8.1.

Subjects were most able ($h = 0.400$; $P < 0.001$) to judge direction when
naked. However, ability was not significantly reduced ($z = 0.348$; P
(one-tailed) $= 0.363$) when wearing the cotton robe ($h = 0.369$; $P <
0.001$). When wearing the polyester robe, however, performance was
weak ($h = 0.073$) and not significantly better than if the subjects had
guessed ($P = 0.257$). Performance when wearing polyester was significantly worse both than when naked ($z = 1.695$; P (one-tailed) $= 0.045$)
and when wearing cotton ($z = 1.839$; P (one-tailed) $= 0.033$).

The experiment shows that clothes *per se* (at least, loose-fitting robes)
do not interfere significantly with ability to judge direction. In contrast,
ability is significantly reduced if clothes are made of 100% polyester.
Levels of performance (see Chapter 5) by people wearing their everyday
clothes (usually up to about 60% polyester) are intermediate between
the levels recorded for people wearing cotton and polyester in this
experiment.

As yet, this apparent influence of polyester material on performance
at judging direction in chair experiments has not been studied further.
The electrostatic fields which are so conspicuously and uncomfortably
generated when such fabrics are worn next to the skin are the obvious
feature to suspect as instrumental in the reduced performance. It should
be stressed, however, that direct investigation of this possibility (e.g. by
manipulating electrostatic gradients) has not yet been attempted. It is
possible that there is some other, less obvious, feature of the material
(e.g. smell) that is the critical factor.

Even if we assume that it is the electrostatic fields associated with
polyester material that is their important feature, the results shown in
Fig. 8.1 cannot be taken as unequivocal support for a whole-body or
diffuse body-surface magnetoreception system. Other possibilities are
that the electrostatic (or other) properties of polyester material have a
general physiological effect (e.g. irritation, headaches, or other dis-

(a)

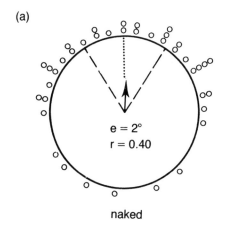

naked

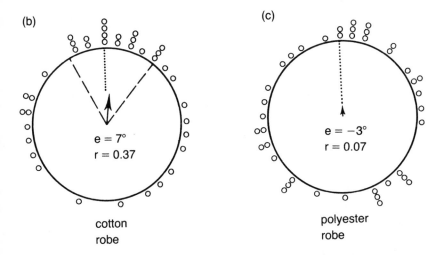

cotton
robe

polyester
robe

Fig. 8.1. The Cheshire nudist experiment: influence of clothing and clothing materials on compass orientation by blindfolded subjects in chair experiments. Each of 39 subjects was tested twice wearing nothing (expect blindfolds and earmuffs), once wearing only a cotton robe and once wearing only a polyester robe. The experimenter wore nothing during all tests. Subjects had a brass bar (which they were told might be a magnet) on the right temple in all tests. Each dot shows the mean error for the eight compass estimates made during a single test (only the first of their two tests while naked). Only naked subjects or subjects wearing cotton could judge compass direction more accurately than expected from guesswork. From Baker (1984b).

comforts) and simply reduce overall performance at a number of tasks, not only judgement of direction.

Finally, even if we assume that the observed reduction in performance does result from an interference between electrostatic fields and magnetoreception, we still cannot rule out the possibility that the magnetoreceptor is a discrete organ in a localized position, such as in the head. The electrostatic field generated by the robe would have extended beyond the head. Any magnetoreceptor in the head would thus be functioning within an unusual electrostatic field. It is, of course, unlikely that this electrostatic field could in any way physically mask the geomagnetic field from the receptor. However, if the magnetoreceptor made any use of induced ac or dc currents to interpret direction, these currents could well be influenced by the spurious electrostatic field generated by polyester garments.

The Cheshire nudist experiment has thus shown that clothes alone do not interfere significantly with magnetoreception. However, there is a possibility, no more, that the physiology of magnetoreception is sensitive to the electrostatic environment within which it is functioning. As the electrostatic cocoon within which many modern humans now lead their lives is of recent origin, it is reasonable to assume that there has been no time (or selection pressure) to evolve a magnetoreceptor that can function efficiently under such conditions. The experiment does not tell us, however, whether we are searching for a diffuse, whole-body sensory system or for a discrete, localised receptor. To pursue this question further, a different approach has been adopted.

8.1.2. *Localised magnetic manipulation*

Electromagnetic coils large enough for a person's whole body to be rotated within the altered magnetic field have a predictable influence on judgement of compass direction. So too do stationary electromagnetic coils that alter the magnetic field through only a person's head and neck (Chapter 6). These two experiments show that there is a magnetoreceptor in the human head. They do not show that there is no magnetoreceptor in the remainder of the body; so far no navigation experiments have changed the magnetic field only through the torso and limbs, not through the head. Experiments on dowsers (Harvalik 1978), however, have tried this approach, and claims have been made that magnetoreceptors involved in the dowsing response are located in the region of the adrenal glands, just above the kidneys, as well as in the front part of the head 13 mm in front of the ear orifice. For further discussion of experiments on dowsing see Kirschvink (1985) and Williamson (1987).

The great majority of experiments reported in Chapters 6 and 7 involved bar magnets placed on the right temple. In this position, just behind and extending from just above to just below the right eye,

INFLUENCE OF MAGNETS
on judging compass direction

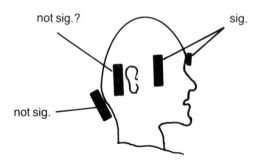

not sig.?   sig.

not sig.

Fig. 8.2. Positions on the head at which magnets have a significant, non-significant, or intermediate effect on orientation.

magnets have a significant effect (Fig. 8.2). Two experiments in the United States (Gould 1980; Adler & Pelkie 1985) used magnets on the forehead just above the nose and between the eyes. Although the influence of these magnets may have been less than when placed on the temple, in combination the two experiments showed that the magnets had a significant influence on orientation (Baker 1985b, 1987c). Experiments at Barnard Castle (Baker 1980d) and at Princeton, USA (Gould & Able 1981) used magnets placed on the back of the head. Any apparent influence (Baker 1980d, 1981b, 1985a) nevertheless failed to reach significance (Baker 1985b, c; Dayton 1985). Finally, magnets positioned just behind the right ear had an intermediate (but insignificant) influence (Baker 1985c). Direct experiments to compare the influence of Nup magnets placed on the back and front of the head also show a significant difference (Baker 1984b, 1985a), orientation being better than guesswork only if the magnet is placed on the back of the head, not the front. Taken all together, these experiments imply a magnetoreceptor forward of the ear, perhaps level with the back of the eyes rather than further forward, and perhaps on a vertical level between the top and bottom of the eyes. This is the same area implicated by the first series of bus experiments at Manchester using electromagnetic helmets (Baker 1981b). The implicated block of tissue encompasses the back of the eyes and the sphenoid/ethmoid sinuses; precisely the areas predicted on the basis of theorising (Leask 1977) and anatomical investigations (Baker *et al.* 1983).

The coincidence has already been noted (Baker 1985a) between this location and, on the one hand, the position claimed by Harvalik (1978) to be the location of a magnetoreceptor involved in dowsing and, on the other hand, the position in which pre-Columbian sculptors of human figures in Guatemala seem consistently to have located magnetic poles (Dunn & Malmstrom, personal communication). At this stage, no further comment can be added.

8.1.3. *The eyes*
As originally formulated, Leask's optical resonance theory predicted that, if the eyes were the site of magnetoreception in birds, some light would be necessary to provide energy for magnetoreception (Leask 1977). The level of light intensity needed may not be great, starlight possibly being sufficient. Shortly after, Schmidt-Koenig (1979) pointed out that, in all experiments on birds in which magnetoreception had been demonstrated, some ambient light had been present. The Wiltschkos then showed that pigeons transported in total darkness were as disoriented upon release as other pigeons, transported in light but treated with bar magnets to deny them geomagnetic information (W. Wiltschko & Wiltschko 1981). Since then, there has been a flurry of neurophysiological investigations. As a result, support for the optical system as the site of magnetoreception has been growing.

Working with homing pigeons, Peter Semm and his colleagues (Semm *et al.* 1984; see also Semm, unpublished data, in W. Wiltschko & Wiltschko 1988) have shown that there are neurones located in the nucleus of the basal optic root (nBOR) that respond with clear changes in electrical activity to gradual inversions of the inclination of the natural magnetic field. The nBOR is part of the accessory optic system, and units in this nucleus are highly sensitive to objects moving through their receptive fields. These units may be classified into two major groups (Britto *et al.* 1981): (a) cells sensitive to movement which project mainly to the oculo-motor area; and (b) cells sensitive to direction which project mainly to the vestibular system (Emmerton 1982). These latter directionally sensitive cells each respond optimally to movements in a particular direction and are inhibited by motion in the opposite direction. It is in this population of direction-sensitive cells that clear-cut responses to directional changes of the magnetic field were found (Semm *et al.* 1984). Moreover, individual cells responded to distinct ranges of field direction with inhibition or augmentation of their spontaneous electrical activity.

Not only did Semm and his colleagues demonstrate responses to specific changes in the magnetic field, their recordings also demonstrated that light was necessary for these responses to occur; in total darkness the spontaneous activity of the cells did not change. Illumination of the eyes with light of different wavelengths showed a peak of magnetic responsiveness at 503 nm, consistent with Leask's (1977) suggestion of the involvement of rhodopsin molecules.

Cells in the nBOR are not the only ones to be selectively sensitive to the direction of optical stimuli. Similar cells are found in the *stratum griseum et fibrosum superficiale* of the *tectum opticum*. Semm & Demaine (1986) have shown that these cells also respond when the direction of the magnetic field is changed. As in the nBOR, individual cells responded only to a narrow range of directions but, as a whole, their various peaks of sensitivity would represent all parts of space.

Taken together, the recordings from the nBOR and *tectum opticum* suggest that the responses of these cells contain sufficient directional information to allow detection of the magnetic field direction as required for compass orientation (Semm & Demaine 1986). At least some students of pigeon navigation (e.g. W. Wiltschko & Wiltschko 1988) suggest that the available evidence supports the view that detection of magnetic field direction takes place in the visual system together with the detection of light. Such bimodal sensitivity of receptors is not unusual, and possible primary processes have been discussed by Schulten & Windemuth (1986).

In the retina of the Quail (*Coturnix coturnix*), the activity of the enzyme Hydroxyindole-O-methyltransferase (HIOMT) is influenced by variations of the Earth's magnetic field (Krause *et al.* 1984). HIOMT catalyses the biosynthesis of methoxyindoles, such as melatonin. Melatonin, in turn, is assumed to play an important role in the dark adaptation of the retina. An involvement of magnetoreception in melatonin synthesis is not confined to birds. There is similar evidence for mammals (Welker *et al.* 1983), and experiments to examine magnetic field effects on pineal melatonin synthesis in the Rat clearly implicate a role for retinal magnetosensitivity (Olcese *et al.* 1985). Moreover, Krause *et al.* (1984) have demonstrated for humans that variations in the ambient magnetic field influence the acuity of human night vision. More recently, Krause & Hennekes (1986) have used an electro-oculogram (EOG) on humans to study the influence of manipulation of the ambient magnetic field on the oscillations of retinal potential. A 50% decrease in the strength of the horizontal component of the Earth's magnetic field causes a distinct phase shift in the potential oscillations of both eyes. They conclude that the human retina shows an objective magnetic field sensitivity, and suggest that this, plus the studies on melatonin synthesis, appoint to the retina an important role in the registration of weak magnetic fields. The remaining and exciting question is whether the magnetoreceptor(s) that these studies by Semm, Krause and their colleagues have apparently identified in the retina of birds and mammals, including humans, are the same as those involved in human orientation and navigation.

Magnets influence human orientation and navigation at night and when blindfolded (Chapter 7) showing that magnetoreception remains possible under such conditions. However, the level of light intensity necessary to power an optical resonance magnetoreceptor is unknown; so too is the amount of light passing through the blindfolds used in chair experiments. Night-time walkabouts have either been starlit and/or subjects have carried torches. It is a moot point, therefore, whether or not the persistence of magnetoreception under such conditions represents evidence against Leask's hypothesis. In Leask's favour is the observation that magnetoreception is more powerful when people can see (Chapter 7). Moreover, the deterioration in orientation in chair experiments in a wooden hut as evening progresses to night (Baker & Mather 1982; Baker 1984b) could be due to the reduction towards zero in the amount of light available to pass through the blindfolds. Even at night, however, there is some light available since the experimenter wears a headlight to allow him or her to see to perform the tests. No experiments have yet been performed in which it is possible to be certain that absolutely zero light energy is striking the retina of the person being tested. There is enough evidence consistent with Leask's hypothesis and insufficient against for optical resonance to remain a viable hypothesis for human magnetoreception.

Whether or not optical resonance is the mechanism, there is sufficient interaction between vision and magnetoreception in the data presented in Chapters 5 to 7 for the eyes to remain viable candidates as the site of the human magnetoreceptor. Alternatively, many of the interactions noted in Chapter 7 could be explained solely as higher order interactions within the central nervous system. Even so, the possibility remains that the interaction occurs because vision and magnetoreception share a common site for reception: the eyes. In this context, the failure of Judge (1985) to find any evidence for orientation to the ambient magnetic field in physiologically blind or visually handicapped subjects could be particularly instructive. However, sample size was small (eight or nine) and the distance of the journey was such that successful orientation might not have been expected even by subjects with intact magnetoreceptors (Chapter 5).

8.1.4. *The ethmoid/sphenoid sinus complex*

Two series of chair experiments have been carried out relating to the suggestion (Baker *et al.* 1982, 1983, Baker 1984a) that the human magnetoreceptor may be located in the ethmoid/sphenoid sinus complex. Both series have been based on the supposition that, if this complex is indeed the site of the magnetoreceptor, irritation of these sinuses with foreign substances may well interfere with ability to judge direction. Naturally, there is little scope for the deliberate introduction of irritants into people's sinuses, and we were limited to two categories of foreign substances that many people inflict on themselves in everyday life: nasal sprays and smoke.

From October 1982 to March 1983, under my supervision, Carol Siddorn carried out experiments on fellow undergraduate students at Manchester University to test for an influence of commercially available nasal sprays on ability to judge compass direction in chair experiments. Two different sprays were used, one of which was introduced to both nostrils by the subjects themselves a few minutes before being tested. In addition, subjects were tested without any spray. The two sprays used were: (1) deionised water (masked); and (2) nasal spray (Vick's Sinex). Each was contained in an identical Sinex container that had been thoroughly rinsed with deionised water before filling. The deionised water spray was masked by having Sinex rubbed around the neck of the container so that the subject could smell Sinex as the deionised water was sprayed into the nasal tract. The experiment was notionally double blind in that neither the subject nor the experimenter knew which jar contained which spray. It is likely, however, that the subject, though perhaps not the experimenter, could detect the difference between the two sprays.

It was intended that each subject would be tested first without spray, then once with each spray in random order with at least one week between consecutive tests. However, in the event, most subjects were only tested twice.

In these chair experiments, subjects were able to judge compass direction after spraying deionised water into their nasal tract but not after introducing nasal spray (Table 8.1). The difference, however, is not significant (P (one-tailed) $= 0.147$). Interpretation of the results is confused in that subjects not exposed to either water or nasal spray also performed no better than could be achieved by guesswork ($P = 0.148$). There was also no way of knowing how much of the decongestant or water, if any, actually reached the ethmoid/sphenoid sinus complex. Moreover, as in all experiments that rely on disorientation rather than misorientation (see Section 4.4.3), it is always possible that any influence of decongestant was general, reducing overall performance, rather than a specific influence on magnetoreception. The results are consistent with the sinal magnetoreceptor hypothesis, but are by no means unequivocal.

Table 8.1. Chair experiments: orientation performance after treatment with nasal spray

Treatment	N	$e \pm CI°$	h	P (V-test)	Wallraff's test z	P (1-tailed)
Nasal spray	24	154°	−0.073	0.696		
Controls						
(a) water spray	34	−47 ± 44°	0.231	0.029	1.050	0.147
(b) no spray	49	−11°	0.105	0.148		
total	83	−36 ± 52°	0.157	0.022		

Significant orientation (*V*-test) underlined.

Data from Carol Siddorn (unpublished).

Analysis of the results of walkabout experiments shows that people who smoke more than one nicotine-based cigarette per day are less able to judge compass direction than people who have never smoked or have not smoked for at least about 6 months. No such difference is found, however, in ability to point towards home (Table 8.2).

From October 1984 to March 1985, under my supervision, Anne Bambridge carried out chair experiments on 'smoker' and 'non-smoker' fellow undergraduates at Manchester University (Table 8.2). Male subjects were unable to orient whether or not they smoked. Females who had never smoked could judge compass direction better than expected from guesswork (Table 8.2); females who smoked more than five cigarettes a day could not.

Thus far, the results were consistent with the hypothesis of a sinal magnetoreceptor while again not providing unequivocal evidence. However, Bambridge then showed that, if her female subjects were allowed to smoke while being spun in the chair, their ability to judge direction improved almost to the level of non-smokers. Bambridge's results have been confirmed by Sarah Moss in a further series using only female subjects, October 1986 to March 1987 (Fig. 8.3). Moreover, Moss has shown that the improved performance shown by smokers begins to deteriorate within minutes of their finishing their last cigarette.

It seems, then, that the deleterious effect of smoking on ability to judge direction is not consistent with the hypothesis of a sinal magnetoreceptor. Rather, the results are of a classical drug or habit response: subjects habituated to function while smoking only perform well when allowed to smoke. This could also provide an explanation for the paradox that, on walkabout experiments, smokers are worse at compass orientation, but not at pointing to home. Compass orientation is invariably an instantaneous estimate at the test site whereas pointing to home is assumed to involve route-based navigation throughout the journey. Smokers often smoke at intervals during the walk, but rarely do so at the test site itself.

These studies have shown that the observed influence of smoking is primarily consistent with a general influence on physiology rather than a specific influence on magnetoreception. In particular, good performance by smokers when smoking and poor performance when not offer no support to the hypothesis of a sinal magnetoreceptor. At the same time, of course, the possibility of such a receptor, but one that is immune to, or untouched by, smoke cannot be dismissed by these data.

8.1.5. *Conclusions*
Localised manipulation of magnetic fields implies that humans have one or more magnetoreceptors in their head, probably located in the block of tissue that includes the back of the eyes and the sphenoid/ethmoid sinus

Table 8.2. Influence of smoking on orientation and navigation as measured in chair and walkabout experiments

	Non-smokers				Smokers				Wallraff's test	
	N	$e \pm CI$	h	P (V-test)	N	$e \pm CI$	h	P (V-test)	z	P (1-tailed)
Sighted										
Walkabouts										
pointing to home	188	$25 \pm 11°$	0.495	<0.001	72	$12 \pm 15°$	0.578	<0.001	−1.413	0.921
compass orientation	181	$-13 \pm 40°$	0.170	<0.001	69	$-84°$	0.011	0.449	1.934	0.027
Blindfolded										
Chair										
compass orientation										
males (AB)	12	$-110°$	−0.103	0.696	7	$-36°$	0.163	0.266	−0.972	0.835
females (AB)	12	$23 \pm 44°$	0.513	0.007	7	$117°$	−0.217	0.797	1.946	0.026
females (SM)	16	$-2 \pm 48°$	0.464	0.005	24	$167°$	−0.136	0.828	2.361	0.009

Combined probability

χ^2_{10}	P
24.470	0.007

Significant values of h, z and χ^2 are underlined.
Walkabout data from Baker (unpublished); chair data from Ann Bambridge (AB) and Sarah Moss (SM) (unpublished).

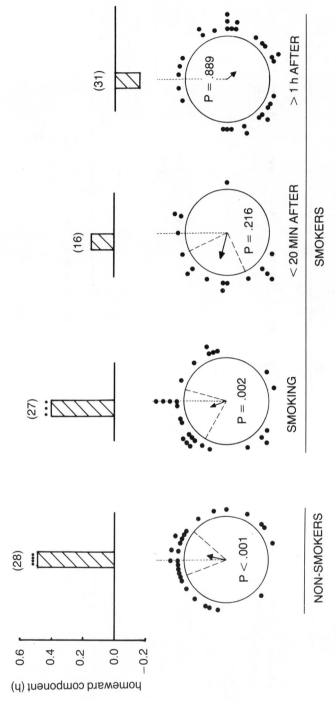

Fig. 8.3. Influence of smoking on strength of compass orientation in chair experiments. Strength of compass orientation was measured in chair experiments for 27 female subjects (18–24 years old). Sixteen were 'non-smokers' (ten had never smoked; six had not smoked for at least 6 months); 11 were 'smokers' who smoked more than five nicotine-based cigarettes each day. Non-smokers were tested between one and four times (one test = nine estimates of direction while blindfolded). Smokers were tested between one and four times in each of three conditions: (a) while smoking; (b) within 20 min of finishing their last cigarette; and (c) more than 1 h after finishing their last cigarette. Dots in the circular diagrams are the mean errors of the nine estimates of direction in a single test. For other conventions see Fig. 4.12. Data from Bambridge & Moss (unpublished).

complex. If there are further areas of magnetoreception elsewhere in the torso and/or limbs, information from these areas is secondary to that collected by the receptor(s) in the head.

Poorer orientation by subjects who introduce high concentrations of foreign substances into the nasal tract could be consistent with the hypothesis of a sinal magnetoreceptor. More detailed study of the orientation of people who smoke more than five cigarettes a day, however, does not support this hypothesis. Rather, the observed influence of smoking is consistent more with a general influence on physiology than a specific influence on magnetoreception.

The tendency for magnets to influence orientation to a greater extent when people can see than when they are blindfolded is consistent with the hypothesis that the magnetoreceptor is located in the eyes. However, people do show magnetic sensitivity both at night and when blindfolded. This does not preclude the possibility of a retinal magneto-receptor but perhaps casts doubts that such a magnetoreceptor may be based on optical resonance. However, the weight of this inference must await clarification of how much light energy is needed to drive a magnetoreceptor based on optical resonance and how much light penetrates the double blindfolds used in the experiments at Manchester.

The disorienting effect of wearing polyester fibre may or may not be due to the electrostatic fields that are such a conspicuous feature of garments made from such material. If electrostatic fields interfere with orientation, the effect is perhaps most likely to be due to, as for smoking, a general influence on performance, rather than a specific influence on magnetoreception. The possibility should still be borne in mind, however, that at some stage in the process of magnetoreception ac, or dc, electric currents are induced that may be influenced in some specifically disruptive way by the ambient electrostatic environment.

8.2. *How the geomagnetic field is 'read'*

8.2.1. *Features of the geomagnetic field*
Few people are so familiar with the form of the Earth's magnetic field that they can easily envisage the information available from the field and the way it is altered by particular experimental manipulations. A review of the main features of the geomagnetic field of interest to students of navigation is provided by Skiles (1985).

For present purposes, the two most important points to bear in mind are: (1) that the magnetic lines of force have polarity (i.e. North–South); and (2) that they are only horizontal at the Earth's magnetic equator. Elsewhere on the Earth's surface the lines have an angle of dip (or inclination). They become steeper at higher latitudes and are more or less vertical at the geomagnetic poles (Fig. 8.4). In numerical terms, the angle of dip is zero at the equator and 90° at the poles.

Geomagnetic field

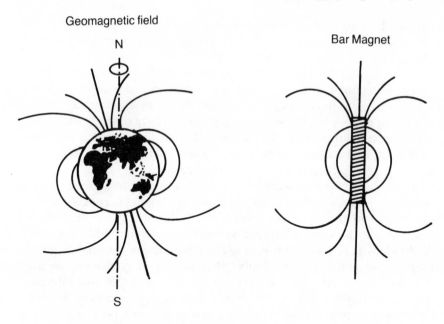

Fig. 8.4. Dipole magnetic field of Earth and bar magnet.

Wherever you are on the Earth's surface (except at the magnetic poles) a hand-held compass needle will show you the direction of North and South. The needle is pivoted so that it aligns itself horizontally along the horizontal component of the lines of force. The North-seeking (usually red-coloured) end of the needle points towards the geomagnetic North Pole; the South-seeking end (usually coloured white) points towards the geomagnetic South Pole. A person, or any other animal, with such a **polarity compass** in their head would be able to identify the direction of North (and therefore other bearings) from anywhere on the Earth's surface (Fig. 8.5) except near the magnetic poles.

However, a conventional polarity compass is not the only way of measuring compass direction. Wherever you are on the Earth's surface (except near the equator) it is also possible to use an **inclination compass**. If a person turns to face the direction in which the lines of force of the Earth's magnetic field are descending into the ground, that person will be facing the nearest geomagnetic pole; the North Pole in the Northern Hemisphere, the South Pole in the Southern Hemisphere. Alternatively, if they turn to face the direction in which the lines of force are climbing upwards, they will be facing the Earth's equator, no matter in which hemisphere they are standing. A person with such an inclination compass in their head, therefore, would be able to identify the direction of the equator and the nearest pole from anywhere on the

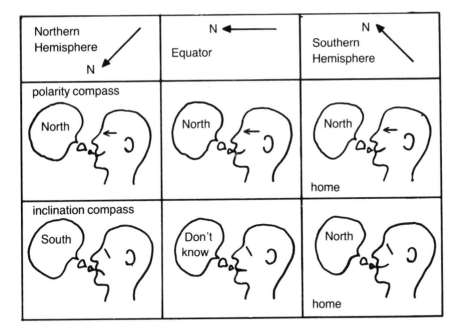

Fig. 8.5. Global use of polarity and inclination compasses. The top row illustrates the angle of inclination of the lines of force of the geomagnetic field in temperate latitudes of Northern and Southern Hemispheres and at the magnetic equator. A person from the Southern Hemisphere, familiar with the Southern Hemisphere magnetic field, could still recognise compass direction (North; South; etc.) at the equator and in the Northern Hemisphere, but only as long as he or she were using a polarity compass (middle row). A person using an inclination compass would be disoriented at the equator and misoriented by 180° in the Northern Hemisphere (bottom row).

Earth's surface (except the equator). On the equator, depending precisely on how it worked, such a compass might allow the person to identify the direction to the two poles (in other words, the pole–pole axis), but would not allow the person to know which was the North and which the South Pole. To know that, a polarity compass would be necessary.

Given that there are at least these two ways of reading the geomagnetic field, the first question to be answered is: do humans and other vertebrates use a polarity or an inclination compass?

8.2.2. *The avian compass: inclination or polarity?*
The first major step in our understanding of the physiology of vertebrate magnetoreception came when W. Wiltschko & Wiltschko (1972) demonstrated that the European Robin (*Erithacus rubecula*) uses a compass

based on inclination rather than polarity. A system of electromagnetic coils around the orientation cage in which the birds were tested allowed both the horizontal and vertical components of the magnetic field to be manipulated independently.

If the vertical component of the geomagnetic field is opposed and reversed by a stronger field produced by coils, the polarity in the horizontal plane remains the same but the lines of force disappear upwards towards the pole instead of descending into the ground. A compass needle still points to the North, but an inclination compass now finds the lines of force diving most steeply into the ground towards the equator, not the pole.

If the horizontal component of the geomagnetic field is reversed, the lines of force are now bent so that (in the Northern Hemisphere) their more northern end disappears into the ground towards the South Pole of the Earth rather than towards the North. Both a polarity and an inclination compass would be reversed, the former pointing South instead of North, the latter pointing towards the equator instead of the pole.

Finally, if both the horizontal and vertical components are reversed, the polarity of the lines is simply reversed. They still dive into the ground towards the pole, as would unaltered lines of force. Now, however (in the Northern Hemisphere), it is their more southerly end that dives into the ground. A polarity compass shows reversal but an inclination compass is unaffected, still finding the lines diving most steeply into the ground towards the pole.

In summary, both polarity and inclination compasses function effectively in an unaltered field. A polarity compass is unaffected by reversing the Earth's vertical component but is reversed if the horizontal component is reversed. An inclination compass is unaffected if both horizontal and vertical components are reversed, but is reversed if either horizontal or vertical components alone are reversed. This rather complicated set of effects is summarised in Table 8.3 and illustrated in Fig. 8.6.

W. Wiltschko & Wiltschko (1972) carried out all of these manipulations and came to the surprising conclusion that, although Robins use the alignment of the lines of force to provide themselves with a North–South axis, they determine which is its poleward end, not by using polarity but by using angle of inclination. The clearest reversal was obtained by reversing either the vertical or the horizontal component (Fig. 8.7). If both components were reversed, the robin's orientation was unaltered. Finally, in a horizontal field with polarity and alignment but with an inclination of zero degrees, such as would be experienced at the equator, orientation was uniform. Viehmann (1979) has since obtained similar results for the Blackcap (*Sylvia atricapilla*).

Table 8.3. Field manipulations to distinguish between inclination and polarity compasses

Field components		Predicted orientation	
Horizontal	Vertical	Inclination compass	Polarity compass
nil	reversed	random	random
normal	reversed	reversed	normal
normal	nil	random	normal
normal	normal	normal	normal
nil	normal	random	random
reversed	normal	reversed	reversed
reversed	nil	random	reversed
reversed	reversed	normal	reversed

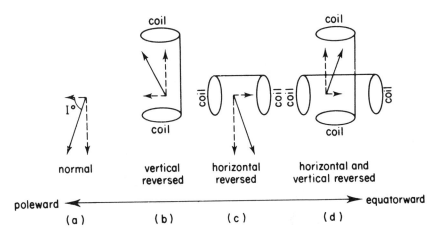

Fig. 8.6. Manipulation of polarity and inclination compasses by reversing the horizontal and vertical components of the geomagnetic field. In mid-temperate latitudes the lines of force of the geomagnetic field (solid line) are not horizontal (a) but have an angle of inclination ($I°$). These lines of force, however, can be resolved into horizontal and vertical components (dashed lines). By opposing either the horizontal or vertical component with a double-strength field generated by appropriate electromagnetic coils (b–d), one or other (b, c) or both (d) of these components can be reversed. When only the vertical component is reversed (b), an inclination compass is reversed but a polarity compass is unaffected. When only the horizontal component is reversed (c), both polarity and inclination compasses are reversed. When both horizontal and vertical components are reversed (d), a polarity compass is reversed but an inclination compass is unaffected. (An inclination compass is unaffected if the lines of force slope from top right to bottom left, irrespective of the direction the arrow is pointing, but is reversed if the lines slope from top left to bottom right. A polarity compass is reversed whenever the arrow points to the right instead of to the left.) See also Table 8.3.

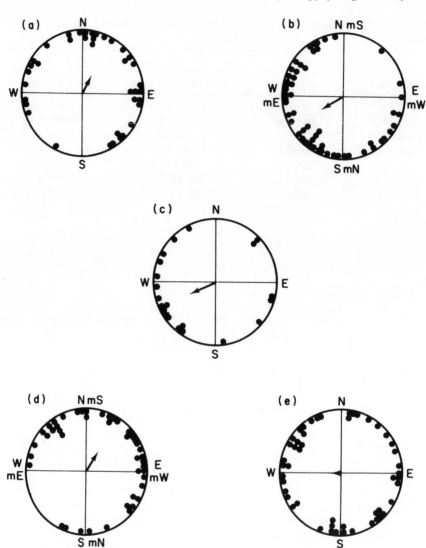

Fig. 8.7. Evidence for an inclination compass in the European Robin (*Erithacus rubecula*). Each dot shows the mean compass bearing of the activity of a single bird in an orientation cage over the course of a single night during the period of migratory restlessness in spring. In the normal geomagnetic field, Robins (in Germany) orient to the North–East (a). They continue to do so (d) when both vertical and horizontal components of the field are reversed (Fig. 8.6d). When either (b) the vertical component is reversed (Fig. 8.6b) or (c) the horizontal component is reversed (Fig. 8.6c), the Robins orient to the South–West. If the lines of force are made horizontal, orientation is random with a tendency toward bimodality (e). From Baker (1984b) after W. Wiltschko & Wiltschko (1972).

An inability to use a magnetic compass at the equator is no disadvantage to a Robin, which travels no further south than the Mediterranean in its autumn migration. The same is probably also true for Blackcaps, few of which ever reach the magnetic equator. Surprisingly, however, W. Wiltschko (1974) also found that the Garden Warbler (*Sylvia borin*), uses an inclination compass and is unable to judge direction from a horizontal magnetic field. This species breeds through most of Europe between 40° and 65°N and winters in tropical and southern Africa between the latitudes of 10°N and 30°S, with by far the largest part of its winter range lying to the South of the magnetic equator. Most Garden Warblers, therefore, during the course of their annual migrations, have to cross a zone in which the geomagnetic field is horizontal and in which their magnetic compass at best gives them only the North–South axis and at worst gives them no direction at all.

These three birds, therefore, have evolved to use a magnetic compass based on inclination rather than polarity. In so doing, they seem to have sacrificed an ability to use a magnetic compass near to the magnetic equator. For such a magnetoreceptor to persist with such an obvious disadvantage, we might suppose that it must be more than offset by some compensatory advantage. One such advantage comes to mind that would apply with particular force to seasonal migrants such as the three species so far tested.

Species of bird that show seasonal migration are born with an instinctive preference to migrate in a particular compass direction (e.g. Gwinner 1972; Berthold 1973). In the Northern Hemisphere, such birds are born with an instinctive preference to migrate more or less South in their first autumn. This preference may be overridden by parental example (e.g. Schüz 1949, 1950) but offers the bird an opportunity to travel in the optimum direction if, by chance, it finds itself needing to migrate without the company or example of older birds. Some young birds (e.g. the Eurasian Cuckoo (*Cuculus canorus*)) always have to migrate without the company of older birds. Any advantage conferred on a bird by such an innate preference would, of course, be completely negated if the Earth's magnetic field were to change in any significant way. Yet, periodically, this is precisely what does occur; or, at least, it does if the bird happens to be using a magnetic compass based on polarity!

Over the past 5 million years, the polarity of the geomagnetic field has reversed at least 23 times (Skiles 1985). The length of polarity intervals has ranged from about 20 000 years to 730 000 years with a mean of about 217 400 years. The most recent dipole reversal occurred about 730 000 years ago. The transition in polarity requires around 4000–5000 years, though the reduced field intensity that also occurs may last two to four times longer. During reversal, the field is neither dipolar nor zero.

Rather, as the intensity of the dipole component of the Earth's magnetic field decreases, other, non-dipolar components remain unaltered. The global field becomes less ordered, but local fields remain, albeit irregular and changeable. These transitional fields may not be completely chaotic and may well be dominantly quadrupolar or octopolar.

Consider a young bird of a species in the Northern Hemisphere that has evolved an instinctive urge to fly towards magnetic South on its first autumn migration but that uses a polarity compass by which to recognise South. After the next reversal (which, from the current rate of decay of the Earth's dipole component, may be less than 2000 years away; Bloxham 1986), such a bird would head North to spend an uncomfortable (and presumably brief!) winter in the Arctic. A bird that uses an inclination compass, on the other hand, would still be predisposed to fly towards the equator.

Either side of a reversal event, therefore, an inclination compass would give useful information whereas a polarity compass would not. What is not clear is to what extent, and for how long, even an inclination compass would be useless during the reversal period to a bird with an *instinctive* migratory preference. If for 4000–5000 years during each reversal the geomagnetic field offers only a mosaic of contours, rather than an ordered global field, neither a polarity nor an inclination compass would be useful to a bird with an instinctive preference. However, an animal that learns how to use the field (each individual in its own lifetime) could find a use for either compass and would not be greatly inconvenienced by geomagnetic reversals, save perhaps for the decrease in total field intensity that also occurs.

The problem of how trans-equatorial migrants among birds manage to orient as they cross the equator has yet to be resolved, though the Wiltschkos and their students continue to study the question at the University of Frankfurt. It is assumed that the technique used is: (1) to switch to other (e.g. sun and star) compass systems while crossing the rather narrow zone in which the field is perfectly horizontal; then (2) to recalibrate their magnetic compass against these other compasses once the zone has been crossed. Perhaps deviations of only 5–10° from the horizontal are all that are needed before a bird can use an inclination compass (W. Wiltschko, personal communication).

If the only advantage an inclination compass offers over a polarity compass to migrant birds is that it is useful at least on either side of geomagnetic reversal, such a compass may be of less advantage to a non-migrant bird. Here the evidence is less clear cut. Homing pigeons, descendants of North temperate zone Rock Doves (*Columba livia*), have been suggested to have an inclination compass from an observed influence of electromagnetic helmets (Walcott & Green 1974). Releases on the geomagnetic equator at noon with the sun near the zenith were not homeward oriented (Ranvaud *et al.* 1983). However, by origin, homing pigeons are from temperate regions where an inclination compass would suffer no disadvantage relative to a polarity compass. Studies of compass orientation by species of non-migratory birds that have evolved near to the geomagnetic equator would be instructive.

8.2.3. *The human compass: inclination or polarity?*

In the above context, the way that humans read the geomagnetic field could be particularly instructive, as well as of interest in its own right. Humans are probably of roughly equatorial origin and do not have an innate compass preference as a mechanism for performing annual, long-distance, trans-equatorial migrations. A polarity compass might seem to be more suited than an inclination compass to human needs. On the other hand, of course, it may be unrealistic to consider simply the type of compass that may be best suited to human navigational behaviour. Presumably we inherited our compass from non-human forebears. In the absence of strong selection for a particular type of compass, the type we possess could be there almost by default, as are many of our vertebrate and mammalian characteristics.

Since 1984, I have carried out two series of experiments aimed at testing whether humans use a polarity or inclination compass. Both series used chair experiments. One was carried out in the laboratory at Manchester; the other involved transporting subjects thousands of kilometres from both Northern and Southern Hemispheres to a test site in the Northern Hemisphere on Grand Bahama.

Laboratory studies   Under my supervision, two undergraduate students at the University of Manchester (Roz Brian, October 1985 to March 1986; Simon Bennett, October 1986 to March 1987) have attempted to repeat for humans the experiments used by the Wiltschkos (W. Wiltschko & Wiltschko 1972) to demonstrate the type of compass used by European Robins. Brian & Bennett used two sets of large Helmholtz coils to manipulate the polarity and angle of inclination of the geomagnetic field. The larger set (radius 1 m; Fig. 6.1) stood on the floor and produced a field that opposed or complemented the horizontal component of the geomagnetic field. The smaller set (radius 0.5 m) was suspended from the larger and produced a field that opposed or complemented the vertical component of the geomagnetic field. Variable resistors and a transformer allowed the angle of inclination and polarity to be adjusted while keeping total field intensity between 45 000 and 55 000 nT. Orientation of human subjects (2 male, 11 female; aged 18–22 years) was then tested using chair experiments, the chair being located so that the person's head was at about the mid-point of the smaller coils. All 13 subjects were tested in a normal field and in a field with the horizontal component reversed. Only seven were also tested in fields with reversed vertical and reversed vertical and horizontal components. The aim was to test all subjects four times in each of the fields in which they were to be tested and, with a few absentees, this was achieved. Seven of the subjects were also tested twice in a perfectly horizontal field, once with the declination unchanged (artificial N = geomagnetic N), once with it reversed (artificial N = geomagnetic S). Each test involved nine estimates of direction (Chapter 4); the interval between tests was at least 48 hours and usually 5–7 days. Sequences of field types were randomised between subjects.

All experiments were double blind. Neither experimenter nor subject knew the field setting during any particular experiment. Moreover, nobody involved in the experiment had any clear expectation or preference over what pattern of results should emerge.

Figure 8.8 compares the orientation performance with those expected if subjects were using polarity or inclination compasses. Of the two, the polarity compass hypothesis may be rejected. All field settings give results predicted by the inclination compass hypothesis except the critical setting in which both vertical and horizontal components are reversed. This anomaly is discussed further below.

Trans-equatorial displacement   When people cross the Earth's magnetic equator, they experience a change in the geomagnetic field equivalent to that experienced from reversing the vertical component in the above experiment. Thus, a person using a polarity compass should experience no difficulty in judging compass direction after crossing the equator; a person using an inclination compass, on the other hand, while still correctly recognising the direction of pole and equator, would incorrectly attach the labels 'South' and 'North' (unless they consciously reversed their estimate to allow for the fact that they have crossed the equator). Under the protocol of normal chair experiments, therefore, in which subjects use the labels 'North', 'South', 'East' and 'West', people who have crossed the equator should appear misoriented by an error of 180° until they learn to read the local field correctly.

In collaboration with the Scientific Exploration Society and Operation Raleigh, orientation experiments were performed on subjects newly arrived on Grand Bahama Island in the Caribbean. Subjects were flown from a variety of countries in both the Northern and Southern Hemispheres (Fig. 4.3). Within 36 h of arrival on Grand Bahama, all subjects took part in a walkabout experiment. At intervals during the following four weeks, subjects then took part in chair experiments. These took place in the open in woodland and involved one estimate of direction when blindfolded, one when sighted. Details of the protocol have been given in Chapter 5 (Section 5.1.1). Of necessity, testing was opportunistic

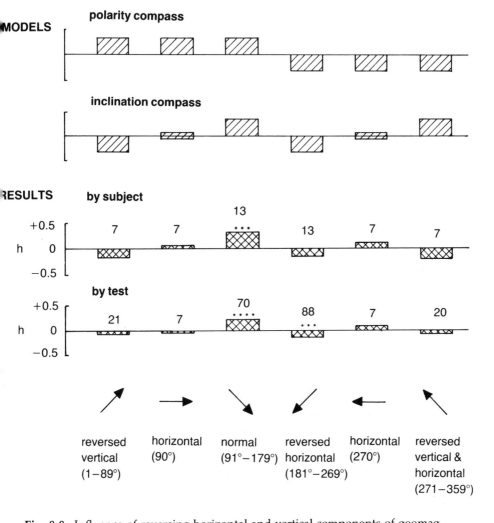

Fig. 8.8. Influence of reversing horizontal and vertical components of geomagnetic field on ability of blindfolded humans to judge compass direction in chair experiments: comparison with prediction of inclination and polarity compass hypotheses. The bottom row shows the polarity and inclination of lines of force through a subject's head produced by two pairs of large (radii: 1 m, 0.5 m, respectively) electromagnetic coils. Arrow head shows N-end of lines of force. *Models:* the top two rows show the changes in strength of orientation in true geomagnetic compass direction (i.e. beyond coils) predicted (see Table 8.3) by polarity and inclination compass hypotheses (histograms show hypothetical *h*-values). *Results:* observed changes in *h*-value analysed by test and by subject (for conventions, see Fig. 4.12; significance test for reversed horizontal data is against a predicted error of 180°). The data are a better, but not perfect, fit to the inclination compass hypothesis. Data from Brian & Bennett (unpublished).

and brief so as to fit in with subjects' other activities in connection with Operation Raleigh.

Throughout the four weeks, subjects were tested while wearing a brass bar that they were told might be a magnet. Apart from the initial walkabout, however, subjects were not exposed to magnets during this 4-week period so as not to interfere with any natural adaptation to the local geomagnetic field. At the end of the four weeks, Northern Hemisphere subjects were given magnetic pretreatment (Chapter 4) and tested within ten minutes of the magnets being removed. Results (Table 6.15) confirm that subjects were using magnetoreception to judge compass direction under the test conditions, at least while blindfolded and perhaps also while sighted.

Both Northern and Southern Hemisphere subjects had travelled several thousand kilometres to reach the test site. Both sets of subjects were unable to judge compass direction when blindfolded for two weeks after arrival on Grand Bahama (Fig. 8.9). Thereafter, blindfolded Northern Hemisphere subjects were able to use the ambient geomagnetic field for compass orientation (Table 6.15; Fig. 8.9) whereas Southern Hemisphere subjects did not. Even after four weeks on Grand Bahama, when the experiment had to end, Southern Hemisphere subjects were judging compass direction when blindfolded no better than they could have achieved by guesswork.

Discussion   Results from both laboratory and trans-equatorial experiments concur that the human magnetoreceptor does not read the magnetic field in the same way as a conventional hand-held polarity compass. Many of the results are consistent with the view that the human receptor, like the avian receptor, reads the angle of inclination of the geomagnetic field. The final proof, however, remains elusive. In neither the laboratory ($e = 112°$; $h = -0.205$; $n = 7$) nor Bahama experiments ($e = 178°$; $h = -0.235$; $n = 21$; Southern Hemisphere subjects, weeks 3–4) does reversal of the vertical component of the normal field produce significant misorientation by 180° ($P = 0.217$ and 0.064, respectively; V-test versus $e = 180°$), as should have happened with an inclination compass, though, taking the two experiments as a whole, the results are not far from significance ($P = 0.073$; combined probability).

More seriously for the inclination compass hypothesis, double reversal of field components (vertical + horizontal) does not produce orientation in the laboratory that is as good as in a normal field (Fig. 8.8). Instead, the results show disorientation, subjects again performing no better than expected from guesswork ($e = -158$; $h = -0.412$; $n = 7$; $P = 0.940$; V-test against $e = 0°$). One possible explanation for the failure of orientation in this double-reversed field is that the electromagnetic coils used

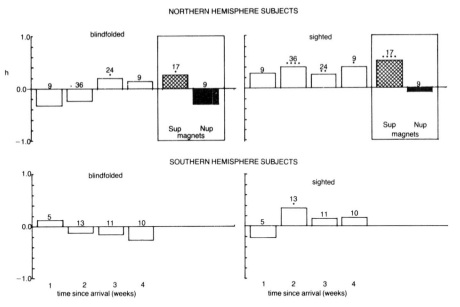

Fig. 8.9. Bahama chair experiments: ability of Northern and Southern Hemisphere subjects to judge compass direction after long-distance (>2000 km) displacement to a site in the Northern Hemisphere. Tests were carried out in the open in woodland on Grand Bahama. Each test involved one estimate of direction made while blindfolded; then one while sighted (see Chapter 4). Histograms show level of compass orientation (*h*) for subjects tested in each of the 4 weeks after arrival on Grand Bahama following long-distance displacement (Fig. 4.3). Some subjects were tested in more than one of the 4 weeks. Data are separated for subjects from Northern and Southern Hemispheres and for estimates made while blindfolded and sighted (see Fig. 4.12 for conventions). Open histograms are for subjects given 15-minute pretreatment with brass bars while continuing with normal activity. Southern Hemisphere subjects, after trans-equatorial displacement, are generally unable to recognise (and/or label correctly) North, South, East and West, even when sighted and even 4 weeks after arrival in the Northern Hemisphere. Over the 4 weeks, compass orientation by Southern Hemisphere subjects when sighted was significantly weaker than that by Northern Hemisphere subjects ($z = 1.894$; P (1-tailed) = 0.029; $N = 78$, 39; analysed by test). When blindfolded, orientation was not significantly weaker during the first 2 weeks ($z = -0.900$; P (1-tailed) = 0.816; $N = 45$, 18) but was during the second 2 weeks ($z = 2.122$; P (1-tailed) = 0.017; $N = 33$, 21). Blindfolded Northern Hemisphere subjects are misoriented by 180° until 2 weeks after displacement; thereafter they are significantly oriented. During the fourth week, 26 Northern Hemisphere subjects (E–W sleepers) were pretreated with Nup or Sup magnets rather than brass bars. Protocol was double-blind. Magnets had a significant influence both when blindfolded ($z = 2.403$; P (1-tailed) = 0.008) and when sighted ($z = 1.793$; P (1-tailed) = 0.036). Moreover, subjects pretreated with disruptive Nup magnets were unable to recognise compass direction whether blindfolded or sighted. Data from Baker (unpublished).

in our laboratory do not produce a field that, by virtue of some unknown factor, is a suitable match to the normal dc field of the Earth. For
example, although the ac mains electricity was passed through an ac–dc
transformer before entering the coils, it is possible that the field was not
sufficiently as static as the Earth's field. The result could be a field that
was unreadable by the receptor, thus leading to disorientation. Against
this explanation are two other facts: the same coils, when used simply
to reverse the horizontal component, led to misorientation by 180°,
rather than disorientation. Secondly, Southern Hemisphere subjects,
transported across the equator to the Bahamas, produced an orientation
response about equivalent to that observed in the appropriate (reversed
vertical) artificial laboratory field in Manchester (i.e. disorientation, with
a tendency to reversal).

The laboratory experiment will be continued with further subjects
and, inevitably, different experimenters. Clearly, it would be premature
to conclude that the human magnetoreceptor does not function as a
simple inclination compass comparable to that of birds. For the moment,
however, the possibility has to be considered that the human magnetoreceptor simply cannot read a field that is either horizontal or which
has a vertical component reversed relative to that in which the receptor
normally functions. In other words, while not reading polarity, nor does
the receptor simply read inclination. Even four weeks was insufficient
time for Southern Hemisphere subjects to read a Northern Hemisphere
magnetic field, even though they had been able to judge direction when
sighted (Fig. 8.9). Perhaps the period of significant misorientation by
180° by *Northern Hemisphere* subjects during the second week after arrival
on Grand Bahama is also a clue as to the problem experienced by the
magnetoreceptor after long-distance travel.

8.2.4. *What is read: orientation within the field or changes in orientation?*
Even when perfectly stationary, a normal, *hand-held* polarity compass
indicates magnetic declination and, presumably, the same could be true
for the compass in the head. Thus, an animal could detect its orientation
within the geomagnetic field without moving. From time to time, however, students of avian magnetoreception have concluded that birds
need to move through the geomagnetic field in order to sense direction
(e.g. Bookman 1978; Wallraff & Gelderloos 1978). Bookman, for example,
showed that homing pigeons could be conditioned to the geomagnetic
field if free to move but not if strapped down. Perhaps most significantly, the neurophysiological studies by Peter Semm and his colleagues (Semm *et al.* 1984; Semm 1988) showed that nerves from the eye
of the homing pigeon would only fire in response to changes in the
ambient magnetic field if the head also moved, thus triggering input
from the vestibular system.

If magnetoreception does require the animal (or, more precisely, the magnetoreceptor) to move through the ambient magnetic field, it could indicate that the magnetoreceptor is measuring changes in its relationship to the ambient field, rather than the stationary field itself. In this context, experiments in which a fixed artificial field is applied through the head while the animal is detecting the field might be crucial. This is because the fixed field only changes the stationary field experienced by the animal at any given time. However, the contribution of this fixed field to the total field is constant. *Changes* in the field through the receptor as the head moves through the ambient field remain entirely due to changes in the animal's orientation within the ambient field. This is no different from what applies to an animal without a fixed artificial field through the head. It is more than possible, therefore, that if the magnetoreceptor responds, not to the ambient field itself, but to the animal's changes relative to the ambient field, a fixed field through the head might be totally transparent to the animal. Direction may be judged just as accurately with a fixed artificial field through the head as with no artificial field.

In the light of these considerations, it might seem a simple matter to test whether the magnetoreceptor detects simply its orientation within the ambient field or changes within the ambient field. If it does the former, a fixed field through the head will be effective in generating misorientation. If it does the latter, such a field will be ineffective.

The fixed fields produced by electromagnetic helmets may have been totally ineffective in producing misorientation (Section 6.2), supporting the view that the human magnetoreceptor, perhaps like its avian counterpart, detects changes in its orientation relative to the ambient field. However, there were indications that electromagnetic helmets may sometimes have been effective (Section 6.2) and no doubt that bar magnets, which also produced a fixed field through the head, were effective (Section 6.3). In both cases, however, the observed effects may have been due, not to the influence of the treatment on the field being sensed, as would be of interest here, but to an action of producing changes in the magnetoreceptor itself. When bar magnets are removed, even a normal field cannot be read accurately (Section 6.4).

The evidence, therefore, is still not clear. In any case, I prefer, and now offer, a hypothesis for the way magnetoreceptors read the geomagnetic field that not only assumes they detect changes in their orientation relative to the ambient field, but at the same time predicts that a fixed field through the head may not be transparent.

8.2.5. *How the field is read: a hypothesis*
Suppose, in using some form of inclination compass, an animal, in effect, needs to identify the direction in which the lines of force through

the head pass through at a particular angle (e.g. when the animal was facing North). Suppose that, when facing this direction, the magnetoreceptor gave its maximum neural signal; when facing the opposite direction, its minimum. Sensing direction might thus involve the animal turning its head (through up to 180°, depending on starting orientation) in effect to scan the different directions and identify that of maximum (or minimum) signal. In the above example, this position would be that of North (or South). On such a system, it is quite possible that the magnetoreceptor detects only two positions out of the 360°; directions of maximum and minimum signal. Quite possibly, intermediate directions might be judged in interaction with the vestibular system: the magnetoreceptor detects the direction of maximum or minimum signal, the vestibular system judges how far from one of these directions the head has to turn to face the current intermediate direction.

Any such system as this requires movement of the head through the ambient field for two reasons: (1) to allow the magnetoreceptor to scan the field to determine the direction of maximum or minimum signal; and (2) to allow the vestibular system (or, perhaps, neck receptors) to judge the angle of turn between this direction and the direction of travel or orientation. As amplified below, in Section 8.3, however, maximum or minimum signal is postulated to derive from the relative alignment of: (a) something within the magnetoreceptor; and (b) the lines of force of the ambient field. Movement of the magnetoreceptor is important, but so too is the actual alignment of the net ambient field.

With such a system for magnetoreception, a fixed field through the head may or may not be transparent to the receptor. Everything will depend on how much the component due to the fixed field obliterates any modulation from maximum to minimum signal from the receptor and how much it rotates the actual direction of maximum and minimum signal. As such, the rather confused results in Sections 6.2 and 6.3 for experiments with electromagnetic helmets or bar magnets on the head are quite compatible with the hypothesis.

8.3. *The influence of magnets*

8.3.1. *The aftereffect*
Bar magnets, placed on the head, have a significant influence on compass orientation and navigation. However, this influence is not simply due to the magnets altering the field that the magnetoreceptor is trying to read. This is evident from the observation that magnets continue to have an effect on orientation for some time after the magnet is removed (Figs 6.7 and 6.8).

Figure 8.10 shows, in simplified form, the curve of recovery from a 10- to 15-minute exposure to 10–20-mT bar magnets, illustrating the way

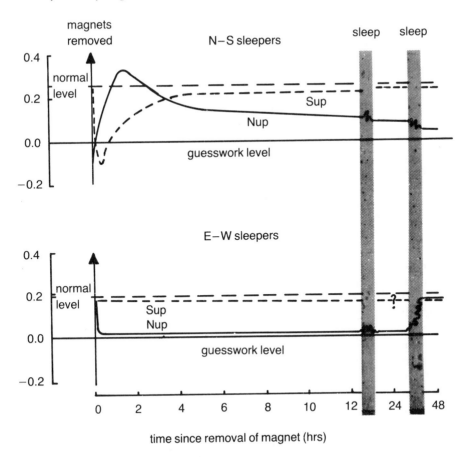

Fig. 8.10. Ability of blindfolded subjects to judge compass direction in chair experiments: change with time after exposure to magnets aligned vertically on the right temple. Solid line, Nup magnets; dashed line, Sup magnets. Curves of *h*-value shown separately for N–S and E–W sleepers. Diagram is a simplified and interpretative version of the data in Fig. 6.8.

that the pattern of recovery is a function of magnet polarity and bed orientation of subjects.

The data in Fig. 8.10 show the recovery from a 10- to 15-minute exposure to bar magnets of fixed strength. Between October 1985 and March 1986, under my supervision, Karen Perchard measured the influence of exposure of N–S and E–W sleepers to different strengths of vertical field generated by electromagnetic coils. The field was polarised N down, as would be experienced at the Northern Hemisphere geomagnetic pole and as experienced by a magnetoreceptor alongside the central part of a Nup bar magnet. Sighted subjects were exposed to the artificial field for 5 minutes and then tested immediately afterwards (i.e. 0–10 minutes) for ability to judge compass direction when blindfolded in chair experiments. Her results are given in Fig. 8.11 and show that after an apparent initial enhancement by a weak field, increasing strength of field produced a gradually decreasing strength of orientation.

The only reasonable explanation for the aftereffect is that the magnetic field due to the bar magnet has in some persistent way altered some part of the process by which the magnetoreceptor reads the ambient field. This persistence could be due to an influence of the bar magnet on either: (a) the magnetoreceptor itself; or (b) some part of the process by which neural signals from the magnetoreceptor are carried to the central nervous system, decoded, and integrated with information from other sensory systems. However, while not ruling out the latter, the fact that the nature of the aftereffect is a function of magnet polarity and bed orientation would seem to make the former the more likely.

There is some tenuous evidence that aspects of human physiology are influenced by compass orientation during sleep. For example, electro-encephalogram studies have shown that human brain rhythms during sleep are influenced by bed alignment (Kotleba *et al.* 1973). The only reasonable explanation (other than chance) is that some aspects of human physiology are a function of orientation within the geomagnetic field. One possibility, therefore, for the way that the aftereffect is a function of magnet polarity and bed orientation, is that some feature of the magnetoreceptor is in some way set during sleep into a pattern that differs for N–S sleepers and E–W sleepers. These patterns then interact with magnets of different alignments and polarities to produce the patterns illustrated in Figs 8.10 and 8.11. Given that the pattern is susceptible to change by an applied magnetic field, it seems reasonable to suppose that the initial pattern setting is also an effect of the ambient magnetic field.

The only ambient field normally available during sleep is the geo-magnetic field. There is a problem, however, with the view that the geomagnetic field fixes some feature of the magnetoreceptor during 8 hours of relative horizontal immobility overnight. Any feature set during this period would surely be altered during the 16 hours of relative activity while vertical within the geomagnetic field the following day. This daytime influence would surely, for most people, generate a new pattern that would be different from, but perhaps still a function of, that produced by overnight bed orientation.

It is difficult to discuss the aftereffect any further in general terms. However, as Walcott (1982) argued with respect to the possibility of a similar aftereffect in homing pigeons (Chapter 3), there are clear implications for the magnetite hypothesis of magnetoreception.

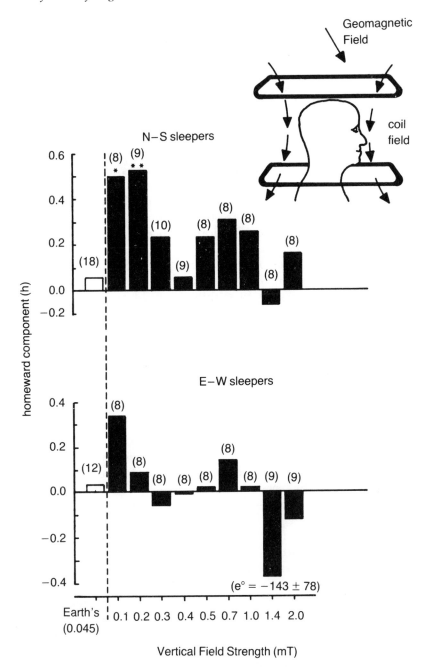

Fig. 8.11. Compass orientation by blindfolded subjects in chair experiments, 0–10 min after a 5-minute exposure to a vertical N-down field of different strengths generated by electromagnetic coils (0.5 m radius) around the head. Histogram shows *h*-values for N–S and E–W sleepers. Increasing strength of treatment leads to greater levels of disorientation or, for E–W sleepers, perhaps misorientation. Data from Perchard (unpublished).

8.3.2. *The aftereffect and the magnetite hypothesis*

For many people (see papers in Kirschvink *et al.* 1985a), of all the hypotheses reviewed in Chapter 3, the one with the greatest lure is that of a magnetoreceptor based on magnetite. In the present context, the proposal would be that the human magnetoreceptor, located somewhere in the front half of the head, consists of an array of magnetite particles. These share common alignment and are ramified by nerves which communicate with the central nervous system. As this array of magnetic particles moves within the geomagnetic field, electric, magnetic or pressure events take place, the pattern of which is a function of the head's orientation within the geomagnetic field. This invokes a patterned firing of the ramifying nerves that, when relayed to the central nervous system, is decoded into directional information. This, in turn, is integrated with other directional information being relayed by other sensory systems (Chapter 3).

As described in Chapter 3, the particles could be free to rotate as the head turns or they could be fixed in some semi-persistent way so that they retain their alignment within the head as the head turns. As Perchard (Fig. 8.11) found that stronger fields produced greater aftereffects, it seems the more likely that the particles are fixed rather than simply free to rotate. Let us assume, therefore, that the array of particles (if such an array exists) is actually fixed in some resistant material. In normal magnetoreception, therefore, the particles will actually move relative to the Earth's field and not simply stay aligned with the Earth's field as the head turns (as would a normal, hand-held compass needle). Presumably, however, although the particles are held in a matrix such that they are resistant to realignment during normal movement within the geomagnetic field, realignment may occur if the ambient field is strong enough and/or exposure is long enough.

Reconciliation of the observed characteristics of the aftereffect (Chapter 6) with the magnetite hypothesis may now proceed along the following lines.

Overnight, the geomagnetic field influences the alignment of particles within the magnetite array. Either existing particles are aligned or realigned, or new particles are laid down with an alignment dictated by the ambient field (Baker 1985a). The result is that each person obtains an array of particles aligned with a polarity and axis determined by the combined influence of that person's bed orientation and sleeping habits. How much time a person spends on their back, front or left and right sides, how much they roll from side to side or curl into a ball may all influence their particular net alignment of particles. However, we cannot rule out more sophisticated physiological mechanisms, such as new magnetite particles being laid down only when the person is on their back.

Each person will have their own individual alignment of array (though broad categories should exist, such as according to bed orientation). The result is that the signal received by different people when, for example, they turn to face North, will be different. Putting this in the context of the model introduced above in Section 8.2.5, different people will obtain the maximum signal from their magnetoreceptor when facing different directions. For some people, maximum signal will be when facing North, others when facing South–West, and so on. Each person, there-fore, has to learn the pattern of signals generated by their own array as they face in different directions. Any sudden, enforced change in alignment of particles, if it produces a different pattern of signals, will lead either to disorientation (if either no clear maximum signal is pro-duced in any direction or a clear maximum is produced in several directions) or misorientation (if, for example, a clear maximum signal that used to be generated when facing West is now generated when facing North–East).

Such a model could make sense of pretreatment results such as those illustrated in Fig. 7.1. There it is only necessary to postulate that, in the 15 minutes or so between removal of Nup magnets and testing, the direction of maximum signal slowly shifted through 100° or so.

The magnetite hypothesis would continue, therefore, that exposure to bar magnets and their strong (from 4 to 200 times Earth strength in the case of the bar magnets used at Manchester, depending on whether the sense organ is in the centre of the head or near the right temple) magnetic fields produces just such a sudden change in particle alignment. The result is dis- or misorientation, as explained. Karen Perchard's discovery that the extent of disorientation depends on the strength of the applied field could imply that realignment is a gradual and graded response, as if the particles are being rotated against a resistance, such as a viscous matrix. Thus, the stronger the field the further the particles are rotated away from their natural alignment and towards alignment with the artificial ambient field. Unfortunately, we do not yet have data on variation in aftereffect according to length of exposure to applied fields of different strengths.

The observation (Fig. 8.10) that disorientation persists after the mag-net is removed implies that the array of magnetite particles do not imme-diately revert back to their original alignment. On the other hand, the fact that changes do occur and that perhaps there is even some sem-blance of recovery within two hours after exposure implies that the new alignment produced by the applied field is only temporary. Figure 8.10 rather suggests that orientation is almost normal again after 2–6 hours, though it is not absolutely clear that recovery is total until 48 hours or so have elapsed (Fig. 6.7).

The change in pattern of performance at orientation in the hours immediately following exposure to magnets seems most likely to be due to the influence of the geomagnetic field on the alignment of the magnetite particles (though, just conceivably, it could be due to some self-restoring property of the magnetite array or some 'elastic' property of the matrix in which the magnetite particles are embedded). Whether we should consider the changes that take place in the hours immediately after exposure as true 'recovery', however, is a moot point. Only N–S sleepers exposed to Nup magnets actually seem to 'recover' under the influence of the geomagnetic field after exposure, and even these seem to pass through a phase of orientation before once more becoming disoriented (Fig. 8.10). N–S sleepers exposed to Sup magnets actually become disoriented with time after the magnet is removed. E–W sleepers are either unaffected (by Sup magnets) or are disoriented (by Nup magnets) with no indication of recovery on the day of exposure. Actual 'recovery' seems to require one or more night's sleep.

Suppose that the changes that occur immediately after the bar magnets are removed are due to an influence of the geomagnetic field on the alignment of the previously manipulated particles. Then perhaps we should also accept that, even in normal daytime activity, the geomagnetic field acts gradually to change the alignment of particles achieved during sleep. Alternatively, we could postulate that the geomagnetic field only realigns particles during the day if the magnetoreceptor has been exposed to, perhaps even damaged by, strong, applied, magnetic fields.

There is yet another way we could postulate that the geomagnetic field is adequate to affect particle alignment overnight, but does not then alter alignment significantly during normal activity by day. Suppose there is a diel rhythm of resorption-of-old and deposition-of-new magnetite particles within the magnetoreceptor. Deposition is greatest, or even confined to, periods of sleep, perhaps when the person is in a particular position (e.g. on their back). The matrix within which the particles are held goes through a diel cycle of softening and hardening so that there is resistance to change in particle alignment during the person's daytime activities, but the possibility of realignment and particle deposition at night.

The process of realignment and deposition overnight may be seen as a form of tissue repair, the correction of any problems raised, for example, by the clumping of magnetite particles (perhaps through knocks to the head as well as magnetic influences) that may have occurred since the previous night (Baker 1984b). As the only fields normally experienced by humans throughout evolution will have been little different in intensity from the geomagnetic field, we should expect evolution to have set the threshold of matrix viscosity rather finely either side of that necessary level. Even marginally stronger applied fields may therefore be effective in producing realignment and/or damage. Only if the array is forcibly changed, perhaps damaged, during the day, such as by exposure to strong magnetic fields, does a contingency response of matrix softening and realignment of old or deposition of new particles set in by day rather than night.

Such a model would require that the array is a site of considerable generation of magnetite from magnetite precursors. Kuterbach *et al.* (1982) have shown for Honey Bees that, in the region of the abdomen that shows magnetic remanence due to magnetite (Gould *et al.* 1978), there are deposits of a ferric material that has been identified as hydrous iron oxides. These could be biochemical precursors of magnetite. Such hydrous iron oxides are often biological storage materials for iron and are precursors to magnetite formation in chitons and magnetotactic bacteria (Towe & Lowenstam 1967; Frankel *et al.* 1979). Only 0.33% of the iron visible in the bee's abdomen need be magnetite to account for the level of remanence in the region (Kuterbach *et al.* 1982). The observations could well indicate that the site of this putative magnetoreceptor in Honey Bees is one of considerable turnover of magnetite particles, as postulated here for humans.

Consider the model. The human magnetoreceptor consists of an array of magnetite particles, fixed by a viscous matrix into a resistant alignment throughout the day, realigned and redeposited in a softened matrix during sleep at night (or when damaged). These aligned particles move through the geomagnetic field when the head turns. When facing a particular direction, the alignment of the particles within the array and the alignment of the lines of force of the geomagnetic field interact to generate a maximum neural signal which the individual has learned means he or she is facing a particular direction.

To me (naturally), the model is both pleasing and seductive. No part of the observed characteristics of the human magnetoreceptor described in Chapters 5 to 7 potentially cannot be accommodated by such a model. Nevertheless, a word of caution is necessary. In the wider context of investigation into animal magnetoreception, there are problems.

8.3.3. *A case against the magnetite hypothesis*
The scientific and lay press still show considerable interest, verging even on excitement, every time there is a new report of the discovery of magnetite in a particular animal or tissue. Much less coverage is given to the more negative discoveries. Yet, the fact remains that the presence of magnetite in specific tissue is proving to be notoriously inconsistent. For example, magnetite in the dura of the first few homing pigeons examined by Walcott *et al.* (1979) was not present in the next 80 (Walcott & Walcott 1982); nor could magnetite at this site be found by other authors (Presti & Pettigrew 1980) though it was reported from the neck

muscles. Presti & Pettigrew found greater magnetic remanence in the heads of long-distance migrant birds than among residents. However, Ueda *et al.* (1982) found no significant magnetic remanence in either. Histological studies of the pigeon head (Walcott & Walcott 1982) found little consistency in the location of deposits of ferric iron. Kuterbach *et al.* (1982) were unable to demonstrate magnetite among ferric deposits in the abdomen of Honey Bees where magnetic remanence had previously been reported (Gould *et al.* 1978).

In my own studies, the apparent ferric deposits that were such a conspicuous feature of the sinus bones of human corpses were not evident in ethmoid sinus bones removed from a living person (Baker, Kennaugh & Canty, unpublished). Perhaps (Boyde, personal communication) the ferric deposits we observed in corpses (Baker *et al.* 1983) were artefacts due to breakdown products of haemoglobin and a 2-day delay between death and fixation. Certainly, proton probe analysis of *unstained* sinus bones from human corpses also failed to find a layer of ferric iron (Baker 1985a) as did electron microscopy of the analogous ethmoturbinal bones of Woodmice (Jorgenson, in Mather 1985).

Bees without single-domain magnetite nevertheless appear to show magnetic sensitivity (Gould *et al.* 1980). Salmon fry, although able to orient to the ambient magnetic field, show no significant magnetic remanence (Ueda *et al.* 1982). Cave salamanders, which are sensitive to magnetic fields (Phillips & Adler 1978), show no consistent ferric deposits other than at the base of the teeth (Walcott & Walcott 1982).

An inability to find magnetite in a particular animal may, of course, mean only that the material is present in quantities too small to detect. Such small amounts may nevertheless be sufficient for magnetoreception (Kirschvink 1982). Even so, the continuing absence of a demonstrable link between magnetite and magnetoreception, magnetite's erratic occurrence and distribution in animal tissue and its possible absence in animals capable of magnetoreception, all suggest that the current excitement surrounding the magnetite hypothesis as applied to all vertebrates may be premature.

8.3.4. *Discussion*

The observed influence of magnets on human magnetoreception requires that the receptor must have the following characteristics: (1) a physical basis in a pattern that varies between individuals and is dictated by orientation during sleep; (2) normal resistance to realignment by the geomagnetic field during the day; (3) proneness to realignment by stronger applied fields followed by reduced resistance to realignment by the geomagnetic field; and (4) a response to applied fields that is a function of the polarity of the applied fields.

The characteristics of magnetite, if held in a viscous matrix, could nicely fit, or be made to fit, these characteristics. Yet the world-wide push to demonstrate that magnetite is the basis of vertebrate magneto-reception is currently foundering on a bed of inconsistencies. It has to be admitted that, though it remains a persuasive idea, there is still not a scrap of positive evidence to link vertebrate magnetoreception with a magnetoreceptor based on magnetite. In contrast, there is increasing evidence that the magnetoreceptor of birds and mammals is located in the visual system and is linked in some way to the perception of light (Section 8.1.3).

In searching for alternatives to magnetite that would still accommodate a patterned aftereffect as observed (Fig. 8.10), two suggestions have emerged. Adey (personal communication) points out that the pattern of distribution of calcium ions on cell membranes is altered by an applied magnetic field and that the change persists for several hours after the applied field is removed. Similarly, Leask (personal communication) has pointed out that the triplet states of some large molecules may also persist long enough to generate an aftereffect. Such suggestions at least hold out the hope that there are avenues to pursue other than magnetite; avenues that would link with the neurophysiological evidence for birds.

Whether the resistant pattern or 'alignment' that seems to lie at the heart of the magnetoreceptor consists of molecular triplet states, calcium ions, magnetite or whatever, there are still details that remain unexplained and elusive. I have tried persistently to produce a detailed version of the model developed in Section 8.3.2; a version that would accommodate not only the way that different magnetic fields are read (Section 8.2) but also the precise interactions of bed orientation and magnetic treatment that are observed. My first model (Baker 1984a) predicted that N sleepers and S sleepers should respond oppositely to the polarity of magnetic pretreatment. Initial data were encouraging (Baker 1984a) but first Murphy (1987) and now I have shown that this does not happen. N and S sleepers respond to magnetic pretreatment similarly, but differently from E and W sleepers. It is the *axis* of bed orientation that is important, not its polarity (Chapter 6). Yet the polarity of magnets *is* important.

It would help if certain basic decisions could be made. For example: (1) would maximum signal be generated when the alignments of magnetoreceptor and lines of force are parallel or at right angles; (2) need we consider only the axes of the two alignments or must the polarity of one or both components also be considered; (3) when a given pretreatment has no effect (e.g. Sup magnets on E–W sleepers), does it indicate that the alignment of the applied field exactly matches that of the particle array; and (4) is at least the alignment of particles during sleep proposed in Fig. 8.12 correct?

Perhaps the final completion of the jigsaw is not far away.

8.4. *Clinical considerations*

All known senses differ in their levels of acuity from person to person. The major part of this variation is due to normal variation about the population mean. More extreme departures (e.g. blindness, deafness) from the population mean, however, are often symptoms of some clinical condition, either genetic, infectious, or induced. It would be a surprise if magnetoreception did not share these clinical characteristics.

For convenience, the following discussion is divided into three headings. In reality, the distinctions may be far less clear and the headings should not be taken too literally.

8.4.1. *Genetic deficiencies in magnetoreception*

In the loosest sense, both dyslexia and agoraphobia involve spatial problems: dyslexics confuse things with lateral symmetry, particularly letters and words, but also 'right/left'; agoraphobics have a morbid fear of being away from their home base. In each case, at the request of organisations studying these two conditions, we have considered the problem from the point of view of defective magnetoreception.

Working with Gai Murphy and Sarah Bird, I carried out two major series of chair experiments on dyslexics and their families attending a clinic in Watford, UK. Some non-dyslexic controls were recruited from visitors to an open day at the clinic. The tests were blind in the sense that the experimenters did not know which of their subjects were dyslexic and which were not. Moreover, even non-dyslexic subjects did not know if they were expected to perform well, for all subjects were fitted with a brass bar on the head which they were told could be a magnet which might disrupt their ability to judge direction. Ages ranged from 6 to 60 years and the sex ratio was about even.

Dyslexic subjects performed no worse than the wider population (Table 8.4) and in fact performed marginally but not significantly better than non-dyslexic, unrelated controls. The parents of dyslexic subjects, however, performed no better than expected from guesswork; in fact, there was a tendency for them to be misoriented by nearly 180° (Table 8.4).

There is no evidence here of genetic magnetoreceptive deficiency. The intriguing possibility that dyslexics may have misoriented parents perhaps merits further investigation.

Our consideration of the problem of agoraphobia has not progressed far. Large-scale experiments of the type performed on dyslexics are out of the question for chronic agoraphobics, resistant as they are to leaving their own homes. Home tests on enough subjects are impracticable and might also be resisted when subjects are at the peak of their symptoms. Despite liaison with agoraphobia societies, the problem of how to test the magnetoreceptive ability of agoraphobics has not yet been solved. The only, albeit extremely tenuous, link so far is the observation that

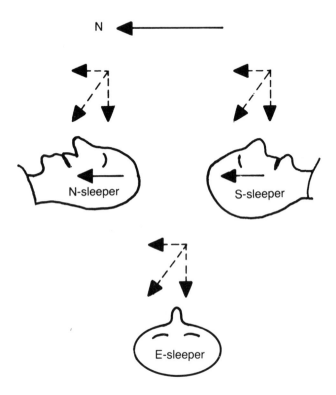

Fig. 8.12. A model of the influence of bed orientation on the alignment of magnetic particles in the human magnetoreceptor. Horizontal and vertical components (dashed arrows) of the geomagnetic field are shown for a location in mid-temperate latitudes in the Northern Hemisphere. As a N-sleeper rolls from side to side during sleep, the vertical component cancels out giving a net alignment as shown. In consequence, when a N sleeper stands and walks around during the day, any dipole in the head will more or less complement the geomagnetic field. When a S sleeper stands, any dipole will be opposed to the geomagnetic field. As E–W sleepers roll from side to side during sleep, both vertical and horizontal components cancel out. Net alignment results only if the person spends asymmetric times during sleep on right or left sides *or* if realignment and particle deposition only occur while the person is in a particular posture (e.g. on the back). From Baker (1984a).

Table 8.4 Ability of dyslexic subjects, their parents and other relatives to judge compass direction in chair experiments

	Dyslexics				Parents				Other relatives			
	N	$e \pm CI$	h	P (V-test)	N	$e \pm CI$	h	P (V-test)	N	$e \pm CI$	h	P (V-test)
Males	29	36 ± 51°	0.269	0.020	14	156°	−0.125	0.749	22	22°	0.055	0.356
Females	11	−80°	0.035	0.434	26	−129°	−0.022	0.564	21	48°	0.036	0.407
Total	40	23 ± 81°	0.205	0.034	40	179°	−0.058	0.699	43	34°	0.046	0.335

Significant orientation (V-test) underlined.

Data from R.R. Baker, Gai Murphy, Sarah Bird and Violet Brand (unpublished).

agoraphobia is most common in females and symptoms peak premen-strually. Chair experiments by Angela Ganss & Pam Walker (1982/83), Judith Ogden (1983/84) and Karen Tricker (1984/85) on 12 female subjects over four menstrual cycles suggested that orientation performance troughs premenstrually. The possibility of a specific cycle of magnetore-ceptive acuity, however, cannot be separated from the possibility that more general physiological aspects (e.g. of concentration or comfort) are the main factors.

Judge (1985) at Albany, USA, found no evidence of any ability at magnetoreception in visually handicapped subjects. Sample size was small (9) and the distance to the test site was long (> 40 km). Orientation that could not statistically be separated from guesswork would be expected even for non-handicapped people (Table 5.13). Nevertheless, an open mind should perhaps be kept on the possibility of a link between visual and magnetoreceptive 'blindness'.

8.4.2. *Infections of the magnetoreception system*
So far, there is nothing in our data to show that any infectious disease influences the acuity of magnetoreception. Nor have we yet examined whether disease such as the cold or other virus reduce performance in chair, bus or walkabout experiments.

8.4.3. *Self- and environmentally induced interference with magnetoreception*

Self-induced Smoking, nose sprays and clothing made of polyester material are all associated with poor performance in navigation and orientation tasks. In no case, however, has it been proved that the influence is specifically on magnetoreception rather than generally on performance. Indeed, in the case of smoking, Bambridge & Moss (Section 8.1.4) have demonstrated that the influence is probably simply that of a habit or drug on general performance.

Exposure of the head to strong magnetic fields, as in pretreatment experiments (Chapters 4 and 6), has a clear influence specifically on magnetoreception. Although many treatments induce disorientation, enough produce misorientation (e.g. Figs 6.6, 7.4, 7.8) for there to be no doubt that we are dealing with a specific influence on magneto-reception, not simply general performance. In their everyday lives, many people expose themselves to magnetic fields as strong, or stronger, than those experienced in orientation and navigation experi-ments. Many people's employment involves working in strong magnetic fields (Barnothy 1964; Ketchen *et al.* 1978). Moreover, the recent popularity of personal portable stereo radios and tape players, complete with magnetic headphones, means that even in their recreation a growing number of people are exposing their heads to strong magnetic fields.

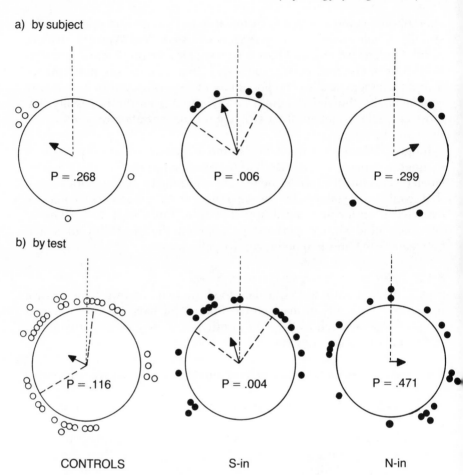

Fig. 8.13. Influence of stereo headphones on ability of blindfolded female subjects to judge compass direction in chair experiments. Each subject was tested eight times with a set of headphones with magnet removed; four times with the magnet polarity S-in (as bought) and four times with the magnets reversed (N-in). Each dot in the bottom row is the mean error of estimates by a person in a single test (nine estimates); each dot in the top row the mean error per person over all tests (36 or 72 estimates). None of the differences is formally significant. (Controls vs S-in: $z = 1.081$; P (2-tailed) = 0.280. Controls vs N-in: $z = 0.481$; P (2-tailed) = 0.631. N-in vs S-in: $z = 1.729$; P (2-tailed) = 0.084. Wallraff's test (analysis by test, not subject.) Data from Doyle (unpublished).

Headphones are normally placed over the ears. In our experiments in which the location of magnets was varied (Baker 1984b), magnets behind the ears had an apparently slight but non-significant effect; magnets in front of the ears had a significant effect that persists for up to 6–48 hours after the magnet is removed. Under my supervision, between October 1986 and March 1987, Katrina Doyle tested six female subjects in chair experiments to test for an influence of headphones. Each subject was tested 12 times: eight times with a pair of headphones with the magnets removed; four times with a pair with the magnets as bought (N pole out); four times with the magnets removed and replaced with reversed polarity (N pole in). The results are shown in Fig. 8.13. The polarity of the magnets in the headphones had an influence that was on the verge of significance, N-ins tending to disorient, S-ins tending to enhance, relative to controls. This experiment was not double blind, the experimenter, though not the subject, knowing the design of the experiment and which set of headphones was being used in any particular test. The fact that S-in magnets tended to enhance, when both experimenter and her subjects would have expected disruption, implies that the experimenter did not influence the results, at least not in the direction that would have matched her prejudices.

A popular experiment that has been carried out at Manchester concerns the possibility that alcohol may influence magnetoreceptive acuity. Some volunteers expressed the expectation that they would be found to navigate equally as well, if not better, after drinking alcohol as before. The research hypothesis, however, was the converse: alcohol would lead to a deterioration in performance. Two series of experiments have been carried out: Jade Davidson (1983/84) used chair experiments; I used a bus experiment (June 1986).

Davidson's experiment took place in the evenings, after 19.00 h GMT, in her apartment at Hulme, Manchester. Volunteers were tested in the chair, then given a drink. Half an hour later, they were tested again, and given another drink. The experiment lasted 2 hours. Some subjects were given 70 ml of vodka, with 100 ml of dry ginger mixer; other subjects were given 70 ml of water with 100 ml of mixer. The experimenter, but not the subject, knew which drink had been given; the experiment was therefore only single blind. Results are shown in Fig. 8.14. Sample size (five controls, six experimentals) was small and subjects were mainly male. Both controls and experimentals deteriorated in performance over the course of the evening; those drinking alcohol deteriorated faster and more severely, but the differences were not significant ($P > 0.05$).

In my own bus experiment, a group of 40 subjects were driven by bus from the University of Manchester to Delamere Forest (39 km away) where they took part in a walkabout experiment. After the experiment

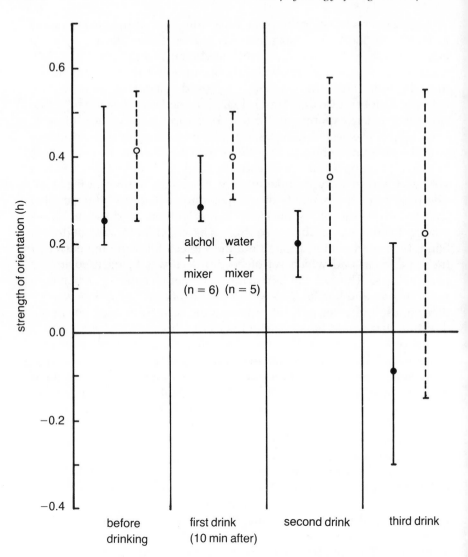

Fig. 8.14. Influence of increasing amounts of alcohol on ability to judge compass direction in chair experiments during the course of a single night. Figure shows median and inter-quartile ranges of h-values for five controls (open dots) and six experimentals (solid dots), 10 minutes after each of 0–3 drinks at 30-minute intervals. Controls drank 50 ml water +100 ml ginger; experimentals drank 50 ml vodka +100 ml ginger every 30 minutes. Performance by subjects drinking alcohol deteriorates faster than that by controls, but differences are not significant. Data from Davidson (unpublished).

was over, the subjects were taken to a public house for 'refreshments', unaware that this was part of a second experiment. The group stayed for 3 hours at the inn, during the course of which some subjects drank no alcohol, others drank up to 12 units (1 unit = half a pint of bitter, etc. or 1 measure of gin/whisky/vodka). The group was then taken by bus back to Manchester. They were sighted throughout the journey. Before arriving at the university and while still in an unfamiliar part of the city, the bus stopped and the subjects were tested for their ability to judge the direction of the place in which they had spent their lunchtime. Airline distance from test site to pub was 35 km; distance travelled was 45 km. On the test sheet, subjects were asked to write down what refreshments they had taken over lunch. Estimates were then analysed with respect to the alcohol intake (Fig. 8.15). Best performance was by subjects who had drunk no alcohol over lunch. The expected deterioration due to drinking any alcohol was significant ($z = 1.776$; P (one-tailed) $= 0.038$) with respect to pointing, but not with respect to judging distance ($z = 0.886$; P (one-tailed) $= 0.188$), and certainly not with respect to judging compass direction ($z = -1.347$; P (one-tailed) $= 0.910$).

Both of these experiments suffer from the same difficulty of interpretation as those on the effect of smoking and nose-sprays, etc.: the observed deterioration in performance may reflect a non-specific influence on general physiology, rather than a specific influence on magnetoreception.

Environmentally induced   There are two main potential sources of interference with magnetoreception that are 'environmental' in origin: (1) magnetic storms; and (2) the electromagnetic jungle that is the modern urban environment.

Small but irregular fluctuations in the geomagnetic field occur as protons and electrons brush past the Earth's atmosphere (Skiles 1985). These charged particles originate in the outer layer of the sun, particularly in sun-spots, and are carried across space by the 'solar wind'. The more extreme fluctuations in geomagnetic field generated in this way are known as 'magnetic storms'. Even the most extreme magnetic storm, however, causes no more than about a 5% perturbation in the geomagnetic field.

Despite the small, but rapid, changes in intensity that are involved, magnetic storms have been claimed to influence a wide range of behaviour and physiology. In an extensive review, Srivastava & Saxena (1980) supported claims that the incidence of (1) hospital admissions for myocardial infarction, (2) road accidents, and (3) air accidents due to pilot error, all correlate in some way with the level of magnetic storm

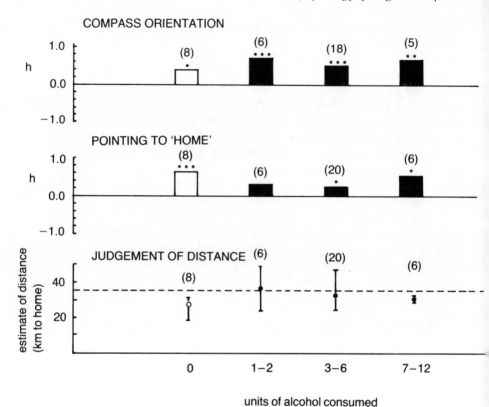

Fig. 8.15. Influence of alcohol on orientation and navigation by sighted subjects on a bus experiment. Subjects were allowed to drink alcohol *ad lib.* for a 3-hour period before being taken on a 45-km bus journey. Some drank no alcohol; others up to 12 units (1 unit = half a pint of beer; 1 measure of spirit). Histograms show *h*-values (for compass orientation and pointing to 'home' (see text) and median (+IQR) errors for judgement of distance (actual distance to 'home' was 35 km, shown by horizontal dashed line). For conventions for compass orientation and pointing, see Fig. 4.12. Best performance at navigation (pointing and judging distance) was by subjects who drank no alcohol; worst by those who drank a little. Compass orientation was unaffected. Any alcohol had a significantly disruptive effect on pointing to home ($z = 1.776$; P (1-tailed) = 0.038) but not on judgement of compass direction ($z = -1.347$; P (1-tailed) = 0.913). The tendency of subjects who drank nothing to underestimate distance relative to those who drank was not significant ($z = 1.157$; P (2-tailed) = 0.250), nor were such subjects absolutely more accurate ($z = 0.886$; P (1-tailed) = 0.188). Data from Baker (unpublished).

activity. Gould (1985) warns that such analyses for humans are post-hoc, but nevertheless places great weight on claims that the ability of birds to navigate may also be influenced by magnetic storms.

Yeagley (1951) showed that the speed at which winning pigeons return home in pigeon races correlates with sun-spot activity the day before the race. Schreiber & Rossi (1976, 1978) found similar evidence in an analysis of 18 years of pigeon racing in Italy. Southern (1971) showed that gull chicks were influenced in their orientation by magnetic storms, and some radar studies (e.g. Richardson 1974; Moore 1977) reported that the scatter of directions of migrant birds correlated with the K-index of magnetic storm activity. Keeton *et al.* (1974) also found a correlation between accuracy of navigation of homing pigeons and the K-index of magnetic storm activity during the 12 hours preceding the experiment. However, other pigeons with bar magnets glued to their backs showed no correlation (Larkin & Keeton 1976). Finally, Klinowska (1987) relates the timing of beaching by whales in Britain to magnetic storms at critical periods in their navigation a short time previously.

I have shown that the ability of people to judge the compass direction of home on bus and walkabout experiments (Fig. 8.16) also deteriorates with an increase in the K-index of magnetic storm activity. The best (but not the only) correlation is with storm activity during the 6 hours prior to the test, not during the journey itself. Artificial magnetic fields through the head during the journey, however, significantly reduce the correlation (Baker 1985a, b). The ability to point towards home, however, shows no such correlation with magnetic storm activity (Baker 1985a). This last point was evidently missed by Westby & Partridge (1986) in their paper entitled: 'Human homing: still no evidence despite geomagnetic controls'. Westby & Partridge tested their subjects by asking them to point (draw an arrow) towards home in bus experiments. From my published data (Baker 1985a), no influence of magnetic storms should have been found; Westby & Partridge's entire discussion of this matter is therefore inappropriate.

Even if all of these demonstrations of a possible link between magnetic storms and orientation are valid, they are almost all concerned with disorientation, not misorientation. The most likely explanation, therefore, would be that there is primarily a non-specific influence on general physiology (perhaps acting through other correlates, such as weather) rather than a specific influence on magnetoreception. Such an explanation would be reinforced by the rather dramatic range of behavioural and physiological correlates documented for humans by Srivastava & Saxena (1980). Only the results for homing pigeons obtained at Cornell by Keeton *et al.* (1974) seem to show misorientation rather than disorientation. Even these results, however, now have to be

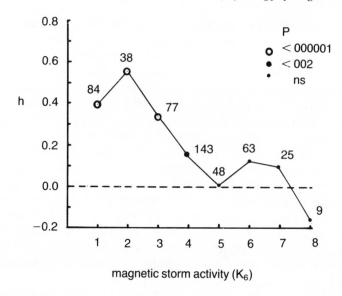

Fig. 8.16. Relationship between magnetic storm activity and ability to estimate the compass direction of home during bus and walkabout experiments on humans. Magnetic storm activity is given by the sum of the two K-indices for the two 3-hour blocks immediately preceding the test (i.e. K_6); orientation performance by the homeward component (h) of compass estimates of home direction. Numbers show total individuals tested at each K-value. One mean error per person per K-value was calculated before calculating h. P-values show results of V-test. From Baker (1984b).

interpreted with caution. According to Able (1987), a recent large series of homing pigeon releases by McIsaac & Kreithen (unpublished data) failed to find any indication of the magnetic storm effect previously reported from Cornell. Equally, Able (1987) failed to find any indication of a deterioration in consistency of orientation by migratory birds, even though some of his observations overlapped in space and time with those by Moore (1977), who did find such an effect.

Able (1987) is clearly unconvinced that magnetic storms have any influence on orientation. I am prepared to accept that there may be a correlation, but not as a specific influence on magnetoreception, only as a non-specific influence on general physiology, acting in all probability through other correlated factors. Other authors, however, not only see the effect as being directly on magnetoreception, but see this effect in turn as evidence that birds (Moore 1980; Gould 1982a; Walcott 1982) and whales (Klinowska 1987) make use of a geomagnetic grid map (Chapter 2; Fig. 2.5C).

The argument, briefly, is that, in order to use a geomagnetic grid map, an animal would need a phenomenal sensitivity to the geomagnetic field. On average, total magnetic field intensity increases only at the rate of about 5 nT per kilometre travelled to the North (in NE United States; Gould 1982a). Such changes have to be detected against a background intensity of about 50 000 nT. To be useful, therefore, field intensity needs to be detected to within about 30 nT in most navigation experiments. At this level of sensitivity, magnetic storms would be disruptive. Hence, their apparent influence has been taken by some authors as support for the hypothesis that birds use a geomagnetic grid of some sort for navigation. These authors (Gould 1982a; Walcott 1982) see further support in the apparent confusion that is perhaps sometimes seen when birds are released at magnetic anomalies; perturbations in the Earth's global field due to magnetic rock deposits near the Earth's surface. If an influence of magnetic storms on the orientation of birds and whales is taken as evidence that they use a geomagnetic map, then presumably the same should be concluded for humans from Fig. 8.16.

Some authors evidently consider that the evidence for the existence and use of geomagnetic maps is persuasive (e.g. Gould 1982a; Presti 1985; Klinowska 1987). Others, including myself (Lednor 1982; Wallraff 1983; Baker 1984b), do not find it so and see no need to postulate that such maps are at all a real phenomenon. How birds or humans could perceive the required small changes in field intensity when transported in vehicles and through urban landscapes that show fluctuations in field intensity that are orders of magnitude greater remains unexplained. So, too, does the way that a geomagnetic map system would cope with large-scale anomalies that completely mask the average global pattern (Lednor 1982). Given: (a) these problems; (b) the probability that, if there is any correlation between orientation and magnetic storm activity, it is the non-specific result of a general influence on physiology; and (c) the lack of any direct evidence for the use of a magnetic map by any animal, I feel there are few grounds for considering the question any further. All of the results in this book may be accommodated by the methods for implementation of magnetoreception illustrated in Figs 2.5A and B. In my opinion, the method illustrated in Fig. 2.5C is, and remains, a hypothetical curiosity.

In comparison with the miniscule fluctuations in electromagnetic environment attributable to magnetic storms, those that are generated by the modern man-made environment are huge. Quite conceivably there are elements in the electromagnetic jungle in which most of us live that not only have non-specific influences on general physiology but may also have specific influences on the magnetoreceptor and magnetoreception. However, whereas our questionnaires (Section 4.3.2) have asked people, for example, whether they have travelled by electric train within the previous 48 hours, these data have not yet been analysed.

At the time of writing, a study has also been instigated to test whether some makes of car, by virtue of differences in electromagnetic fields, may be more prone to lead to dis- or misorientation among their drivers and passengers than others.

The study of clinical aspects of magnetoreception has so far received only minor consideration in our studies at Manchester. It is a safe prediction that this situation will soon change.

8.5. *Summary*

Orientation and navigation experiments suggest that humans possess one or more magnetoreceptors in the front part of the head, probably somewhere within the block of tissue that encompasses the backs of the eyes and the sphenoid/ethmoid sinus complex. Neurophysiological evidence is mounting that the actual location is somewhere in the visual system, perhaps the retina of the eyes. The possibility has to be considered that normal function of the magneto-receptor requires a normal electrostatic environment.

The human magnetoreceptor does not read the polarity of the geomagnetic field but does make at least some use of the angle of inclination. The observed pattern of influences of magnets on human magnetoreception requires that the receptor have the following characteristics: (1) a physical basis in a pattern that varies between individuals and is influenced by orientation during sleep; (2) normal resistance to repatterning by the geomagnetic field during the day; (3) proneness to repatterning by stronger applied fields followed by reduced resistance to repatterning by the geomagnetic field; and (4) a response to applied fields that is a function of the polarity of the applied fields.

It is hypothesised that the human magnetoreceptor consists of a physical, patterned array (possibilities include: calcium ions on membrances; triplet states of large molecules; particles of magnetite). This array is fixed in a resistant pattern (perhaps within a viscous matrix) throughout the day, then repatterned (perhaps in a softened matrix) during sleep at night (or when damaged). As the head turns, this patterned array moves through the geomagnetic field. In effect, the magnetoreceptor scans directions until the alignment of the array within the receptor and the alignment of the lines of force of the geomagnetic field interact to generate a maximum neural signal which the individual has learned means he or she is facing a particular direction. Orientation may involve interaction of magnetoreceptor and vestibular systems, the latter measuring angles relative to the direction of maximum signal from the magnetoreceptor.

It is likely that part of the observed variation in individual performance at orientation and navigation relates to clinical variation in the function of the magnetoreceptor. Genetic, infectious and self- and environmentally induced effects are all to be expected. Of the aspects studied, only the wearing of stereo headphones may have a specific influence on magnetoreception. Any influence of smoking, nasal sprays, polyester clothing, menstrual cycles, alcohol or magnetic storms are all more probably attributable to non-specific influences on general physiology.

There is no reason to suppose that humans, or any other animals, use a geomagnetic map for navigation. All results so far may be interpreted in terms of monitoring twists and turns relative to a reference system of magnetic compass directions (Figs 2.5A and B).

9

The next eight years

At the time of writing, it is just over eight years since the first magnets were placed on people's heads in the navigation experiment at Barnard Castle, and just under eight years since the first results were published (Baker 1980b, c, d). In those publications, I made, in effect, two claims: (1) humans have some non-visual ability that they can use to help solve problems of orientation and navigation; and (2) this non-visual ability is based, at least in part, on magnetoreception. What appears to have happened since these claims were made depends on where one looks.

In the published literature, those eight years were needed for the two claims to pass the most important scientific test of all: replicability by other authors. That they have done so (Baker 1987c) is particularly important at a time when the warning has gone out to students of bird orientation and navigation that they should 'devote more time to replicating past studies lest [they] risk erecting [their] syntheses atop a house of cards' (Able 1987).

On the road to replication, there has been an invigorating air of hostility to the Manchester claims (see Preface) and the intriguing phenomenon of supportive data published under non-supportive titles and embedded in negative discussions and interpretations. Whatever happened, I wonder, to the manuscripts I saw en route to various journals in which the authors not only had data that supported the Manchester claims but actually said so? It would be too cynical of me even to hint that a prerequisite for other authors to have their data published was that they claimed not to support the Manchester findings, no matter what their data actually showed, so I shan't. After all, science does not work that way.

However, all this should now be in the past. The combined data obtained by other scientists in Britain, the United States and Australia now replicate the Manchester experiments with a conservative probability of having occurred by chance that is less than 0.001 with respect to non-visual orientation and less than 0.005 with respect to magneto-reception (Baker 1987c). Of course, at the time of writing I have seen only one reaction to this paper (Turner 1988), publication of which is still only 12 months in the past. Maybe I am being optimistic in thinking that levels of <0.001 and <0.005 will have been convincing to the objective sceptic, but I think I am not. I have enough faith in my fellow scientists to feel confident that they will now publicly accept that the point has been proved: humans do possess magnetoreceptive ability.

The published literature of the past eight years, therefore, has been, quite rightly, concerned with replication. Research at Manchester, however, while not ignoring questions of replicability (e.g. Murphy 1987), has at the same time been pushing ahead with questions that, though not more important, are certainly more interesting. Their findings have formed the basis of this book.

Consider what we now know. Somewhere in the front half of the human head, possibly in the eyes (by analogy with work on birds) but at least in the block of tissue including the backs of the eyes and the sphenoid/ethmoid sinus complex, lie(s) one or more magnetoreceptor system(s) (Chapter 8). Some feature of this receptor is set overnight and is resistant, but not impervious, to change during the day (Chapter 8). Once changed by application of a magnetic field sufficiently stronger than the Earth's field, this feature of the receptor requires at least hours, maybe days, to recover (Chapter 6). It is this feature that interacts with the geomagnetic field to produce estimates of direction (Chapters 5–7), the interaction being more similar to that of an inclination than a polarity compass (Chapter 8). The ability to sense direction by magnetorecep-tion, then to use the information to judge the direction and distance of home during natural exploration, is weak but real (Chapters 5–7). Normally, magnetoreception and vision work together for navigation, information from one continually checking the other (Chapter 7). Either sense can work on its own, with some reduction in acuity, but, without both senses, orientation and navigation are reduced to the level of guesswork (Chapter 7). The main role of magnetoreception is as a sub-conscious aid to navigation (Chapter 7), presumably thus freeing other senses, such as vision, to concentrate on other important aspects of exploration, such as vigilance for resources or dangers (Chapter 2).

These data have led to hypotheses of the way the magnetoreceptor works (Chapter 8) and of the way the directional information it produces is used relative to other information (Chapter 7).

My favoured hypothesis (at present) concerning the nature of the human magnetoreceptor is that it consists of, or contains, a patterned array of ions, molecules and/or particles. This array is fixed by a viscous matrix (or something with the characteristics of a viscous matrix) into a resistant pattern throughout the day, then repatterned or redeposited in a softened matrix during sleep at night (or when damaged). As the head turns, this patterned array moves through the geomagnetic field. In effect, the magnetoreceptor scans directions until the alignment of the array and the alignment of the lines of force of the geomagnetic field interact to generate a maximum neural signal which the individual has learned means he or she is facing a particular direction. Orientation may involve interaction of magnetoreceptor and vestibular systems, the latter measuring fine angles relative to the direction of maximum signal from the magnetoreceptor.

There is no shortage, here, of hypotheses to test during the coming eight years. Whereas the reality of human magnetoreception has passed the tests of replicability, most of these detailed hypotheses have not. Even at Manchester, most of such details are still based on first-generation experiments and are waiting to be tested for replication by ourselves.

It is my hope, therefore, that the next eight years will see a mushrooming of work on human navigation and magnetoreception in more and more departments and laboratories around the world. Most of the experiments are cheap and simple. This does not mean, of course, as warned by Adler & Pelkie (1985), that they can also be casual. Their design and execution must be rigorous and preferably should follow all the guidelines laid down by the different authors and discussed in Chapter 4. A continuous vigilance must be maintained to avoid spurious levels of performance. Some causes have been identified (Section 4.3.1), but others may yet lie in wait.

As long as the experiments are rigorous and the interpretation of results is as fair and objective as for tests on other animals, humans offer so many advantages as experimental animals in the study of animal navigation. I am still convinced that we are going to discover more about the nature, physiology and use of magnetoreception from studies on humans than from studies on any other species.

An obvious priority over the next eight years is to locate the magnetoreceptor itself, now assuming that it is at least relatively discrete and not a diffuse sensor scattered over or through the entire body (Chapter 3). Of no less importance in allowing the most productive design of experiments involving magnetic treatment is to unravel the precise way that the geomagnetic field is read and the way the magnetoreceptor is affected by unusually strong applied fields. I feel confident in the generalities of the hypothesis developed in Chapter 8, but: is the physical basis of the magnetoreceptor of humans, or any metazoan, really magnetite? Or will the case against magnetite (Section 8.3.3) continue to grow?

As a behavioural ecologist, rather than a sensory physiologist or experimental psychologist, my own fascination is with the role of magnetoreception in exploration and navigation and its relative importance to celestial and other information. I shall hope to continue to perform walkabout experiments for many more than the next eight years; preferably under an increasingly wide range of conditions, over longer and longer distances, with more and more *experienced* navigators, and in locations that are increasingly exotic (and nearer the equator). I recommend the walkabout experiment to would-be researchers, both for its pleasure in execution and for its potential ability to contribute to our understanding of animal migration and navigation.

Finally, the more we discover about magnetoreception, the more vulnerable this new-found sensory apparatus appears to be to the influences of everyday modern life, not least such medical practices as NMR imaging (e.g. Morris 1986; see Baker 1986). It really is time for serious study of the more clinical aspects of magnetoreception (Section 8.4), if only so that we may reassure ourselves either that the magnetoreceptor is really a most robust organ or that, if it is damaged, the worst that happens is that we lose one component of our sense of direction.

It is time that I stopped writing about human magnetoreception and got back into the laboratory or field. My hope is that, over the next eight years, many more scientists will not only do the same but this time also publish their results, even if they are positive.

References and author index

(Figures in brackets after each reference give the page numbers on which the publication is quoted.)

Aarde, R.J. van & Skinner, J.D. 1986. Pattern of space use by relocated servals *Felis serval. Afr. J. Ecol.* **24**:97–101. (9)

Able, K.P. 1987. Geomagnetic disturbance and migratory bird orientation: is there an effect? *Anim. Behav.* **35**:559–601. (14, 278, 282)

Able, K.P., Bingman, V.P., Kerlinger, P. & Gergits, W. 1982. Field studies of avian nocturnal migratory orientation. II. Experimental manipulation of orientation in white-throated sparrows (*Zonotrichia albicollis*) released aloft. *Anim. Behav.* **30**:768–773. (136)

Able, K.P. & Gergits, W.F. 1985. Human navigation: attempts to replicate Baker's displacement experiment. In: *Magnetite Biomineralization and Magneto-reception in Organisms: A new Biomagnetism* (Ed. by J.L. Kirschvink, D.S. Jones & B.J. MacFadden), pp. 569–572. New York: Plenum. (xi, 46, 51, 55, 65, 69, 72, 73, 107)

Adey, R. (personal communication). (267)

Adler, K. & Pelkie, C.R. 1985. Human homing orientation: critique and alter-native hypotheses. In: *Magnetite Biomineralization and Magnetoreception in Organisms: A new Biomagnetism* (Ed. by J.L. Kirschvink, D.S. Jones & B.J. MacFadden), pp. 573–594. New York: Plenum. (xi, 46, 51, 55, 65–75, 78, 94, 96, 103, 106, 107, 153–5, 157, 160–3, 235, 284)

Alexander, J.R. & Keeton, W.T. 1974. Clock-shifting effect on initial orientation of pigeons. *Auk* **91**:370–374. (206)

Aneshansley, D.J. & Larkin, T.S. 1981. V-test is not a statistical test of 'home-ward' direction. *Nature, Lond.* **293**:239. (60)

Baker, R.R. 1978a. *The Evolutionary Ecology of Animal Migration*. London: Hodder & Stoughton. (3, 4, 5, 6, 8, 9)

Baker, R.R. 1978b. Demystifying vertebrate migration. *New Scientist* **80**:526–528. (3, 8)

Baker, R.R. 1980a. The significance of the Lesser Black-backed Gull to models of bird migration. *Bird Study* **27**:41–50. (6, 9, 160)

Baker, R.R. 1980b. Man. In: *The Mystery of Migration* (Ed. by R.R. Baker), pp. 220–243. London: Macdonald/Harrow. (282)

Baker, R.R. 1980c. A sense of magnetism. *New Scientist* **87**:844–847. (x, 151, 198, 282)

Baker, R.R. 1980d. Goal orientation by blindfolded humans after long-distance displacement: possible involvement of a magnetic sense. *Science* **210**:555–557. (x, 46, 49, 51, 103, 157, 198, 235, 282)

Baker, R.R. 1980e. We may have an inner compass that points us toward home. *Psychology Today* **14**:60–73.

Baker, R.R. 1981a. The human magnetic sense. *Theoria to Theory* **14**:241–246. (14, 211)

Baker, R.R. 1981b. *Human Navigation and the Sixth Sense*. London: Hodder & Stoughton. (ix, 3, 7, 10, 12–14, 35, 46, 47, 49–51, 103, 108, 118, 121, 147, 151, 157, 160, 198, 235)

Baker, R.R. 1981c. Man and other vertebrates: a common perspective to migration and navigation. In: *Animal Migration* (Ed. by D.J. Aidley), pp. 241–260. Cambridge: University Press. (6, 8)

Baker, R.R. 1982. *Migration: Paths through Time and Space*. London: Hodder & Stoughton. (4, 6, 8, 9, 10)

Baker, R.R. 1984a. Sinal magnetite and direction finding. *Physics in Technology* **15**:30–36. (23, 30, 78, 163, 164, 238, 267, 269)

Baker, R.R. 1984b. *Bird Navigation: Solution of a Mystery?* London: Hodder & Stoughton. (6, 9, 10, 14, 23, 69, 76, 78, 130, 133, 145, 163, 164, 196, 198, 206, 209, 233, 235, 238, 248, 264, 278–9)

Baker, R.R. 1985a. Magnetoreception by man and other primates. In: *Magnetite Biomineralization and Magnetoreception in Organisms: A New Biomagnetism* (Ed. by J.L. Kirschvink, D.S. Jones & B.J. MacFadden), pp. 537–562. New York: Plenum. (19, 23, 28, 46, 65, 67–9, 71, 94, 103, 106, 107, 133, 157, 163–4, 235, 262, 266, 277)

Baker, R.R. 1985b. Human navigation: a summary of American data and interpretations. In: *Magnetite Biomineralization and Magnetoreception in Organisms: A new Biomagnetism* (Ed. by J.L. Kirschvink, D.S. Jones & B.J. MacFadden), pp. 611–622. New York: Plenum. (xi, 46, 51, 55, 67, 71, 73–5, 95, 103, 106–7, 157, 160, 235, 277)

Baker, R.R. 1985c. Exploration and navigation: the foundation of vertebrate migration. In: *Migration: Mechanisms and Adaptive Significance. Contributions in Marine Science Supplement* (Ed. by M.A. Rankin), **27**:466–477. (9, 35, 46, 71, 74, 106, 157, 211, 235)

Baker, R.R. 1986. Clinical applications of NMR (Book Review). *Trends in Biochemical Sciences* **11**:407. (285)

Baker, R.R. 1987a. Integrated use of moon and magnetic compasses by the heart-and-dart moth *Agrotis exclamationis*. *Anim. Behav.* **35**:94–101. (137, 204)

Baker, R.R. 1987b. Accuracy of map-building and navigation by humans during 'natural' exploration: relative roles of magnetoreception and vision. In: *Cognitive Processes and Spatial Orientation in Animal and Man. Vol. 1 Animal Psychology and Ethology* (Ed. by P. Ellen & C. Thinus-Blanc), pp. 217–232, NATO ASI. Dordrecht: Martinus Nijhoff. (35, 46, 63, 78–9, 91–2, 99, 126, 196, 207, 214, 224, 228)

Baker, R.R. 1987c. Human navigation and magnetoreception: the Manchester experiments do replicate. *Anim. Behav.* **35**:691–704. (xi, xii, 46, 55, 70–1, 73, 94–5, 103, 106–7, 196, 235, 282–3)

Baker, R.R. 1988. Human magnetoreception for navigation. In: *Electromagnetic Waves and Neurobehavioural Function. Progress in Clinical and Biological Research, Vol. 257* (Ed. by M.E. O'Connor & R. Lovely), pp. 63–80. New York: Liss. (35, 46, 78, 94, 108)

Baker, R.R. & Bailey, S.E.R. *in* Baker (1981b). (235)

Baker, R.R. & Mather, J.G. 1982. A comparative approach to bird navigation: implications of parallel studies on mammals. In: *Avian Navigation* (Ed. by F. Papi & H.G. Wallraff), pp. 308–312. Heidelberg: Springer. (68, 130, 137, 238)

Baker, R.R. & Murphy, R.G. (unpublished data). (93, 99, 193)

Baker, R.R., Kennaugh, J.H. & Canty, P. (unpublished data.) (266)

Baker, R.R., Mather, J.G. & Kennaugh, J.H. 1982. The human compass? *EOS* **63**:156. (25, 68, 130, 238)

Baker, R.R., Mather, J.G. & Kennaugh, J.H. 1983. Magnetic bones in human sinuses. *Nature, Lond.* **301**:78–80. (25, 30, 235, 238, 266)

Baker, R.R., Murphy, R.G. Bird, S. & Brand, V. (unpublished data). (270)

Baker, R.R. *et al.* (unpublished data). (171)

Bambridge, A. (unpublished data). (241–2)

Banerjee, S.K. & Moskowitz, B.W. 1985. Ferrimagnetic properties of magnetite. In: *Magnetite Biomineralization and Magnetoreception in Organisms: A New Biomagnetism* (Ed. by J.L. Kirschvink, D.S. Jones & B.J. MacFadden), pp. 17–42. New York: Plenum. (22)

Barlow, J.S. 1964. Inertial navigation as a basis for animal navigation. *J. Theoret. Biol.* **6**:76–117. (16, 73, 98)

Barnothy, M.F. (ed.) 1964. *Biological Effects of Magnetic Fields*, Volume 1. New York: Plenum Press. (271)

Batschelet, E. 1981. *Circular Statistics in Biology*. London: Academic Press. (57, 59–61, 64–5, 68, 79, 89)

Bauer, G.B., Fuller, M., Perry, A., Dunn, J.R. & Zoeger, J. 1985. Magnetoreception and biomineralization of magnetite in cetaceans. In: *Magnetite Biomineralization and Magnetoreception in Organisms: A New Biomagnetism* (Ed. by J.L. Kirschvink, D.S. Jones & B.J. MacFadden), pp. 489–588. New York: Plenum. (25)

Bayliss, R., Bishop, N.L. & Fowler R.C. 1985. Pineal gland calcification and defective sense of direction. *British Medical Journal* **291**:1758–1759. (71)

Bayliss, R. (personal communication). (71)

Beason, R.C. & Nichols, J.E. 1984. Magnetic orientation and magnetically sensitive material in a transequatorial migratory bird. *Nature, Lond.* **309**:151–153. (25)

Bellamy, J.C. 1839. *The Natural History of South Devon*. Plymouth: Jenkin Thomas. (ix)

Benvenuti, S., Baldaccini, N.E. & Ioalé, P. 1982. Pigeon homing: effect of altered magnetic field during displacement on initial orientation. In: *Avian Navigation* (Ed. by F. Papi & H.G. Wallraff), pp. 140–148, Heidelberg: Springer. (143)

Berthold, P. 1973. Relationships between migratory restlessness and migration distance in six *Sylvia* species. *Ibis* **115**:594–599. (249)

Bingman, V.P. 1981. Savannah sparrows have a magnetic compass. *Anim. Behav.* **29**:962–963. (136)

Blakemore, R.P. 1975. Magnetotactic bacteria. *Science* **190**:377–379. (21)

Blakemore, R.P. & Blakemore, N. *in* Maugh (1982). (22)

Bloxham, J. 1986. Geomagnetic reversals: evidence for asymmetry and fluctuation. *Nature, Lond.* **322**:13–14. (250)

Bookman, M.A. 1978. Sensitivity of the homing pigeon to an earth-strength magnetic field. In: *Animal Migration, Navigation and Homing* (Ed. by K. Schmidt-Koenig & W.T. Keeton), pp. 127–134. Heidelberg: Springer. (256)

Bovet, J. 1987. Cognitive map size and homing behaviour. In: *Cognitive Processes and Spatial Orientation in Animal and Man. Vol. 1 Animal Psychology and Ethology* (Ed. by P. Ellen & C. Thinus-Blanc), pp. 252–265, NATO ASI. Dordrecht: Martinus Nijhoff. (114)

Boyde, A. (personal communication). (266)

Brian, R.A. (unpublished data). (139)

Brian, R.A. & Bennett, S. (unpublished data). (253)

Britto, L.R.G., Natal, C.L. & Marcoudes, A.M. 1981. The accessory optics system in pigeons: receptive field properties of identified neurons. *Brain Res.* **206**:149–154. (236)

Brown, H.R., Ilyinsky, O.B., Muravejko, V.M., Corshkov, E.S. & Fonarev, G.A. & 1979. Evidence that geomagnetic variations can be detected by lorenzinian ampullae. *Nature, Lond.* **277**: 648–649. (20)

Buchler, E.R. & Wasilewski, P.J. 1985. Magnetic remanence in bats. In: *Magnetite Biomineralization and Magnetoreception in Organisms: A New Biomagnetism* (Ed. by J.L. Kirschvink, D.S. Jones & B.J. MacFadden), pp. 483–488. New York: Plenum. (25)

Buskirk, R.E. & O'Brien, W.P. Jr. 1985. Magnetic remanence and response to magnetic fields in Crustacea. In: *Magnetite Biomineralization and Magnetoreception in Organisms: A New Biomagnetism* (Ed. by J.L. Kirschvink, D.S. Jones & B.J. MacFadden), pp. 365–384. New York: Plenum. (25)

Campion, M. (in prep.) Basic evidence that some humans have a natural sense of orientation (MS). (58, 96)

Campion, M. (personal communication). (78, 97, 223)

Campion, M. (unpublished data). (94, 96, 107, 178, 182–3, 185)

Cherfas, J. 1980 Introduction. In: *The Mystery of Migration* (Ed. by R.R. Baker), pp. 7–13. London: Macdonald/Harrow. (x)

Cox, S. (unpublished data). (157)

Danilov. V., Demirochaglyan, G., Avetysan, Z,. Aelakhnyerdyan, M., Grigoryan, S. & Saribekhyan, G. 1970. Possible mechanisms of magnetic sensitivity in birds (in Russian). *Biol. Zh. Arm.* **23**:26–34. (21)

Darwin, C. 1873. Origin of certain instincts. *Nature, Lond.* **7**:417–418. (x)

Davidson, J.M.J. (unpublished data). (274)

Dayton, T. 1985. A comment on Baker's methodology and statistics. In: *Magnetite Biomineralization and Magnetoreception in Organisms: A New Biomagnetism* (Ed. by J.L. Kirschvink, D.S. Jones & B.J. MacFadden), pp. 563–568. New

York: Plenum. (65–6, 68, 106–7, 157, 235)

Dodge, R.I. 1890. *Our Wild Indians*. Connecticut: Hartford. (7)

Doyle, K. (unpublished data). (272)

Dunn, P.A. & Malmstrom, V.H. (personal communication). (30, 236)

Edrich, W. & Keeton, W.T. 1977. A comparison of homing behavior in feral and homing pigeons. *Z. Tierpsychol.* **44**:389–401. (206)

Ellen, P. 1987. Cognitive mechanisms in animal problem-solving. In: *Cognitive Processes and Spatial Orientation in Animal and Man. Vol. 1 Animal Psychology and Ethology* (Ed. by P. Ellen & C. Thinus-Blanc), pp. 20–35. NATO ASI. Dordrecht: Martinus Nijhoff. (10)

Emmerton, J. 1982. Functional morphology of the visual system. In: *Physiology and Behavior of the Pigeon* (Ed. by M. Abs), pp. 221–244. London: Academic Press. (236)

Etienne, A.S. 1987. The control of short-distance homing in the golden hamster. In: *Cognitive Processes and Spatial Orientation in Animal and Man. Vol. 1 Animal Psychology and Ethology* (Ed. by P. Ellen & C. Thinus-Blanc), pp. 233–251, NATO ASI. Dordrecht: Martinus Nijhoff. (13, 98)

Etienne, A.S., Maurer, R., Saucy, F. & Teroni, E. 1986. Short-distance homing in the golden hamster after a passive outward journey. *Anim. Behav.* **34**:696–715. (13)

Fildes, B.N., O'Loughlin, B.J., Bradshaw, J.L. & Ewens, W.J. 1984. Human orientation with restricted sensory information: no evidence for magnetic sensitivity. *Perception* **13**:229–236. (xi, 58, 72, 91–2, 94–7, 106, 120)

Fitter, R. 1984. Operation Oryx — the success continues. *Oryx* **18**:136–137. (9)

Foà, A., Wallraff, H.G., Ioalé, P. & Benvenuti, S. 1982. Comparative investigations of pigeon homing in Germany and Italy. In: *Avian Navigation* (Ed. by F. Papi & H.G. Wallraff), pp. 232–238. Heidelberg: Springer. (108)

Forster, J.R. 1778. *Observations Made during a Voyage Round the World (in the Resolution 1771–5)*. London: G. Robinson. (46)

Frankel, R.B., Blakemore, R.P. & Wolfe, R.S. 1979. Magnetite in freshwater magnetic bacteria. *Science* **203**:1355–1357. (21, 25, 265)

Frankel, R.B., Papaefthymiou G.C. & Blakemore, R.P. 1985. Mossbauer spectroscopy of iron biomineralization products in magnetotactic Bacteria. In: *Magnetite Biomineralization and Magnetoreception in Organisms: A New Biomagnetism* (Ed. by J.L. Kirschvink, D.S. Jones & B.J. MacFadden), pp. 269–288. New York: Plenum. (24–5)

Frisch, K. von 1967. *The Dance Language and Orientation of Bees*. London: Oxford University Press. (7)

Fuller, M., Goree, W.S. & Goodman, W.L. 1985. An introduction to the use of SQUID magnetometers in biomagnetism. In: *Magnetite Biomineralization and Magnetoreception in Organisms: A New Biomagnetism* (Ed. by J.L. Kirschvink, D.S. Jones & B.J. MacFadden), pp. 103–154. New York: Plenum. (24)

Ganss, A. (unpublished data). (171, 271)

Gärling, T., Böök, A. & Lindberg, E. 1979. The acquisition and use of an internal representation of the spatial layout of the environment during locomotion.

Man-Environ. Syst. **9**:200–208. (34)

Gärling, T., Böök, A. & Lindberg, E. 1984. Cognitive mapping of large-scale environments. *Environment and Behaviour* **16**:3–34. (34)

Gatty, H. 1958. *Nature is Your Guide.* London: Collins. (1, 12, 16, 90)

Golledge, R.G., Smith, T.R., Pellegrino, J.W., Doherty, S. & Marshall, S.P. 1985. A conceptual model and empirical analysis of children's acquisition of spatial knowledge. *J. Environ. Psychol.* **5**:125–152. (34, 103)

Gould, J.L. 1980. Homing in on the home front. *Psychology Today* **14**:62–71. (46, 51, 55, 71–3, 78, 107, 157, 160, 198, 235)

Gould, J.L. 1982a. The map sense of pigeons. *Nature, Lond.* **296**:205–211. (14, 278–9)

Gould, J.L. 1982b. Reply to Wallraff, Benvenuti & Papi. *Nature, Lond.* **300**:294. (14)

Gould, J.L. 1985. Absence of human homing ability as measured by displacement experiments. In: *Magnetite Biomineralization and Magnetoreception in Organisms: A New Biomagnetism* (Ed. by J.L. Kirschvink, D.S. Jones & B.J. MacFadden), pp. 595–600. New York: Plenum. (xi, 46, 51, 55, 65, 68, 72–3, 106, 277)

Gould, J.L. *in* Jacobs (1982). (x)

Gould, J.L. (unpublished data). (162)

Gould, J.L. & Able, K.P. 1981. Human homing: an elusive phenomenon. *Science* **212**:1061–1063. (xi, 46, 51, 55, 64–5, 68, 72, 78, 84, 106–7, 157, 160, 198, 235)

Gould, J.L., Kirschvink, J.L. & Deffeyes, K.S. 1978. Bees have magnetic remanence. *Science* **102**:1026–1028. (22–5, 265–6)

Gould, J.L., Kirschvink, J.L., Deffeyes, K.S. & Brines, M.L. 1980. Orientation of demagnetized bees. *J. Exp. Biol* **86**:1–7. (266)

Gould, P.R. & White, R. 1974. *Mental Maps.* Harmondsworth: Penguin. (31)

Green, J., Green, R. & Jefferies, D.J. 1984. A radio-tracking survey of otters *Lutra lutra* on a Perthshire river system. *Lutra* **27**:86–145. (10)

Greenwood, P. (unpublished data). (107)

Gwinner, E. 1972. Adaptive functions of circannual rhythms in warblers. *Proc. XV Int. Orn. Congr., Berlin,* pp. 218–236. (249)

Harvalik, Z.V. 1978. Anatomical localization of human detection of weak electromagnetic radiation: experiments with dowsers. *Physiol. Chem. Phys.* **10**:525–534. (234–5)

Hoffmann, K. 1954. Versuche zu der im Richtungsfinden der Vögel enthaltenen Zeitschätzung. *Z. Tierpsychol.* **11**:453–475. (209)

Holekamp, K.E. 1984. Dispersal in ground-dwelling sciurids. In: *The Biology of Ground-Dwelling Squirrels: Annual Cycles, Behavioral Ecology, and Sociality.* (Ed. by J.O. Murie & G.R. Michener, pp. 297–320. Lincoln: University of Nebraska Press. (9)

Hollen, N. & Saddler, J. 1968. *Textiles,* 3rd edn. London: Macmillan. (231)

Howitt, A.W. 1873. *in* Gatty (1958). (1)

Hutchison, H.E. 1953. The significance of stainable iron in sternal marrow sections. *Blood* **8**:236–240. (24)

Jacobs, P. 1982. Magnetic field: tests point away from 6th sense. US findings negative. *Los Angeles Times* **19 July 1982**:1, 10–11. (x, 84)

Jefferies, D.J., Wayre, P., Jessop, R.M. & Mitchell-Jones, A.J. 1986. Reinforcing the native Otter *Lutra lutra* population in East Anglia: an analysis of the behaviour and range development of the first release group. *Mammal Rev.* **16**:65–79. (9)

Jones, D.S. & MacFadden, B.J. 1981. Induced magnetization in the monarch butterfly, *Danaus plexippus* L. (Insecta, Lepidoptera). *J. exp. Biol.* **96**:1–9. (25)

Jorgensen, J.M. *in* Mather (1985). (266)

Jorgensen, J.M. (personal communication). (28–9)

Judge, T.K. 1985. A study of the homeward orientation of visually handicapped humans. In: *Magnetite Biomineralization and Magnetoreception in Organisms: A New Biomagnetism* (Ed. by J.L. Kirschvink, D.S. Jones & B.J. MacFadden), pp. 601–604. New York: Plenum. (xi, 46, 51, 55, 72, 107, 238, 271)

Juurmaa, J. 1966. An analysis of the ability for orientation and operations with spatial relationships in general. *Work Environ. Health* **2**:45–52. (34)

Kalmijn, A. 1978. Experimental evidence of geomagnetic orientation in elasmobranch fishes. In: *Animal Migration, Navigation and Homing* (Ed. by K. Schmidt-Koenig & W.T. Keeton), pp. 345–353. Heidelberg: Springer. (20)

Kalmijn, A. (1988) Electromagnetic orientation: a relativistic approach in: *Electromagnetic Waves and Neurobehavioural Function. Progress in Clinical and Biological Research, Vol. 257* (Ed. by M.E. O'Connor & R. Lovely), pp. 23–46. New York; Liss. (20)

Kalmijn, A. & Blakemore, R.P. 1978. Magnetic behaviour of mud bacteria. In: *Animal Migration, Navigation and Homing* (Ed. by K. Schmidt-Koenig & W.T. Keeton), pp. 354–355. Heidelberg: Springer. (21)

Keeton, W.T. 1971. Magnets interfere with pigeon homing. *Proc. Nat. Acad. Sci., USA* **68**:102–106. (151, 156, 206)

Keeton, W.T. 1972. Effects of magnets on pigeon homing. In: *Animal Orientation and Navigation* (Ed. by S.R. Galler, K. Schmidt-Koenig, G.J. Jacobs & R.E. Belleville), pp. 579–594. Washington, D.C.: NASA Sp-262, US Govt Printing Office. (16)

Keeton, W.T. in Gould (1980). (71)

Keeton, W.T., Larkin, T.S. & Windsor, D.M. 1974. Normal fluctuations in the earth's magnetic field influence pigeon orientation. *J. Comp. Physiol.* **95**: 95–103. (277)

Ketchen, E.E., Porter, W.E. & Bolton, N.E. 1978. The biological effects of magnetic fields on man. *Am. Ind. Hyg. Assoc. J.* **39**:1–11. (271)

Khan, S. (unpublished data). (171)

Kiepenheuer, J. 1978. Pigeon navigation and magnetic field: information collected during the outward journey is used in the homing process. *Naturwiss.* **65**:113. (13, 144)

Kiepenheuer, J., Ranvaud, R. & Maret, G. 1986. The effect of ultrahigh magnetic fields on the initial orientation of homing pigeons. In: *Biophysical Effects of Steady Magnetic Fields* (Ed. by G. Maret, N. Boccara & J. Kiepenheuer), pp. 189–193. Berlin: Springer-Verlag. (171)

Kirschvink, J.L. 1981a. Biogenic magnetic (Fe_3O_4): a ferrimagnetic mineral in bacteria, animals, and man. In: *Ferrites: Proceedings of the 3rd International*

Conference, Japan, 1980 (Ed. by M. Sigimoto), pp. 135–137. New York: Plenum. (25)

Kirschvink, J.L. 1981b. Ferromagnetic crystals (magnetite?) in human tissue. *J. exp. Biol.* **92**:333–335. (25)

Kirschvink, J.L. 1982. Birds, bees and magnetism. A new look at the old problem of magnetoreception. *Trends in Neuroscience* **5**:160–171. (266)

Kirschvink, J.L. 1983. Biogenic ferrimagnetism: a new biomagnetism. In: *Biomagnetism: an Interdisciplinary Approach* (Ed. by S. Williamson), pp. 501–532. New York: Plenum. (30)

Kirschvink, J.L. 1985. A cautionary note on magnetoreception in dowsers. In: *Magnetite Biomineralization and Magnetoreception in Organisms: A New Biomagnetism* (Ed. by J.L. Kirschvink, D.S. Jones & B.J. MacFadden), pp. 243–256. New York: Plenum. (234)

Kirschvink, J.L. *in* Jacobs (1982). (x)

Kirschvink, J.L. (personal communication). (28)

Kirschvink, J.L. & Gould, J.L. 1981. Biogenic magnetite as a basis for magnetic field detection in animals. *BioSystems* **13**:181–201. (22–3)

Kirschvink, J.L. & Walker, M.M. 1985. Particle-size considerations for magnetite-based magnetoreceptors. In: *Magnetite Biominderalization and Magnetoreception in Organisms: A New Biomagnetism* (Ed. by J.L. Kirschvink, D.S. Jones & B.J. MacFadden), pp. 243–256. New York: Plenum. (22)

Kirschvink, J.L., Jones, D.S. & MacFadden, B.J. (eeds) 1985a. *Magnetite Biomineralization and Magnetoreception in Organisms: A New Biomagnetism.* New York: Plenum. (xi, xii, 24, 262)

Kirschvink, J.L., Peterson, K.A., Chwe, M., Filmer, P. & Roder, B. 1985b. An attempt to replicate the spinning chair experiment. In: *Magnetite Biomineralization and Magnetoreception in Organisms: A New Biomagnetism* (Ed. by J.L. Kirschvink, D.S. Jones & B.J. MacFadden), pp. 605–608. New York: Plenum. (58, 67, 72, 79, 94–5, 137, 140–1)

Klinowska, M. 1987. No through road for the misguided whale. *New Scientist* **113**:46–48. (14, 277–9)

Kotleba, J., Bielek, J., Glos, J. & Bárta, J. 1973. O moznom vplyve magnetického pol'a zeme na spánok cloveka. *Cs. Fysiol.* **22**:459–460. (260)

Krause, K. & Hennekes, R. 1986. Magnetfeld Empfindlichkeit des menschlichen Auges: objective Befunde. *Fortschr. Ophthalmol.* **83**:245–247. (237)

Krause, K., Cremer-Bartels, G., Küchle, H.J., Weitkämper, U. 1984. Der Einfluss schwaches Magnetfeldvariationer auf die Menvchliche Dammerungssehschärfe. *Fortschr. Ophthalmol.* **81**:183–185. (237)

Kuterbach, D.A., Walcott, B., Reeder, R.J. & Frankel, R.B. 1982. Iron-containing cells in the honey bee (*Apis mellifera*). *Science* **218**:695–697. (25, 265–6)

Larkin, T.S. & Keeton, W.T. 1976. Bar magnets mask the effect of normal magnetic disturbances on pigeon orientation. *J. Comp. Physiol.* **110**:227–231. (69, 277)

Leask, M.J.M. 1977. A physico-chemical mechanism for magnetic field detection by migratory birds and homing pigeons. *Nature, Lond.* **267**:144–146. (21, 198, 235–6)

Leask, M.J.M. (personal communication). (267)

Lednor, A.J. 1982. Magnetic navigation in pigeons: possibilities and problems. In: *Avian Navigation* (Ed. by F. Papi & H.G. Wallraff), pp. 109–119. Heidelberg: Springer. (279)

Leitner, L., Weitzman, M. & Williams, T. (unpublished data). (107)

Lewis, D. 1972. *We, the Navigators*. Canberra: Australian National University Press. (12, 224)

Lindberg, E. & Gärling, T. 1978. Acquisition of locational information about reference points during blindfolded and sighted locomotion: effects of a concurrent task and locomotion paths: *Umeå Psychological Reports No. 144*, pp. 1–19. (34)

Lord, F.E. 1941. A study of spatial orientation of children. *J. Educ. Res.* **34**:481–505. (46, 114, 120)

Lowenstam, H.A. 1962. Magnetite in denticle capping in recent chitons. *Geol. Soc. Am. Bull.* **73**:435–438. (25)

MacFadden, B.J. & Jones, D.S. 1985. Magnetic butterflies: a case study of the Monarch (Lepidoptera, Danaidae). In: *Magnetite Biomineralization and Magnetoreception in Organisms: A New Biomagnetism* (Ed. by J.L. Kirschvink, D.S. Jones & B.J. MacFadden), pp. 407–416. New York: Plenum. (25)

Magarey, A.T. 1899. Tracking by the Australian aborigine. *Proc. Roy. Geogr. Soc. Australasia* **3**:120. (1)

Malmstrom, V.H. 1976. Knowledge of magnetism in pre-Columbian Mesoamerica. *Nature, Lond.* **259**:390–391. (30)

Mann, S. 1985. Structure, morphology, and crystal growth of bacterial magnetite. In: *Magnetite Biomineralization and Magnetoreception in Organisms: A New Biomagnetism* (Ed. by J.L. Kirschvink, D.S. Jones & B.J. MacFadden), pp. 311–332. New York: Plenum. (25)

Mather, J.G. 1981. Wheel-running activity: a new interpretation. *Mammal Rev.* **11**:41–51. (9)

Mather, J.G. 1985. Magnetoreception and the search for magnetic material in rodents. In: *Magnetite Biomineralization and Magnetoreception in Organisms: A New Biomagnetism* (Ed. by J.L. Kirschvink, D.S. Jones & B.J. MacFadden), pp. 509–533. New York: Plenum. (28, 266)

Mather, J.G. & Baker, R.R. 1980. A demonstration of navigation by rodents using an orientation cage. *Nature, Lond.* **284**:259–262. (13)

Mather, J.G. & Baker, R.R. 1981a. Magnetic sense of direction in woodmice for route-based navigation. *Nature, Lond.* **291**:152–155. (13, 28, 30, 144–5)

Mather, J.G. & Baker, R.R. 1981b. Reply to Aneshansley & Larkin. *Nature, Lond.* **293**:239. (13)

Mather, J.G., Baker, R.R. & Kennaugh, J.G. 1982. Magnetic field detection by small mammals. *EOS* **63**:156. (28)

Matthews, G.V.T. 1968. *Bird Navigation*, 2nd edn. Cambridge: University Press. (13)

Maugh, T.H. II. 1982. Magnetic navigation: an attractive possibility. *Science* **215**:1492–1493. (22)

McIsaac & Kreithen *in* Able (1987). (278)

Meharg, M. (unpublished data). (148)

Mellor, V. (unpublished data). (171)

Merkel, F.W. & Wiltschko, W. 1965. Magnetismus und Richtungsfinden zugun-ruhiger Rotkehlchen (*Erithacus rubecula*). *Vogelwarte* **23**:71–77. (x, 136)

Middendorf, A. von 1855. Die Isepipetsen Russlands; Grundlagen zur Erfors-chung der Zugzeiten und Zugrichtungen der Vögel Russlands. *Mem. Acad. Sci. St. Petersbourg* **8**:1–143. (x)

Mittlestaedt, H. & Mittlestaedt, M.-L. 1982. Homing by path integration. In: *Avian Navigation* (Ed. by F. Papi & H.G. Wallraff), pp. 290–297. Heidelberg: Springer. (98)

Moore, B.R. 1980. Is the homing pigeon's map geomagnetic? *Nature, Lond.* **285**:69–70. (14, 278)

Moore, F.R. 1977. Geomagnetic disturbance and the orientation of nocturnally migrating birds. *Science* **196**:682–684. (277–8)

Moore, F.R. 1986. Book review. *Q. Rev. Biol.* 27:104–5. (106)

Morris, P.G. 1986. *Nuclear Magnetic Resonance Imaging in Medicine and Biology.* Oxford: Clarendon Press. (285)

Moss, S. (unpublished data). (241–2)

Murphy, R.G. 1987. Development of compass orientation in children. PhD Thesis, University of Manchester. (57–8, 76, 90, 94, 96–7, 114, 117–8, 120–2, 133, 140, 153–4, 163–6, 169–70, 174–5, 216, 218–9, 221, 267, 283)

Nelson, F. (unpublished data). (157)

Nesson, M.H. & Lowenstam, H.A. 1985. Biomineralization processes of the radula teeth of chitons. In: *Magnetite Biomineralization and Magnetoreception in Organisms: A New Biomagnetism* (Ed. by J.L. Kirschvink, D.S. Jones & B.J. MacFadden), pp. 333–364. New York: Plenum. (25)

Ogden, J. (unpublished data). (271)

Olcese, J., Reuss, S., Vollrath, L. 1985. Evidence for the involvement of the visual system in mediating magnetic field effects on pineal melatonin syn-thesis in the rat. *Brain Res* **333**:382–384. (237)

Panagakis, S. (unpublished data). (156–9)

Papi, F. 1976. The olfactory navigation system of homing pigeons. *Verh. Deut. Zool. Ges.* **1976**:184–205. (13)

Papi, F. 1982a. Olfaction and homing in pigeons: ten years of experiments. In: *Avian Navigation* (Ed. by F. Papi & H.G. Wallraff), pp. 149–159. Heidelberg: Springer. (13)

Papi, F. 1982b. The homing mechanism of pigeons. *Nature, Lond.* **300**:293–294. (14)

Papi, F., Ioalé, P., Fiaschi, V., Benvenuti, S. & Baldaccini, N.E. 1978. Pigeon homing: cues detected during the outward journey influence initial orienta-tion. In: *Animal Migration, Navigation and Homing* (Ed. by K. Schmidt-Koenig & W.T. Keeton), pp. 65–77. Heidelberg: Springer. (143)

Pelkie, C. (personal communication). (60)

Pelkie, C, Brown, I. & Baker, R.R. (unpublished data). (72, 107, 112)

Perchard, K. (unpublished data). (261)

Perry, A., Bauer, G.B. & Dizon, A.E. 1981. Magnetite in the green turtle. *EOS* **62**:849. (25)

Perry, A., Bauer, G.B. & Dizon, A.E. 1985. Magnetoreception and biomineralization of magnetite in amphibians and reptiles. In: *Magnetite Biomineralization
and Magnetoreception in Organisms: A New Biomagnetism* (Ed. by J.L. Kirschvink,
D.S. Jones & B.J. MacFadden), pp. 439–454. New York: Plenum. (25, 30)

Philips, J.B. & Adler, K. 1978. Directional and discriminatory responses of salamanders to weak magnetic fields. In: *Animal Migration, Navigation and Homing* (Ed. by K. Schmidt-Koenig & W.T. Keeton), pp. 325–333, Heidelberg:
Springer. (266)

Presti, D. 1985. Avian navigation, geomagnetic field sensitivity, and biogenic
magnetite. In: *Magnetite Biomineralization and Magnetoreception in Organisms:
A New Biomagnetism* (Ed. by J.L. Kirschvink, D.S. Jones & B.J. MacFadden),
pp. 455–482. New York: Plenum. (279)

Presti, D. & Pettigrew, J.D. 1980. Ferromagnetic coupling to muscle receptors as
a basis for geomagnetic field sensitivity in animals. *Nature, Lond.* **285**:99–101.
(25, 265)

Randi, J. 1982. *The Truth about Uri Geller* Buffalo: Prometheus Books.

Randi, J. *in* Jacobs (1982). (84)

Ranvaud, R., Schmidt-Koenig, K., Kiepenheuer, J. & Gasparotto, O.C. 1983.
Initial orientation of homing pigeons at the magnetic equator with and without sun compass. *Behav. Ecol. Sociobiol.* **14**:77–79. (251)

Richardson, W.J. 1974. Autumn migration over Puerto Rico and the Eastern
Atlantic: a radar study. *Ibis* **118**:309–332. (277)

Rosenblum, B. & Jungerman, R. 1981. Induction-based magnetoreception
(theoretical analysis), *EOS* **62**:849. (21)

Rosenblum, B., Jungerman, R.L. & Longfellow, L. 1985. Limits to induction-
based magnetoreception. In: *Magnetite Biomineralization and Magnetoreception
in Organisms: A New Biomagnetism* (Ed. by J.L. Kirchvink, D.S. Jones & B.J.
MacFadden), pp. 223–232. New York: Plenum. (21)

Rosenthal, A. (unpublished data). (107)

Saint Paul, U. von 1982. Do geese use path integration for walking home? In:
Avian Navigation (Ed. by F. Papi & H.G. Wallraff), pp. 298–307. Heidelberg:
Springer. (11)

Schmidt-Koenig, K. 1979. *Avian Orientation and Navigation.* New York: Academic
Press. (73, 198, 209, 236)

Schmidt-Koenig, K. *in* Baker (1985c). (9–10)

Schreiber, B. & Rossi, O. 1976. Correlation between race arrivals of homing
pigeons and solar activity. *Boll. Zool* **43**:317–320. (277)

Schreiber, B. & Rossi, O. 1978. Correlation between magnetic storms due to
solar spots and pigeon homing performances. *IEEE Trans. Magn.* **14**:961–963.
(277)

Schulten, K. & Windemuth, A. 1986. Model for a physiological magnetic compass. In: *Biophysical Effects of Steady Magnetic Fields.* (Ed. by G. Maret, N.
Boccara & J. Kiepenheuer). pp. 99–106. Berlin: Springer-Verlag. (237)

Schüz, E. 1949. Die Spat-Auflassung ostpreussischer Jungstorche in West-
Deutschland durch die Vogelwarte Rossitten 1933. *Vogelwarte* **15**:63–78. (249)

Schüz, E. 1950. Fruh-Auflassung ostpreussischer Jungstorche in West-

Deutschland durch die vogelwarte Rossitten 1933–36. *Bonner zool. Beitr.* **1**:239–253. (249)

Semm, P. 1983. Neurobiological investigations on the magnetic sensitivity of the pineal gland in rodents and pigeons. *Comp. Biochem. Physiol* **76A**:683–689. (30)

Semm, P. 1988. The magnetic detection system of the pigeon: involvement of pineal and retinal photoreceptors and the vestibular system. In: *Electromagnetic Waves and Neurobehavioral Function* (Ed. by M.E. O'Connor & R. Lovely). pp. 47–62. New York: Liss. (30, 198)

Semm, P. (unpublished data) *in* Wiltschko & Wiltschko (1988). (236)

Semm, P. & Demaine, C. 1986. Neurophysiological properties of magnetic cells in the pigeon's visual system. *J. Comp. Physiol.* **59**:619–625. (237)

Semm, P., Nohr, D., Demaine, C. & Wiltschko, W. 1984. Neural basis of the magnetic compass: interactions of visual, magnetic and vestibular inputs in the pigeon's brain. *J. Comp. Physiol. A* **155**:1–6. (30, 198, 236, 256)

Semm, P., Schneider, T., Vollrath, L. & Wiltschko, W. 1982. Magnetic sensitive pineal cells in pigeons. In: *Avian Navigation* (Ed. by F. Papi & H.G. Wallraff), pp. 329–337. Heidelberg: Springer. (30)

Shepard, J.F. *in* Ellen (1987). (10)

Siddorn, C. (unpublished data). (239)

Siegel, S. 1956. *Nonparametric Statistics for the Behavioral Sciences.* New York: McGraw-Hill. (61, 63–4, 69, 89)

Skiles, D.D. 1985. The geomagnetic field: its nature, history and biological relevance. In: *Magnetite Biomineralization and Magnetoreception in Organisms: A New Biomagnetism* (Ed. by J.L. Kirschvink, D.S. Jones & B.J. MacFadden), pp. 43–102. New York: Plenum. (243, 249, 275)

Slepian, J. 1948. Physical basis of bird navigation. *J. Appl. Phys.* **19**:306. (19)

Sokal, R.R. & Rohlf, F.J. 1969. *Biometry.* San Francisco: W.H. Freeman. (64, 70)

Southern, W.E. 1971. Gull orientation by magnetic cues: a hypothesis revisited. *Ann NY Acad. Sci.* **188**:295–311. (277)

Southern, W.E., Hanzely, L., Bailey, R.L. & Molsen, D.V. 1982. Is the avian eye a magnetic sensor? In: *Avian Navigation* (Ed. by F. Papi & H.G. Wallraff), pp. 344–351. Heidelberg: Springer. (21)

Spencer, C. & Blades, M. 1986. Pattern and process: a review essay on the relationship between behavioural geography and environmental psychology. *Progress in Human Geography* **10**:230–248. (34)

Srivastava, B.J. & Saxena, S. 1980. Geomagnetic–Biological correlations: some new results. *Indian J. Radio Space Phys.* **9**:121–126. (275, 277)

Stewart, O.J.A. 1957. A bird's inborn navigational device. *Trans, Ky. Acad. Sci.* **18**:78–84. (19)

Swingland, I.R. 1983. Intraspecific differences in movement. In: *The Ecology of Animal Movement* (Ed. by I.R. Swingland & P.J. Greenwood), pp. 102–115. Oxford: Clarendon. (6)

Swingland, I.R. 1984. Book review. *Anim. Behav.* **32**:310. (9)

Talkington, L. 1967. Bird navigation and geomagnetism. *Am. Zool.* **7**:199. (21)

Thinus-Blanc, C. 1987. The cognitive map concept and its consequences. In: *Cognitive Processes and Spatial Orientation in Animal and Man. Vol. 1 Animal Psychology and Ethology* (Ed. by P. Ellen & C. Thinus-Blanc), pp. 1–19, NATO

ASI. Dordrecht: Martinus Nijhoff. (31)

Towe, K.M. 1985. Studying mineral particulates of biogenic origin by transmission electron microscopy and electron diffraction: some guidelines and suggestions. In: *Magnetite Biomineralization and Magnetoreception in Organisms: A New Biomagnetism* (Ed. by J.L. Kirschvink, D.S. Jones & B.J. MacFadden), pp. 167–180. New York: Plenum. (24)

Towe, K.M. & Lowenstam, H.A. 1967. Ultrastructure and development of iron mineralization in the radular teeth of *Cryptochiton stelleri* (Mollusca). *J. Ultrastruct. Res.* **17**:1–13. (21, 265)

Tricker, K. (unpublished data). (171, 271)

Turner, A. (1988). Getting it right. *New Scientist* **117**:70–71. (97, 283)

Ueda, K., Kusunoki, M., Kato, M., Kakizawa, R., Nakamura, T., Yaskawa, K., Koyama, M. & Maeda, Y. 1982. Magnetic remanences in migratory birds. *Journal Yamashina Institute of Ornithology* **14**:166–169. (266)

Viehmann, W. 1979. The magnetic compass of Blackcaps (*Sylvia atricapilla*). *Behaviour* **68**:24–30. (246)

Visalberghi, E. & Alleva, E. 1979. Magnetic influences on pigeon homing. *Biol. Bull.* **156**:246–256. (151, 156, 206)

Walcott, B. 1985. The cellular localization of particulate iron. In: *Magnetite Biomineralization and Magnetoreception in Organisms: A New Biomagnetism* (Ed. by J.L. Kirschvink, D.S. Jones & B.J. MacFadden), pp. 183–196. New York: Plenum. (24)

Walcott, B. & Walcott, C. 1982. A search for magnetic field receptors in animals. In: *Avian Navigation* (Ed. by F. Papi & H.G. Wallraff), pp. 338–343. Heidelberg: Springer. (30, 265–6)

Walcott, C. 1977. Magnetic fields and the orientation of homing pigeons under sun. *J. exp. Biol.* **70**:105–123. (151, 156, 206)

Walcott, C. 1982. Is there evidence for a magnetic map in homing pigeons? In: *Avian Navigation* (Ed. by F. Papi & H.G. Wallraff), pp. 99–108. Heidelberg: Springer. (14, 22, 169, 194, 260, 278–9)

Walcott, C. & Gould, J.L. *in* Walcott (1982). (169, 194)

Walcott, C. & Green, R.P. 1974. Orientation of homing pigeons is altered by a change in the direction of an applied magnetic field. *Science* **184**:180–182. (151, 250)

Walcott, C., Gould, J.L. & Kirschvink, J.L. 1979. Pigeons have magnets. *Science* **205**:1027–1029. (22, 25, 30, 265)

Walker, M.M. & Dizon, A.E. 1981. Identification of magnetite in tuna. *EOS* **62**:850. (25)

Walker, M.M., Kirschvink, J.L., Chang, S.-B.R. & Dizon, A.E. 1984. A candidate magnetic sense organ in the yellowfin tuna, *Thunnus albacares. Science* **224**:751–753. (25, 30)

Walker, M.M., Kirschvink, J.L. & Dizon, A.E. 1985a. Magnetoreception and biomineralization of magnetite: fish. In: *Magnetite Biomineralization and Magnetoreception in Organisms: A New Biomagnetism* (Ed. by J.L. Kirschvink, D.S. Jones & B.J. MacFadden), pp. 417–438. New York: Plenum. (25)

Walker, M.M., Kirschvink, J.L., Perry, A. & Dizon, A.E. 1985b. Detection, extraction and characterization of biogenic magnetite. In: *Magnetite Biomineralization and Magnetoreception in Organisms: A New Biomagnetism* (Ed. by J.L. Kirschvink, D.S. Jones & B.J. MacFadden), pp. 1565–166. New York: Plenum. (24)

Walker, P. (unpublished data). (171, 271)

Wallraff, H.G. 1978. Proposed principles of magnetic field perception in birds. *Oikos* 30:188–194. (19)

Wallraff, H.G. 1982. The homing mechanism of pigeons. *Nature, Lond.* 300:293. (14)

Wallraff, H.G. 1983. Relevance of atmospheric odours and geomagnetic field to pigeon navigation: what is the "map" basis? *Comp. Biochem. Physiol.* 76A:643–663. (14, 279)

Wallraff, H.G. & Gelderloos, O.G. 1978. Experiments on migratory orientation of birds with simulated stellar sky and geomagnetic field: method and preliminary results. *Oikos* 30:207–215. (137–8, 256)

Welker, H.A., Semm, P., Willing, R.P., Commentz, J.C., Wiltschko, W. & Vollrath, L. 1983. Effects of an artificial magnetic field on serotonin-N-acetyltransferase activity and melatonin content of the rat pineal gland. *Exp. Brain Res.* 50:426–432. (237)

Westby, G.W.M. & Partridge, K.J. 1986. Human homing: still no evidence despite geomagnetic controls. *J. exp. Biol.* 120:325–331. (xi, 46, 51, 72, 106–8, 121, 277)

Wilkinson, D.H. 1949. Some physical principles of bird orientation. *Proc. Linn. Soc. Lond.* 160:94–99. (20)

Williamson, T. 1987. A sense of direction for dowsers? *New Scientist* 113:40–43. (234)

Wiltschko, R. 1983. The ontogeny of orientation in young pigeons. *Comp. Biochem. Physiol.* 76A:701–708. (206)

Wiltschko, R. & Wiltschko, W. 1978. Evidence for the use of magnetic outward-journey information in homing pigeons. *Naturwiss.* 65:112–113. (13, 73, 136, 143, 206)

Wiltschko, R. & Wiltschko, W. 1984. The development of the navigational system in young homing pigeons. In: *Localization and Orientation in Biology and Engineering* (Ed. by Varjù/Schnitzler), pp. 337–343, Heidelberg: Springer. (206)

Wiltschko, R., Nohr, D. & Wiltschko, W. 1981. Pigeons with a deficient sun compass use the magnetic compass. *Science* 214:343–345. (156)

Wiltschko, R., Wiltschko, W. & Keeton, W.T. 1978. Effect of outward journey in an altered magnetic field on the orientation of young homing pigeons. In: *Animal Migration, Navigation and Homing* (Ed. by K. Schmidt-Koenig & W.T. Keeton), pp. 152–161. Heidelberg: Springer. (144)

Wiltschko, W. 1974. Der Magnetkompass der Gartengrasmücke (*Sylvia borin*). *J. Orn.* 115:1–7. (249)

Wiltschko, W. (personal communication). (250)

Wiltschko, W. & Wiltschko, R. 1972. Magnetic compass of European Robins. *Science* 176:62–64. (136, 150, 245–6, 248, 251)

Wiltschko, W. & Wiltschko, R. 1981. Disorientation of inexperienced young pigeons after transportation in total darkness. *Nature, Lond.* 291:433–434. (144,

151, 198, 236)

Wiltschko, W. & Wiltschko, R. 1988. Magnetic orientation in birds. In: *Current Ornithology, Vol. 5* (Ed. by R.F. Johnston), pp. 67–121. New York: Plenum. (206, 237)

Wiltschko. W., Wiltschko, R. & Keeton, W.T. 1976. Effects of a "permanent" clock-shift on the orientation of young homing pigeons. *Behav. Ecol. Sociobiol.* 1:229–243. (206)

Wolton, R.J. 1985. The ranging and nesting behaviour of Wood mice, *Apodemus sylvaticus* (Rodentia: Muridae), as revealed by radio-tracking. *J. Zool., Lond. (A)* 206:203–224. (10)

Worchel, P. 1951. Space perception and orientation in the blind. *Psychol. Monogr.* 65 (332). (34)

Yeagley, H.L. 1947. A preliminary study of a physical basis of bird navigation. *J. Appl. Phys.* 18:1035–1063. (14, 19)

Yeagley, H.L. 1951. A preliminary study of a physical basis of bird navigation. II. *J. Appl. Phys.* 22:746–760. (277)

Yorke, E.D. 1985. Energetics and sensitivity considerations of ferromagnetic magnetoreceptions. In: *Magnetite Biomineralization and Magnetoreception in Organisms: A New Biomagnetism* (Ed. by J.L. Kirschvink, D.S. Jones & B.J. MacFadden), pp. 233–242. New York: Plenum. (22)

Zoeger, J., Dunn, J.R. & Fuller, M. 1981. Magnetic material in the head of the common Pacific dolphin. *Science* 205:1027–1028. (25, 30)

Zusne, L. & Allen, B. 1981. Magnetic sense in humans? *Perceptual and Motor Skills* 52:910. (xi, 58, 72, 78, 94–5, 151, 154, 163)

Subject index

ability (at orientation and navigation)
  factors influencing
    age, variation with 121–4
    bed alignment 133
    cloud cover 124–7
    sun, height of 126, 128–9
    time of day 130–3
  levels of
    at navigation 71–8, 97–135
    at orientation 71–8, 89–97,
      108–35
aborigine (Australian) 1–2, 12
adrenal glands 234
African bushmen 12
agoraphobia 268–9, 271
alcohol 273–6, 280
Amerindian 7
ampullae of Lorenzini 20
Apis mellifera (honey bee) 7, 22–5,
  265–6
Apodemus sylvaticus (woodmouse) 10,
  25, 28–30, 143–5, 266

bacteria 21, 22, 25, 265
bar magnets 151–69, 234, 258–60,
  263–4
  strength of 186–94
basal optic root, nucleus of (nBOR)
  236–7
bats 25
bed orientation 23, 77–8, 133, 164–9,
  175–6, 178, 259–60, 262–3, 267, 269
Bedouin 6

bees, see *Apis mellifera*
biological clock 14, 18, 130
bus experiments 33, 45–55, 86, 91–3,
  96–8, 103–8, 110–13
  outward journey
    complexity of 108, 110, 113–4
    length of 108, 110–13
  protocol of 46–51
  replication (by other authors) 55
  subjects, age of 52–4, 111
butterflies 25

cap-and-collar coils 151
cats 6
celestial cues 16, 90
cetaceans 25, 30, 277, 279
chair experiments 33, 55–9, 86, 90–1,
  94–7, 216–8, 252
  location of 55
  protocol of 55–7
  replication (by other authors) 58
chitons (polyplacophora) 21, 25, 265
circular statistics 59–62
  second-order analysis 65–7
  see also statistics
clock
  circadian 130
  see also biological clock; time, sense
    of
cognitive maps, *see* mental maps
Columbia livia (homing pigeon, racing
  pigeon, dove) 13, 22, 108, 143–4,
  171, 198, 206, 236–7, 250–1, 256,

performance in, factors affecting
  age of subjects 39, 41–2, 101, 111
  complexity of walk 108, 110,
    113–4
  length of walk 37, 101, 108,
    110–11
whales, *see* cetaceans

whole-body hypotheses (of
  magnetoreception) 19–20, 230, 232,
  234

zenith (= overhead) sun 126
Zugunruhe, *see* migratory
  restlessness)